ALCOHOLISM:
CHALLENGE FOR SOCIAL WORK EDUCATION

by HERMAN KRIMMEL

Council on Social Work Education
345 East 46th Street, New York, N.Y. 10017

Library of Congress No. 70-176194

Preface

Alcoholism is a major social problem, one which intensifies many of the other problems that are targets of social work concern. Yet social work, along with other helping professions, has all too often considered the problem as not amenable to professional treatment and has left the field to law enforcement and a limited group of specialized institutions and agencies. The complex reasons for this neglect are treated in this volume. Here it is sufficient to note that recently changing circumstances and attitudes are creating a climate more conducive to professional treatment of alcoholism. The social work profession is in a strategic position to participate in this change, but only if it is prepared to concern itself with the problem. This concern cannot be limited to the direct treatment of the identified alcoholic by social workers specializing in such treatment but must also include the ability on the part of social workers generally to recognize alcoholism and to be aware of its implications for other social problems. In the belief that social work neither can nor wishes to prolong its neglect of this serious social problem, CSWE has commissioned this source book. It is intended to provide social work students, faculty, and practitioners with a basic knowledge of alcoholism and its treatment and to suggest ways in which social workers may be constructively involved in this field.

The production of the source book is a cooperative effort on the part of many people to whom CSWE wishes to give its thanks. Major credit goes to Herman Krimmel, the author, who brings to its writing the unusual combination of education as a professional social worker and years of experience as a practitioner and administrator in the treatment of alcoholism. Grateful acknowledgement is also made to those who permitted Mr. Krimmel the use of illustrative case material from their practice.

The Council also wishes to thank the advisory committee, whose breadth of knowledge and experience added new dimensions to the content of the book. The committee* included: Joseph F. Meisels (Chairman), Dean, Boston University School of Social Work; James Alford, M.D., Atlanta, Georgia, Department of Preventive Medicine and Community Health; Pauline Cohen, Director of Staff Development, Family Service Association of America; Charles Garvin, Associate Professor, University of Michigan School of Social Work; Milton A. Maxwell, Executive Director, Rutgers University Summer School of Alcohol Studies; John O'Neill, Associate Professor, Fresno State College School of Social Work; Harry Russell, Assistant to the Director for Community Affairs and Director of Social Work, Perth Amboy General Hospital; Burt Shachter, New York University School of Social Work; Joan Skelly, Public Health Nurse, Florida Alcoholic Treatment and Research Center; Deenah Stolman, Associate Professor and Director of Casework, University of Connecticut School of Social Work; and Elizabeth G. Watkins, Staff Associate, Division of Direct Services, American Public Welfare Association. Working with the committee on a liaison basis* representing the National Center for Prevention and Control of Alcoholism, National Institute of Mental Health, were: Thomas A. Plaut, Assistant Chief; George Retholtz, Chief, Manpower and Training Section; and Grace Bell, Chief, Community Services Section.

Thanks are also due to the social work faculty who met as a group to review an early draft of the source book. Their suggestions added significantly to its usefulness for schools of social work.

CSWE is especially grateful to the Institute on Alcohol Abuse and Alcoholism, National Institute of Mental Health, for the grant which made the book possible, and to George Retholtz, Chief, Manpower and Training Section, for his sustained interest and encouragement.

We hope that students and faculty of schools of social work and staff of social agencies will find this publication useful as they deal with this severe social problem.

Lilian Ripple
Acting Executive Director

September, 1971

*Affiliations given are those at the time of membership on the committee.

Foreword

This book has gone through many revisions and the author has somehow survived meetings with an advisory committee and one with delegates from graduate schools of social work. In all fairness, the survival powers of the committees should also be acknowledged. Be that as it may, each meeting had its quota of pain and pleasure. Ideas and suggestions seemed to be born almost every minute but the mortality was also high. In the end, those that were most pertinent were summarized and an effort has been made to include as many as possible in the final version. The fact remains, however, that the book was never intended to be nor can it be all things to all faculty and students. There are omissions – many of them. Some have been imposed by restrictions of space; others, alas, by the boundaries of the author's training and knowledge.

Within these limits, material had to be selected from an overwhelming surplus. Other writers might have organized the data differently or made selections which would have altered the emphasis. I happen to be a social worker who has been in practice and administration in the field of alcoholism for fifteen years and the book inevitably reflects the viewpoint of a practitioner. The advisory committee, incidentally, was about equally populated by practitioners and teachers who frequently clashed in their approach. An uncertain author occasionally felt like a shuttle in a badminton game, flying from one side of the net to the other. In the end there was (I think) substantial agreement on major points as opposing views were clarified under the persuasive leadership of Dean Joseph Meisels of the Boston University School of Social Work. He is a chairman of considerable diplomacy and skill and I will always be grateful to him.

A full disclosure requires more than confessing that I am a practitioner. For better or worse, I am a casework practitioner which may explain even more. This does not imply any effort to slight the areas of group work and community organization but it is impossible to award equal time in a relatively brief volume. I tried at least to recognize the invaluable contributions of other areas in working with alcoholics and their families. Whatever guilt remains is assuaged by the words of Helen Harris Perlman in *Social Casework* (April, 1970). The casework method, she wrote, "takes as its unit of attention, as the unit to be helped, one person or one family, suffering some clear and present problem or obstacle to satisfactory or satisfying social functioning, either in carrying necessary task or interpersonal relationships." Surely, that applies to alcoholics.

This does not preclude recognition of the fact that alcoholism, like other social problems, cannot be eradicated, or even significantly diminished, by the exclusive use of this method. It will only succumb to social action resulting in basic social changes. However, continues Perlman: "There is no 'love of mankind' except as fraudulent rhetoric, unless there is compassion for a single human being . . ." and "A person's problems today will not wait for the wheels of justice or social reform to grind out change. Grind they must, and it is hoped that social work will accelerate them. But the man who is their victim wants help *now* because his problems in personal and family life hurt now. And if these problems are the result of yesterday's causes, they are at the same time the causes of tomorrow's new problems."

The imbalance in favor of the individual approach may be most apparent in the vignettes following the chapters and in the longer cases that are available separately. Considerable effort was made to find a usable case in community organization but the material accumulated did not seem to lend itself to teaching. Perhaps diligent students interested in the field of alcoholism will fill the void.

Throughout the text there are references to research projects although there is no section devoted exclusively to research. Anyone who wants to know what research is in progress is urged to consult the *Quarterly Journal of Studies on Alcohol,* especially Part B of each issue, which is a separate compendium of the latest papers with abstracts from many.

An effort has been made to show the increasing role of the systems approach to social problems. Few social problems demand this approach more than alcoholism because the alcoholic affects and is affected by family, friends, job, courts, indeed, the total community. Moreover, his rehabilitation needs are frequently determined by where and how he enters the treatment system. The needs of the working executive are quite different from those of the skid row derelict although both are alcoholics. What happens to the alcoholic may depend on whether he first encounters help in the medical department of a large industry or in a municipal court. This has not been examined as extensively as it might have been, but as more professionals of all disciplines work with alcoholics they will gather and interpret data.

Many parts of the book are tinctured with the bias of my own experience; some parts are vigorously opinionated because in a hotly controversial field I have opinions. This may violate strict academic objectivity, although every effort has been made to document factual material and to present varied points of view. In alcoholism, everyone talks about "hard data" but, whatever that is, precious little of it has been produced.

My basic premise is that alcoholism is primarily a *social problem* with medical complications rather than primarily a medical problem. The latter has long been a traditional view which may have had the effect of a constructive catalyst for a while but in recent decades has created an intellectual and emotional smog that has impaired the vision. When this hypothesis was presented at the National Conference on Social Welfare in 1967 in a paper, "Alcoholism, A Social Problem for Social Workers," it was reported in a Cleveland newspaper with the comment that I saw social workers as having far more skills necessary to the total treatment of alcoholics than physicians do. Solicitous friends suggested that I would do well to avoid acute illness for a while. It wasn't really that serious and in the intervening years a few apostate doctors have joined the wave of the future.

One of the most pleasant aspects of completing this book is the opportunity to acknowledge in print the help I have received during the long months of organization and writing.

In January, 1971, more than sixty representatives of graduate schools of social work convened in St. Louis to discuss a late draft and to exchange ideas about its possible use in the curriculum. Out of two days of general and section meetings came a potpourri of ideas—some in accord, some in conflict, and the summarized reports were invaluable in preparing the final manuscript. The number involved makes it impossible to name each individual but all were helpful.

The assembling of case material would have been far more difficult without the generous help of many people. Assistance was freely offered by Dr. James Alford, Associate Professor of Preventive Medicine in Community Health, Assistant Dean, School of Medicine and Nursing, Emory University; Dr. Peter Bourne, Georgia Narcotics Treatment Program, Health Center in Atlanta, Georgia; Dan Anderson, executive director, Hazelden, Center City, Minnesota; Dr. Charles Garvin, Associate Professor, University of Michigan; Mrs. Vera Lindbeck and the staff of the Alcoholism Project of the Family Service Association of Cincinnati, Ohio; Francis A. Smith and Robert Strayer, respectively of the Hartford and Bridgeport offices of the Connecticut Commission on Alcoholism; Gladys Price, director of Social Services of the Washingtonian hospital in Boston; and Gertrude Nilssen, Division of Alcoholism Control, State Department of Mental Hygiene, Baltimore, Maryland. In each of these locations members of the staffs were as helpful as the executives named.

Inevitably, much material was culled from the records of the Cleveland Center on Alcoholism and Drug Abuse and members of that staff were most helpful in the selection of vignettes and cases. Louise W. Lantz, a caseworker, was always cooperative and there was an abundance of riches in the work of former casework supervisor, Helen R. Spears, a creative and stimulating colleague.

It has been a pleasure to work with staff members at the Council on Social Work Education. Edward Francel, Frank Loewenberg, Margaret Purvine, and Jacqueline Atkins have been patient and tolerant through what must have been exasperating delays, revisions, missed deadlines, and an assortment of irritations imposed by the curious work habits of the author. Dr. Purvine, who has borne a major part of the burden, has been unfailing cheerful and cordial.

It does not diminish the contributions of those mentioned above to say that two people have earned very special gratitude for living through the ordeal of this book from the first outline to the final manuscript. Both insisted on (they would say "suggested") changes, deletions, and additions that, when heeded, were synonymous with improvement. One is my wife, Eleanor, whose patience with a husband's temperament and an apartment strewn with books and papers would have made Job seem like a compulsive complainer. She was also most helpful in revising case material. The other is Bette A. Webster, administrative secretary at the Cleveland Center on Alcoholism and Drug Abuse. She prepared the manuscript through many revisions, brought order out of disorganization, saved me from countless errors, and always made the going a lot easier.

Finally, it is imperative to record that while the advisory committee did its work well and was most helpful, its members are not accountable for the content of this book. All opinions as well as possible errors of fact are the sole responsibility of the author. With that assurance goes gratitude to all who gave unstintingly of their time, experience, and insight.

Herman E. Krimmel
Cleveland, Ohio

May, 1971

Introduction

In 1968, while in my official capacity involving manpower and training problems at the then National Center for Prevention and Control of Alcoholism at the National Institute of Mental Health, Arnulf M. Pins and others of the staff of CSWE were quite persuasive in identifying to me the need for a source book on alcoholism for use by concerned social workers everywhere. After participating as a member of the CSWE advisory committee in the development of such a document, I saw the value of such a publication in view of national goals and the need for enlarged involvement of many more professionals and nonprofessionals in dealing with this massive and distressing problem.

The product encompassed in the body of the resultant publication directs attention to the existence, scope, and specific nature of the materials necessary to the adequate education of social workers in the areas of problem drinking and alcoholism.

At the national level there is little doubt that alcoholism constitutes one of the most serious health problems facing us as a nation. Yet, it is indeed surprising that through the years little official recognition has been given to this area of concern, despite the heavy human and economic waste attributable to it. The Congress, since the depression years of the 1930s, has legislated many acts, statutes, and laws involving social welfare, health, and rehabilitation, but *none of these actions* has, to my knowledge, ever mentioned alcoholism as a special category of interest before 1966. Certainly none of the programs that came into existence reflected a coordinated and integrated attempt to neutralize, if not eradicate, the problems of alcoholism and alcohol misuse.

Only within the last five years has there developed substantial public concern to bring into sufficient visibility and focus the archaic and inadequate ways by which this country has dealt with this major public health problem. This state of affairs is not surprising. Competition for limited funds undoubtedly influences many social policy decisions.

It is not unexpected, therefore, that it takes more than some pronouncement from on high to effectuate change, nor can one simply legislate change. We have seen that even a constitutional amendment concerning alcohol (the 18th amendment) had to be amended to undo the damage caused by that legislation.

On the other hand, recent actions of private citizens, governmental commissions and committees, and courts at both the federal and state levels have helped marshal resources to promote the necessary coordination that resulted in passage of the Comprehensive Alcohol Abuse and Alcoholism Prevention, Treatment, and Rehabilitation Act of 1970. On December 31, 1970, President Nixon signed this Act (PL 91-616) into law.

Among the provisions of this law were those that (1) require the establishment of a National Institute on Alcohol Abuse and Alcoholism; (2) authorized formula grants totaling $180,000,000 for the first three years to help state governments develop and administer programs to deal with the problem area; (3) required the United States Civil Service Commission to establish alcoholism prevention, treatment, and rehabilitation for civilian federal employees and to assure employees suffering from alcoholism the same benefits and conditions of employment as individuals ill from other ailments; and (4) required that the Secretary of Health, Education, and Welfare report to the Congress on the deleterious effects of the use of alcoholic beverages, etc.

We need not belabor the importance of this legislation to social workers. Social workers, heavily engaged in front-line activities, are among the first to interact with individuals suffering from the ravages of alcoholism and alcohol misuse. For some time now, the curricula of schools of social work have been general rather than specialized. Schools have sought to prepare students to be knowledgeable about a variety of problems and to have basic skills of intervention. The aim of this source book is to provide substantive information for use in social work education in a largely neglected area of social concern—problem drinking and alcoholism.

It was extremely gratifying, therefore, that when a two-day meeting was held in January, 1971, in St. Louis to preview the draft materials of the source book, participants (approximately 65 in number) included faculty members from schools of social work from different regions of our country, including representation from Hawaii. Participants included those with expertise in social policy, research, human behavior and the social environment, social work method courses, and field instruction.

The quality of the questions posed by the participants and the issues raised strengthened the belief that the source book indeed represented a vehicle that would prove most useful to social work trainees as well as practitioners. Community organization for dealing with the problem of alcoholism, alcoholism and poverty, alcoholism and the family, and many other subject matter areas were explored with great vigor and interested concern. One could not help believing that the publication of this book would provide the impetus for greater attention and effort on the part of social workers everywhere to the plight of alcoholics than had heretofore been given. Also, it is reasonably safe to say that the model and content used by the Council on Social Work Education would be a highly useful adjunct to materials available to other disciplines and gatekeepers, be they professionals or nonprofessionals.

I am pleased to acknowledge my limited involvement with this publication and to recognize here the prodigious work and effort that Mr. Krimmel exerted to create this valuable resource for social workers and others deeply concerned with one of the major societal problems of our time.

The opinions expressed herein are those of the writer and do not necessarily reflect the official position of the National Institute of Mental Health or the Department of Health, Education, and Welfare.

Dr. George Retholtz
Director, Health Services and
Mental Health Administration
Employee Health Program on Alcoholism
Department of Health, Education,
and Welfare

Table of Contents

CHAPTER I

The Extent of the Problem and the Social Work Role

WHAT IS ALCOHOLISM?

The late Mr. Justice Cardozo wrote that "peril lurks in definition, so runs an ancient maxim of law." Nevertheless, if we are to work with alcoholics, as distinguished from social or even heavy drinkers, we need a usable description of alcoholism.

The key word is *usable* because alcoholism has never lacked definition; several years ago Jellenik and Bowman tabulated thirty definitions in the psychiatric literature alone.[1] Medicine, sociology, psychology, the clergy, and almost everyone else have had their favorites and continued to add others.

There is still lack of consensus but there is increasing agreement that alcoholism should be defined as a pattern of drinking that, on a continuous basis, interferes with adequate functioning in any significant

[1] Mark Keller, "Alcoholism: Nature and Extent of the Problem," *The Annals of the American Academy of Political and Social Sciences*, Vol. 315 (January, 1958), p. 1.

area of a person's life. This means, in the words of the World Health Organization definition, that "dependence on alcohol has attained such a degree that it shows a notable mental disturbance or an interference with [alcoholics'] bodily or mental health, their interpersonal relationships and their smooth social and economic functioning. . . ." [2]

The word *continuous* is important. A person who drinks moderately most of the time, but, on one or two occasions during the year, kicks over the traces at a party and stays home from work to nurse a hangover the next day is not necessarily an alcoholic. Infrequent absences may not be advisable but they are not disastrous. On the other hand, a man who misses fifteen or twenty Mondays annually or who is habitually absent the day after payday is well on the way to alcoholism, or he may have already arrived at that unhappy destination.

There are many variations on this theme in all activities of life, but implicit in a definition based on function impairment is the fact that alcoholism cannot be measured in terms of the amount consumed but only how it *affects* a person's life.

One man may have a cocktail or two before lunch, a few drinks with his friends after work, or possibly a couple with his wife before dinner, and he may add a few highballs during the evening. The total intake is high, but it is spaced over several hours. He doesn't get drunk, he performs well on the job, he gives a large measure of devotion to his family, and he enjoys being with his wife and children. He might be a heavy drinker, but he is not an alcoholic.

Another man may concentrate all that drinking into a few hours. He doesn't use alcohol for relaxation. He uses it to escape from the rat race; he ignores his family and objects to their interference with his drinking so pugnaciously that they learn to leave him alone. His inferior work jeopardizes his job and he has trouble getting through the day to his appointment with the bottle. This man is an alcoholic.

The contrast is not always so clear, but the factor of performance impairment spells the difference. Incidentally, it doesn't make any difference whether he drinks whiskey, gin, or beer; whether before breakfast or only after dinner, alone or with others, at home or abroad. If drinking continues to disrupt his life, he is an alcoholic. The opposite is equally valid. If his drinking does not cause trouble, even if he does drink before breakfast, he is not alcoholic. He may just be like Marquard's character who always started the day with a cold bath and a jigger of gin so he'd be cold on the outside but warm on the inside.

This definition eliminates the need for semantic quibbling about

[2] World Health Organization, *Expert Committee on Alcoholism: First Report* (Geneva: Technical Report Series, WHO, No. 84, 1954).

whether a person is "really an alcoholic" or a "problem drinker" or an "alcohol abuser." All are included. In this book, we will go along with the writer who sees the word *alcoholism* as representing "a useful shorthand designation for a cluster of disorders which have in common some element of drinking pathology, but which vary in the nature of their dependence on alcohol. . . ." [3]

EXTENT OF THE PROBLEM

Alcoholism is recognized as one of the most devastating social and health problems of contemporary life. No one really knows how many alcoholics there are in the United States and there has never been a nationwide census. There is no objective method of making a count because of variations in definition, prejudices about drinking, and other variables. The estimate may depend on who is asked. The total from the Women's Christian Temperance Union will not tally with that from the Licensed Beverage Industries. Unfortunately, statistics are too frequently used as a drunk uses a lamppost – for support rather than illumination.

It is enough to say there are a lot of alcoholics. Most authorities agree that there are at least five million in the nation. Only a small percentage are skid row derelicts, although that does not minimize the problem of the homeless alcoholic. The vast majority live in family units and have jobs – at least most of the time. This means that if the average size of the American family is four, almost every alcoholic intimately affects at least three other people – the spouse and two children. He or she also affects the lives of co-workers, friends, and neighbors.

The dimensions of the problem are so great that one questions why national organizations and groups like Alcoholics Anonymous must attempt to dramatize their case with grim pronouncements to the effect that things are rapidly getting worse because alcoholism is, in their judgment, increasing in geometric progression. Again, no one knows. The statistical impression of a steady rise may reflect and change in professional and public attitudes. The stigma attached to alcoholism has not been erased, but it has certainly decreased so that there is less pressure on physicians to substitute a nonstigmatized diagnosis and families have less need to conceal the alcoholics in their midst. As Keller observed a few years ago, we may not have had a steady rise in alcoholism but rather improvement in reporting. "This would mean that the most recent rates reflect a truer picture of the situation than those of the past. If the rates should now tend to flatten out, it may mean that reports have finally caught up

[3] William J. Plunkert, "Orientation to Alcoholism," in *Alcoholism and Family Casework*, Margaret B. Bailey, ed. (New York: The Community Council of Greater New York, 1969), p. 8.

with reality, or even that the rate of alcoholism has begun to decline." [4] It should be noted that most traditionalists regard that statement as heresy.

Whatever the validity of the statistics, the dimensions of the problem pose a clear and present danger so that any effective attack demands total community participation, with the caretaking professions in the front lines. As Plaut has said:

> Problem drinkers constitute a significant proportion of the clientele of most community helping agencies. However, such agencies usually prefer not to deal with these persons and few have paid particular attention to them. It is only in recent years that some health and social welfare agencies have begun to develop new approaches and special programs to provide care and treatment for this group.
>
> The magnitude of the drinking problem virtually precludes the establishment of special service networks for these patients. Consequently, the burden of providing care has fallen necessarily on the general community helping agencies. The challenge is to overcome neglect by most of these general care-givers and develop adequate community services.[5]

NEGLECT OF ALCOHOLISM

The challenge of alcoholism has not been met by any profession, including social work. Sapir, writing in 1958, observed that social workers had long worked with the consequences of alcoholism but avoided working directly with alcoholics because they felt the prognosis was poor and their training was inadequate to meet the challenge. It had, she said, "become almost a recognized policy in many private agencies to discourage staff from 'becoming involved' with alcoholics because they were too sick psychiatrically to be able to use casework help. Instead, the staff was urged to turn such cases over to an expert." She added that there had been some improvement and that improvement has certainly continued, but there remains widespread resistance.[6]

In many social agencies, it is comparatively easy for the worker to focus on problems other than alcoholism. Despite its high incidence in caseloads, it is seldom the *presenting* problem. A caseworker in a youth agency, for example, worked with a disturbed adolescent who stole cars, was a chronic troublemaker in school, and frequently stayed away from

---

[4] Keller, *op. cit.*, p. 7.

[5] Thomas Plaut, F. A. "Alcoholism and Community Caretakers: Programs and Policies," *Social Work*, Vol. 12, No. 3 (July, 1967), pp. 42-50.

[6] Jean V. Sapir, "Social Work and Alcoholism," *The Annals of the American Academy of Political and Social Sciences*, Vol. 315 (1958), pp. 125-132.

home for two or three days. The boy was a tormented amalgamation of disorders which the worker explored diligently. The boy also happened to have a pair of alcoholic parents who made life utterly miserable for him. The worker, however, paid little attention to the parents because of the presumed hopelessness of alcoholism. Of course, he did try to get the youth to understand his parents, which was a bit difficult when the crockery was flying or when the father hurled the portable television set at his wife.

The boy failed to adjust to this kind of family life despite all the efforts of his caseworker. After eight months, he terminated contact with the agency and the worker noted that the client did not seem ready to make effective use of casework treatment.

Perhaps if the caseworker had worked with the parents for a brief period, lengthy work with their son *might* have been unnecessary. If a direct approach to the problem of the parents had been successful, the boy would have been afforded an opportunity to tackle his own problems in a healthier environment.

The feeling that alcoholism is a problem for specialists is still deeply rooted and widespread. But alcoholism is not and cannot be the exclusive or primary responsibility of specialized agencies. Even if that were desirable, which it is not, there would be insurmountable barriers to financing or staffing enough specialized agencies to cope with even a small pocket of the problem in most communities. One specialized agency in a midwest city serves an area where there are an estimated 75,000 alcoholics and their families. With a limited staff, it can reach only about 600 annually. Obviously, this makes a small impact on a large problem. The agency, therefore, emphasizes and sees its role as a catalyst. Its experience with relatively few clients is employed to train professionals in agencies and clinics throughout the community in order to treat alcoholics in any setting. Thus, the pool of therapists is slowly expanded.

There are other disadvantages to placing major responsibility for treatment in specialized agencies. One is that problems seldom exist in isolation from other social, economic, psychological, and health problems, so it would be unusual to find a person for whom drinking was the sole difficulty. Specialized agencies are seldom equipped to cope with these related problems. Second, a specialized agency tends to become a dumping ground unless there is eternal vigilance to avoid that. And third, the existence of a specialized agency may give the erroneous impression that it can solve all the alcohol problems of the community and that there is little need for further concern.

The specialized agency has its place, but, as Thomas Plaut has emphasized, "General health and welfare agencies, governmental as well as voluntary, must become sources of leadership if substantial care is to be made in providing better care and treatment for the problem drinker. Such agencies will and probably have to assume primary responsibility although valuable contributions can be made by specialized alcoholism programs."

THE ROLE OF SOCIAL WORK

Among the caretaking professions, social work may have the greatest potential for helping alcoholics. This is based partly on mathematics, because social workers are employed in almost every setting where the lame, the halt, and the blind are treated for their social, emotional, and physical infirmities. Consider the scope:

1. Social Agencies – Private

Alcoholism has been called a family illness because it inevitably involves every member of the alcoholic's family. The behavior of the alcoholic dramatically affects his wife and children but, in turn, they influence his need to drink and the neurotic interaction is continuous and usually destructive. Bailey has estimated that 15 to 20 percent of the applications to family service agencies involve a drinking problem that has been related to physical abuse, debts, possible loss of job, and concern about children. In some instances, there have been even more severe symptoms of disorganization.[7]

Most social agencies encounter family problems related to excessive drinking and this includes those working with the young and the aged, the settlement houses, halfway houses for the mentally ill, those working with transients, and those engaged in vocational rehabilitation. Workers in such agencies as the Salvation Army and Volunteers of America see homeless alcoholics and helpless derelicts.

2. Public Welfare

Data on the relationship between alcoholism and economic dependency is limited. In the past, public welfare departments have been understandably shy about advertising the fact that there may be a considerable number of people with drinking problems on the relief roles. Such disclosures, with their innuendos about "shiftless people who drink up hard-earned tax money," are unpopular. Nevertheless, the problem has reached dimensions that demand attention and must be the concern of every social worker on the staffs of these agencies. There is ample

[7] Margaret B. Bailey, "The Family Agency's Role in Treating the Wife of an Alcoholic." *Social Casework*, Vol. 8 (May, 1963), pp. 273-279.

evidence to indicate that alcohol problems are common among welfare recipients, although they may be the result rather than the cause of indigence.

A former director of the Alcoholic Unit of the Cuyahoga County, Ohio Welfare Department (includes Cleveland) estimated that at least 30 percent of the families had drinking problems and thought it might be as high as 40 percent. The difference is explained by the fact that some applicants are not accepted for service. During a radio interview, he said that alcoholism might be the most serious single problem in the caseload.

Other communities have produced comparable data. In 1964, the Westchester (New York) Department of Public Welfare studied various social and health problems in its public assistance caseloads and found alcoholism present in 26 percent of the families.[8] The Massachusetts Department of Public Welfare reported that 14 percent of 2,359 cases requesting disability assistance were suspected of having an alcoholic problem.[9] A Kentucky survey estimated that alcoholism among Child Welfare families was double that of the general population.[10]

With variations in definition of "drinking problems," these statistics are only indicative, but they leave little doubt that social workers in public welfare agencies require some knowledge about alcoholism if they are to help a significant number of clients effectively.

One goal in every welfare department is to prepare clients for jobs to make them self-supporting and to get them off public assistance. It is futile, however, to train the employable alcoholic on welfare unless his alcoholism is treated. If he remains an active alcoholic, he may not be able to obtain employment, or, if he does find a job, he may repeat the pattern of drinking himself out of it.

The importance of helping alcoholics on relief extends beyond those who may be eligible for jobs. Many welfare clients in the Aid to Dependent Children programs are mothers who cannot work because they must be at home caring for their children. Clearly, they will be much better mothers after recovery, and the futures of their children will be far more promising.

Parenthetically, the defeatist attitude that prevails in many welfare departments in relation to working with alcoholics is unjustified. There are failures, but there is also the man from skid row, a derelict who

---

[8] *Monthly Report Bulletin,* County of Westchester, Department of Public Welfare, Vol. 4, No. 10 (October, 1964).

[9] *Massachusetts Mental Health Planning Project Report — Task Force on Alcoholism,* (Boston: Massachussetts Department of Mental Health, 1965), mimeographed.

[10] Research Report No. 41, *Alcohol: Some Kentucky Problems,* Kentucky Legislative Research Commission, p. 12.

spent many of his days in drunken stupors, but who, with help, achieved sobriety and a well-paid job with the city. Another apparently hopeless case became an effective counselor in the welfare department. These illustrations are by no means unique.

3. Courts and Corrections

Social workers in the field of corrections have compelling reasons to be acquainted with the problems of alcoholics because they encounter so many of them. More than 40 percent of all arrests in the United States are for drunkenness–either in public places or while driving. In some large cities, the figure exceeds 50 percent.[11] Many of the persons included in the statistics are arrested more than once, although the actual number of individuals caught in the police legal system is still shockingly high. Not all those arrested are alcoholics, but a large percentage who appear over and over again do have severe alcoholic problems. Unless a skilled person intervenes with help, there is small chance for the defendants to escape the circle of arrest, jail sentence, and rearrest.

Some judges, despite the confusion of higher court decisions, are becoming increasingly aware that the alcoholic needs help and can, in many cases, be made a productive member of society. They are assigning probation officers to the task, sometimes with heartening results.

The court is not the only setting in which the social worker encounters alcoholics. The jails are crowded with inmates convicted of alcohol-related offenses, and to that extent the jail is an important community resource. As long as that is so, it should be used as constructively as possible despite its manifest disadvantages. If incarceration does nothing else, it provides shelter when no other is available. Also, by enforced separation from alcohol, it provides a drying-out period for the alcoholic. The social worker who employs this time to offer treatment and, when the sentence is ended, makes a well-planned referral performs a vital service. A few jails have such programs and they repay the effort.

Probation officers in juvenile courts are constantly exposed to the damage inflicted by alcoholism. They may hear about it in a variety of ways, such as reports of violence, non-support, assaults, or deviant sexual behavior. And, although alcoholism is found primarily in adults, it can develop in adolescence. In one study of 500 male delinquents with an average age of sixteen, 50 were diagnosed as addictive drinkers, and in every one of these families the father was an alcoholic.[12]

---

[11] *Crime in the United States: Uniform Crime Reports, 1968*, (Washington, D.C.: Federal Bureau of Investigation, U.S. Department of Justice, 1969).

[12] James R. McKay, "Drinking and Delinquency," *Alcohol, Alcoholism and Crime*, Report of a Conference at Chatham, Cape Cod, Mass. (1962), pp. 46-57.

4. Hospitals

State hospitals are the most receptive to alcoholics. In one year there were slightly more than 70,000 first admissions to nearly 300 such institutions in the United States, and 22 percent were diagnosed as alcoholics at the time of admission.[13]

The psychiatric wards of general hospitals show a similar incidence of alcoholism. The non-psychiatric services of general hospitals are far less cordial to alcoholics. In 1956, the American Hospital Association and the American Medical Association House of Delegates passed resolutions which recognized alcoholism as a disease and urged that it be treated, when necessary, in general hospitals. In the intervening years, a few progressive institutions have responded, but most seem neither to have seen nor heard the resolutions. Some of the rejections surpass understanding. The chief resident of a large midwestern hospital turned away an alcoholic in obvious need of medical care because "the hospital is not designed to treat social problems."

Despite all the barriers, however, alcoholics do get into hospitals. Some are admitted by physicians who camouflage alcoholism with other diagnoses such as gastroenteritis or "nervous disorders" to outflank the established order. There are others who may have been admitted for some other genuine disorder, and their drinking problem may be discovered accidentally. If this is the case, the chances are that little will be done about it.

Where specific efforts have been made to find alcoholics in the general hospital population, the incidence has been surprisingly high. At North Carolina Memorial Hospital, Pearson surveyed 100 patients (62 medical and 38 surgical) and asked questions about drinking history and patterns, morning drinks, loss of job or family, blackouts, and previous hospitalizations related to drinking. He found 38 patients who might be diagnosed as alcoholic although the word alcoholism was mentioned in only twelve charts.[14]

In any event, alcoholics are there and the treatment of physical needs is the first step in rehabilitation. The second step vital to effective rehabilitation of alcoholics involves the treatment of behavioral, social, and vocational needs. The social service departments of hospitals can and should be active in providing a substantial part of these comprehensive services.

---

[13] *Patients in Mental Institutions, 1964: Part II — State and County Mental Hospitals,* Public Health Service Publication No. 1452 (Washington, D.C.: U.S. Department of Health, Education and Welfare, National Clearinghouse for Mental Health Education, 1964), p. 21.

[14] W. S. Pearson, "The Hidden Alcoholic in the General Hospital: A Study of Hidden Alcoholism In White Male Patients Admitted For Unrelated Complaints," *North Carolina Medical Journal,* Vol. 23, No. 1 (January, 1962), pp. 6-10.

This service is required not only while the patient is in the hospital but after discharge, although it is rarely available at present. To the extent that follow-up care is lacking, the hospital is little better than the jail except for comfort and competent medical care. It becomes part of a circular process because the alcoholic patients discharged without follow-up care will probably return to drinking and will be seen under various guises in hospital after hospital.

In one hospital, an enterprising social work student toured the wards looking for alcoholics and then conducted group sessions with them while they were in-patients. He also invited them to continue in another group after discharge. A surprising number accepted, but without student initiative they might never have been reached.

An encouraging footnote is that many hospitals are becoming slightly more flexible in their policies regarding alcoholics, and, if this continues, the hospital social worker will have more and more work in that field.

5. Industry

The impact of alcoholism on industry is severe and the dollar cost has been widely publicized. It is called the four-billion-dollar hangover, as impaired work performance because of excessive drinking is a major factor. At the executive level, a single error in a judgment made while under the influence of a hangover can cost thousands of dollars. There is also the cost of absenteeism, which is more frequent among alcoholics than any other group of employees. This is compounded by what Harrison Trice has called "on-the-job absenteeism," which is practiced especially by professional, managerial, and other white-collar personnel who go to work even when they cannot do an effective job.

These costs can be tallied on the comptroller's balance sheet. What cannot be measured in dollars, however, is the tragic waste of human resources and lives that go down the drain unless salvaged in time. The majority of alcoholics are in their most productive years—between ages 30 and 55—when their illness is usually at its peak.

Social workers are working daily with employees who seek help because of job dissatisfaction or threatened loss of jobs. Both are disruptive in other areas of their lives and some of the problems are related to excessive drinking. Also, there are social workers employed in industry and labor unions where their relationship to management and employees is on the scene.

6. Other Facilities

There are other settings where social workers see alcoholics or the results of alcoholism. School social workers may cope with the effects of parental alcoholism on children and, in some cases, there is a fairly clear relationship between conditions in the home and substandard performance in school. "Did you ever try to study," asked one junior high school girl, "when your father is cursing and kicking the furniture in a drunken fit, your mother is screaming bloody murder and is half afraid he is going to beat the hell out of her? It happens two or three times a week in our house."

There are churches where social work services are enlisted for counseling, and there are superstructures known as Welfare Federations or Councils of Social Agencies where those in community organization are supposed to plan and mobilize resources for services. The large population of alcoholics and their families deserves more of their time.

PURPOSE OF THE BOOK

This book is not intended to transform social workers into specialists on alcoholism. It does aim, however, to provide a basic knowledge of the subject so that students and faculty will recognize the problem when they encounter it and will furthermore be able to do something about it. Charles Garvin of the School of Social Work at the University of Michigan suspects that many faculty members may not know that their students are working on alcohol-related problems and the students themselves frequently do not recognize such problems.[15]

There is an abundance of evidence to document this suspicion. A physician reported the case of a family whose various members had been seen at *nineteen* different social agencies ranging from welfare departments to hospitals over a period of several years. Almost every member of the family and almost every facet of the family's maladjustment had received attention, except the father's compulsive drinking pattern.

It is also hoped that this book will correct attitudes based on prejudices that color the perceptions and emotional responses of many students and "intrude upon [their] freedom and competence to serve such people and act on their behalf." If that can be accomplished, it may be that future social workers will face the complications of alcoholism with more confidence and enthusiasm than their predecessors.[16]

Alcoholism, one teacher has said, cannot be made a specialization in the social work curriculum because a generic form of education is the best and only practical means for providing basic preparation for social

[15] Charles Garvin, "A Social Work Education in Alcoholism," unpublished paper presented at Annual Meeting of National Council on Alcoholism, New York, April, 1970.

[16] Charles S. Levy, "Introducing Social Work Students to Alcoholism," *Quarterly Journal of Studies on Alcohol*, Vol. 24, No. 4 (December, 1963).

work practice. However, alcoholism is a major problem that will be encountered by most students in their academic and professional careers, so perhaps it does merit "equal time" in the curriculum.[17]

It should be added that this includes all parts of the curriculum. As indicated in the introduction, the pages to follow emphasize the casework approach because that, for better or worse, is the orientation of the author. But the techniques of group work are equally important and the methods of community organization can be applied, as they are in other areas, to planning and implementing the delivery of these services and to the problems of prevention. The Health Department of Pennsylvania recognized this several years ago when its Division of Alcohol Studies and Rehabilitation employed seven community organization representatives and assigned them throughout the state.[18]

Finally, there may be students who do want to become specialists in the field of alcoholism. Despite the limitations indicated, there is and will be a need for them. There are approximately 150 specialized agencies, and, until work with problem drinkers becomes fully assimilated into the activities of helping agencies, there will be an important role for special alcoholism staffs. Even when that goal is fully achieved – which is unlikely to happen tomorrow or the next day – there will be, as Plaut had pointed out, "Specialized services for problem drinkers still will be needed for certain purposes: to demonstrate that problem drinkers can be helped, to provide a training opportunity for personnel who subsequently will work in other generalized agencies, and to undertake research studies." [19]

---

[17] *Ibid.*
[18] Marian J. Wettrick, "The Social Agencies' Responsibility in the Alcoholism Program," National Council on Alcoholism, Inc.
[19] Plaut, *op. cit.*, p. 50.

CHAPTER II

Identifying the Alcoholic

THE WORKING DEFINITION of alcoholism proposed in Chapter One emphasizes the fact that alcoholism cannot be defined in terms of the amount a person drinks, only in terms of what drinking does to him.

There is no single pattern in drinking problems. Some people drink to the point of intoxication every day although they may show varying degrees of dependence on alcohol. Sanford and others think there is a tendency among these alcoholics to require more and more alcohol in order to achieve a desired effect, to crave alcohol, and to suffer when it is not immediately available.[1] However, some alcoholics manage to maintain a desired level of alcohol in their blood for long periods. They never get really drunk but neither are they ever completely sober. They rate the label "alcoholic" because they cannot function to their potential in that condition.

---

[1] Nevitt Sanford, "Conceptions of Alcoholism: What Is It?" *Treatment Methods and Milieus in Social Work with Alcoholics,* Conference Proceedings (Berkeley: Social Work Extension, University of California, Berkeley, December, 1966), pp. 1-14.

Many alcoholics are periodic drinkers who sporadically go on binges lasting from a few days to a few months. In between binges they may not drink at all, but when they start they continue until they are sick to the point of almost total dysfunction. The intervals between sprees may be brief or protracted, but the progression of alcoholism can sometimes be detected in the increased frequency and length of the drinking bouts.

There is no easy way to prove a person is an alcoholic and no rule of thumb to separate alcoholics from normal or heavy drinkers. A physician with some assurance can tell a patient if he has measles, tuberculosis, or diabetes, and reliable laboratory tests and x-rays are available in case of doubt. Alcoholism is not susceptible to similar tests. In an effort to facilitate diagnosis, a number of well-meaning students have composed various questionnaires with fifteen or twenty questions to be answered *Yes* or *No*. They are usually labelled "Test Your A.Q." (Alcohol Quotient) or something equally simple-minded. If the client answers three or four affirmatively, he is suspected of potential alcoholism; if his score is higher, he may be a candidate for the active roster. This approach has no more value than a parlor game. Few alcoholics of reasonable intelligence are likely to be trapped.

Some people seem to be alcoholics almost from the first drink, but the overwhelming majority slip gradually into the condition of uncontrolled habituation after years of social or moderate drinking. Alcoholism, like other abnormal behavior, is continuous with normal behavior rather than apart from it. A man who is a social drinker for a decade or more becomes alcoholic as he becomes increasingly dependent on alcohol to cope with the problems of living.

During this development there are a multitude of signals to warn a family, an employer, friends, and professional helpers that his drinking is on the way to alcoholism. A knowledge of these signals is imperative. The purpose of this chapter is to equip social workers with this knowledge so that they can detect active or incipient alcoholism regardless of the presenting problems.

Detection may come through direct contact with the alcoholic or it may be facilitated by educating others around him and supporting them in constructive action based on insight. Successful intervention at any point depends on this knowledge, and it is especially crucial to early intervention, which can save the alcoholic and his family from years of unnecessary misery.

Recognizing alcoholism, except in the chronic stage, is not easy and a few words of caution are appropriate. These are concerned primarily with excessive dedication to the taxonomic approach that may be useful within limits, but it has many pitfalls.

There have been a variety of charts to show a time-order sequence of symptoms that occur in the life of the so-called "typical" alcoholic, but there are not many typical alcoholics. The majority do not conform to the orderly transition from symptom to symptom as they appear in the meticulously designed curves. Recent studies by Trice and others have indicated that symptoms tend to appear in clusters rather than in sequence. They come at different times for different alcoholics. *When* they appear may not be as important as the fact that they are present and should not be ignored. Some of the most significant signs are:

1. Increasing Dependence on Alcohol

A multitude of criteria have been devised to determine whether or not an individual has a drinking problem, and the one that most authorities emphasize is the degree of dependence on alcohol. The amount of alcohol and behavior while drinking may not be abnormal according to the peer culture in which the person functions, but over-dependence on anything constitutes a problem.

Selden Bacon among others has underlined the importance of this quality of alcoholism:

> Alcoholics may be distinguished from other drinkers primarily by the purpose for which they drink. Some people drink to fulfill a religious ritual, others in order to be polite, still others for a good time, or to make friends, to experiment, show off, get warm or cool, quench thirst, or because they like a particular alcoholic beverage as a condiment or because they want to go on a spree. None of these is the purpose of the alcoholic although he might claim any or all to satisfy some questioner. The alcoholic drinks because he *has* to go on living. He drinks compulsively; that is a power greater than rational planning brings him to drink and to excessive drinking . . .[2]

He elaborated that concept in an article, "Alcoholics Do Not Drink." He pointed out that drinking alcoholic beverages, a widely accepted custom in our society, is enjoyed by most drinkers as a social function that usually involves a kind of "sociality" or reciprocity. When Smith suggests to Jones, "Come on, I'll buy you a drink," it means that Jones' drinking rewards Smith and vice-versa. But, as Jones becomes more dependent on alcohol and gulps drinks at the rate of three to his companion's one, this easy camaraderie is destroyed.

> If Jones is our alcoholic, his use of alcohol is with increasing frequency irritating, perhaps frightening, perhaps even

[2] Selden D. Bacon, "Alcoholics Do Not Drink," *The Annals of the American Academy of Political and Social Sciences,* Vol. 315 (January, 1958), pp. 55-64.

> measurably damaging to Smith. The various Smiths in the group may even verbalize about this, at first only in joking terms but soon in more serious fashion; they may even leave him 'out' of certain situations. But it is equally clear that the drinking of the 'custom bound' Smiths is not only inadequate but rather irritating to our increasingly alcoholic Mr. Jones. He may 'use' the Smith's cocktail party to get alcohol, but the party itself is of little interest, often, in fact, interferes with his perferred patterns of alcohol consumption.
>
> The functions which alcohol serves for any individual drinker are still gained by Jones. Indeed, they are magnified to the point that most members of his group would call them distorted. The others like drinking. Jones *needs* alcohol.[3]

He needs it, according to Keller, for the sedative effect and he begins to drink more and drink more quickly to achieve the necessary solace.[4] At a party, he is on his second or third drink before others have finished their first. He may drink doubles or triples to mask the fact that he is consuming more than other guests. He is the person who volunteers too enthusiastically to serve as bartender, especially if the bar is in the kitchen or some other secluded spot. This enables him to have a few extras while mixing for other guests.

Another indication of dependence is found in a person who has been gregarious and accepted most invitations to social gatherings, regardless of the promise of alcoholic beverages. Now he begins to avoid affairs that do not include drinking. When he does accept an invitation, he is likely to fortify himself with a few drinks before leaving home because he is afraid he will not get enough to drink at the party.

Some men betray their changing behavior in relation to the widespread custom of stopping for a drink or two with friends after work. The friends go home after the first or second drink, but the man with a problem remains in the bar for "just one more," perhaps until late in the evening or until closing time.

Drinking in the morning or throughout the work day, if excessive and used to help the drinker cope with problems or escape from them, is a more advanced sign of dependence. Some people reach for a bottle before they reach for the toothpaste. One man's breakfast seldom varied from four bottles of beer and one egg, although, if hurried, he could skip the egg. Others carry a bottle in the glove compartment of the car and drink on the way to work, or they may have liquor stashed away in the

---

[3] *Ibid.*, p. 61.

[4] John E. Keller, *Ministering to Alcoholics* (Minneapolis, Minnesota: Augsburg Publishing House, 1966), p. 25.

office. Those who can hold out until noon may drink their lunch instead of eating it. Whatever the device, the dependence on alcohol for daily functioning is clear. As the dependence becomes more severe, the alcoholic may be drinking on the job or even not getting to the job at all. As already mentioned, alcoholism is one of the major causes of absenteeism in industry.

The emerging pattern is that a person's life is increasingly arranged around his drinking. He no longer worries about drinking interfering with his activities; he is more concerned with the fact that his activities might interfere with his drinking.

In all problem drinking there is some loss of control. The alcoholic drinks despite his awareness of the damage to his life. As Clinebell points out:

> If a drinker who is not alcoholic finds that his drinking is interfering with his work, he will usually reduce his consumption. In contrast, the alcoholic will not even recognize the causal relationship between his drinking and his job trouble; rather he will project the blame for his trouble on others. He cannot recognize the real cause of his difficulty because alcohol is very important to him. To recognize it as the offender would threaten the center around which he has organized his life. Even if he suspects that alcohol is the cause of his trouble he will not be able to reduce his consumption for any extended period . . .[5]

2. Loss of Control

Loss of control is implicit in increasing dependence, but, in the process of identifying alcoholism by interviewing and history-taking, it should not be confused with simply getting drunk.

There are many social situations in which getting drunk is acceptable as long as it does not impinge on the rights of others. Some groups have occasional parties where it is expected that most participants will get "high." This is behavior that may be ordinarily forbidden but is granted temporary license in given situations. Each group has its rules for the custom of drinking that govern time, place, amounts, frequency, and acceptable deportment. Because ours is a widely diverse society, the rules vary according to the life style of different groups. Behavior that might be viewed as problem drinking in one social group is viewed as being within bounds in another.

A man like Jones in the foregoing illustration reaches a point where

[5] Howard J. Clinebell, Jr., *Understanding and Counselling the Alcoholic* (New York: Abingdon Press, 1968), p. 35.

he no longer observes the rules and, with increasing frequency, exceeds the customary limits of his social group. He goes beyond the allowed license although, as Bacon points out, "he may define certain situations as being appropriate for this license when others do not." [6]

This can be the beginning of the social excommunication suffered by many alcoholics. John Dos Passos, in his autobiography, *The Best Times*, recalled the dilemma that novelist F. Scott Fitzgerald imposed on his friends. "Like every other friend of Scott's the Murphys were in a quandary. They were fond of him. They admired his talent. They were concerned about him. They wanted to be helpful but friendship had its limits. They couldn't go on having every pleasant evening being made a shambles of."

Loss of control means the alcoholic has lost the ability to *choose* when and where he will get drunk and what will happen to him when he does drink. It does not mean he will get drunk every time he takes a drink and sometimes he will stop after one or two. On other occasions, the first drink will trigger a binge lasting for days or weeks. He seldom knows what will happen. It has been said that an alcoholic is one who sets out not to get drunk *this* time but gets drunk anyway.

The quality of control is one factor that distinguishes heavy drinkers from alcoholics; the former have it and the latter do not.

3. Guilt, Rationalization, Denial

Sooner or later the alcoholic begins to feel guilty about his drinking because he sees what it is doing to himself and others but he is not prepared to stop. Indeed, by this time he may be afraid to stop because he has learned to use alcohol to cope with the crises in his life and he sees no effective alternative.

Now, however, there may be pressures from his wife or employer to do something about his drinking, so he begins to rationalize. He tries to eliminate himself from the company of alcoholics by definition. Like the obese person who always knows people who are fatter than he is, the alcoholic always knows someone who drinks more than he does. He may insist that he only has a couple before dinner but forget to mention the fifth he has after dinner. One woman had an impeccable record of abstinence at parties no matter how freely the liquor flowed but she drank to oblivion when she got home.

The alcoholic is never at a loss for excuses to drink, although the excuses may be absurd to everyone except himself. He drinks to celebrate the last day of winter but also to hail the first day of spring. He drinks at funerals and births, at weddings and divorces. One man drank

[6] Bacon, *op. cit.*, p. 60.

only on holidays, but these were not confined to the conventional ones, such as Christmas, Thanksgiving, and Labor Day. He drank on Mother's Day and on the anniversary of the Charge of the Light Brigade. In his book, the birthdays of Lincoln and Chester A. Arthur merited equal observance. He also lifted glasses in countless toasts to the birthdays of all relatives, including second cousins. He managed about fifty holidays a year.

Once the rationalization starts, he drinks at any provocation – when he feels depressed or elated, when he experiences success or defeat, when he wishes to induce sleep or overcome fatigue. He may drink out of self-pity. One man feels sorry for himself because his wife is so wonderful he cannot possibly be worthy of her. Another drinks because he is married to a nagging woman who would send the saintliest man to the bottle.

The alcoholic does not want people to know how much he consumes, so he not only sneaks drinks but hides his private stock to foil those who might watch the diminishing contents of bottles kept in the usual places. Some alcoholics go to great lengths. One man surprised his wife by drinking out of her steam iron. Another hid a bottle in the air filter of his car so he could get it to a party unknown to his wife. Lincoln Williams, in his book *Tomorrow Will Be Sober,* tells of a farmer who secreted a bottle of gin in every one of his beehives. When he went to attend the bees or remove the honey, he covered himself with a heavy black veil – ostensibly to prevent the bees from stinging him – and under cover of this drank to his heart's content. He was quite proud of this deception.

Developing alcoholics may boast about their drinking and their ability to hold their liquor, but with mounting guilt and signs of disapproval all around they make every effort to minimize their intake. Lying becomes necessary. A slogan which, although simplistic, has some truth is that "Alcoholism is reached when certain individuals stop bragging about how much they can drink and begin to lie about how much they are drinking."

At this point, they do not want any discussion of drinking. If an alcoholic's wife broaches the subject, he may ignore her, become angry, or tell her she's crazy and she is the one who needs help. Nor does he want to be "bugged" on the job. He tries to avoid any conversation about drinking, is resentful, complains about invasion of privacy, and is convinced that in a more just society he would be at the top and incumbent executives would be wrapping packages in the shipping department.

The alcoholic's drinking may cause deterioration in job performance and ultimate dismissal, but he feels that it is never his fault. He denounces unreasonable management policies and incompetent superiors.

He may say being fired is the best thing that could have happened and he is glad to be out of that "lousy outfit" where they failed to recognize his skills and, because they didn't like him, placed every possible roadblock in the way of advancement. So his smouldering hostility erupts and he tells the boss to go to hell. Then he gets another job and repeats the pattern. Incidentally, it should be noted that some alcoholics avoid this crisis by quitting before they are fired. They seem to have a radar that warns of impending disaster. This enables them to say that they have never lost a job.

Denial is sometimes accomplished by avoiding symptoms that are so closely associated with alcoholism that they have come to be mistakenly regarded as *sine qua non* for diagnosis. Morning or early drinking is one of these. With this in mind, some alcoholics use their ability to resist the bottle during the day as indisputable "proof" that their drinking is still well under control. They can ask indignantly: "How can I possibly be an alcoholic? Everybody knows a real alcoholic needs a snort for an eyeopener."

Many of these people do not, however, voluntarily reveal that they set a time before which they will not drink but after which anything goes. It may be late afternoon or early afternoon or early evening, and they wait in agony for the designated hour. Then they are off and drinking to oblivion. But they do not drink during the day and with this limited control can delude themselves and sometimes others that they are not alcoholics.

The same kind of rationalization can be applied to the employment situation. Some alcoholics are rarely absent and may even be compulsively punctual, getting to the office no matter how wretched they feel. They may not do much work when they get there or they may make costly errors of judgment, but they persuade themselves that they are not alcoholics because they are on the job every day and, "Everybody knows a *real* alcoholic can't do that."

On the contrary, a *real* alcoholic may summon the will to do almost anything to arrange his life so he can continue drinking. One of the myths about alcoholics is their supposed lack of willpower, but they seem to have inexhaustible resources when it becomes necessary to protect their drinking. (Vignettes #1 and #2)

4. Going On The Wagon

Paradoxically, one of the warning signals of alcoholism is found in planned periods of sobriety. It has been almost proverbial that alcoholics cannot get along without alcohol so a man will prove that he doesn't deserve the label and that he can stop any time he chooses.

Within limits, that is true. Few alcoholics have to drink every day of the year. Most can abstain temporarily if the pressure is severe and the goals worthwhile, but they cannot do it too frequently. In most cases it is futile for a wife or employer to say to a husband or employee: "All right, you say you can get along without liquor. If that's true, prove it by not taking a drink for the next two weeks or a month." Few would flunk that test. It might be painful, but most alcoholics can endure the agony of temporary abstinence if it means saving families or jobs. Almost certainly, however, they are drinking within minutes after the end of the agreed-upon period. This phenomenon is illustrated by some who give up alcohol for Lent and point with pride to their ability to control their drinking. Invariably, they are off on another binge with the rise of the sun on Easter morning.

Marty Mann, in her *New Primer on Alcoholism,* says that a limited period of abstinence is not the genuine test. A better one, she suggests, is for a person to take no less than one but no more than three drinks every day for at least six months. There must be no exceptions, no special occasions, or the test has failed. Few certified alcoholics can make the grade.[7]

5. Blackouts

Among the many symptoms of alcoholism, one of the most dramatic is the blackout, if it occurs in relation to drinking. That relationship is important in diagnosing alcoholism because blackouts can happen to non-alcoholics and to teetotalers. In most charts this symptom is included as one of the early signs, but studies have indicated that blackouts can begin – if they occur at all, and they do not happen to every alcoholic – at any stage.

A blackout is not the same as "passing out" during a too-convivial evening. In a blackout there is no loss of consciousness, but the victim has little or no memory of what has happened in periods that can last from a few hours to a few days. He suffers temporary amnesia. His conduct is not necessarily bizarre and those who encounter him may think he is a little tipsy but nothing more. Occasionally, they are not even aware that he has been drinking. During a blackout a person may drive to a distant city and register in a hotel. When he wakes up the next morning he may have no recollection of the journey or the registration procedure.

The average blackout, however, has to do with the victim's inability to remember what he said or how he got home the night before, but it

[7] Marty Mann, *New Primer on Alcoholism* (New York: Holt, Rinehart and Winston, 1958), p. 83.

can be more frightening. Alcoholics who inflict violence on their families cannot remember striking a single blow and are appalled when told of their behavior.

One woman, in her late thirties with a responsible job and fairly rigid standards of respectability, would find herself in motel beds with strange men whom she did not remember having met. A client said he woke up to see his feet badly lacerated and caked with dry blood. There was no recall of what had happened and he was incredulous when his wife acidly informed him that he had celebrated the previous midnight at a party by performing a tribal dance on broken glass.

Some blackouts are so frightening that they spur a person to seek help. At least they can be used effectively to confront the alcoholic with the potential dangers of his drinking. Alcoholics have said that the inability to recall what one has done is harrowing, but even worse is the inability to deny accusations effectively because they don't remember where they were when the event, perhaps an accident, occurred.

6. Emergency Remedies

As the alcoholic's difficulties increase, he tries an assortment of remedies that seldom work but are themselves signs of alcoholism. Because he knows it is the martinis that defeat him, he switches from gin to bourbon; when that doesn't do any good, he rejects whiskey in favor of vodka. He is a man who would rather switch than fight and he may run the gamut, but he is still an alcoholic. Then, as one writer said:

> During one of his sober periods when he is reviewing his problem for what seems to be the millionth time, he suddenly believes he has found the right answer. It isn't him, it isn't drinking. He just hasn't been going about it right. The real secret is to drink the right kind of beverage and drink only at certain times, and so he sets about to plan it out in great detail. He plans what he will drink and what he won't drink. He plans where he'll drink and where he won't drink. He plans who he'll drink with and who he won't drink with. He plans when he'll drink and when he won't drink. Now at last he has it, so he sets about to put his plan into effect with great care and caution and for a time it may seem to work. But with the increased self-confidence comes lessened discretion in carrying out the plan. Finally, he is painfully awakening from another binge with characteristic familiarity.[8]

Another strategem is geographic change. He attributes excessive drinking to the irresistible temptation of his neighborhood, so he and his

[8] *The Progression of Alcoholism,* Pamphlet distributed by the Milwaukee Council on Alcoholism, Milwaukee, Wisconsin, p. 7.

family move to another part of the city where he soon finds the same irresistible temptations duplicated. He may move from the city to the country because everyone gets loaded in urban areas. Now he can drink the clean rural air instead of booze. Soon, however, he is getting drunk in the village tavern instead of in the cocktail lounge. Some even move to distant cities only to discover that they drink as much in Denver as they did in Baltimore.

7. Personality Changes

In looking for clues to alcoholism, it is important to recognize personality changes. As the alcoholic experiences failure after failure, his self-esteem sinks lower and he may compensate with grandiose behavior. He tries to atone for neglect and betrayal by huge spending binges during which he buys lavish gifts for his family. A new car or a set of furniture, which he cannot afford, is none too good for that loyal and wonderful wife who has remained steadfastly at his side. When he falls behind in payments and the car or furniture is repossessed, he goes on another bender and the cycle, unless interrupted, begins again.

Aggression may replace childish attempts at generosity. The recipients of his misguided extravagance and subsequent disappointment abandon displays of appreciation and resent the efforts to buy affection and good will. As their hostility increases, he responds with anger. One writer pointed out that this aggression is not "always expressed in fights, brawls or physical abuse of his family." He may take out his resentment on something or someone remote. "For example, he may back his car over a hydrant to get even for the unappreciative attitude of his family, kick in a window because his boss or someone else in an authoritative relationship made him angry, or even go down the street slashing tires because a friend offended his increasingly sensitive nature. From this point on he shows ever stronger isolationist tendencies by walking out on his family, friends or employer. This is in anticipation and is intended to save him the embarrassment of being deserted by family and friends or dismissed by his employer."[9]

8. Physical Symptoms

As alcoholism continues toward the chronic stage, physical symptoms appear. Red, bleary eyes, prominent facial veins, and hand tremors are some indications. Poor dietary habits contribute to malnutrition, cirrhosis of the liver, polyneuropathy, and, at the worst, Korsakoff's syndrome. He may need hospitalization for any of these or for delirium tremens.

Brendan Behan's biographer describes him when he reached this

[9] *Ibid.*

stage. His body "was living on an overdraft which could not be repaid in the normal period of rest. He had begun to live on borrowed time. Utterly illogical, he appeared to believe that if he drowned himself long enough in a sea of alcohol, one day a miracle would happen and he would emerge to a new life of golden memories. Added to which he was so ill physically that drinking was a defense mechanism from the pain he was feeling."[10] By the time a man has reached this level of deterioration, he has been an alcoholic for many years.

Parenthetically, H. L. Mencken amusingly illustrated the difference between appropriate and inappropriate drinking. Although he once said, "I drink every known alcoholic drink and enjoy them all," he knew that alcohol did not fuel literary inspiration. He never drank before the day's work was done. He wrote:

> "A man who has taken aboard two or three cocktails is less competent than he was before to steer a battleship down the Ambrose Channel or to cut off a leg, or to draw up a deed of trust, or to conduct Bach's B minor mass, but he is immensely more competent to entertain a dinner party, or to admire a pretty girl, or to hear Bach's B minor mass. The harsh, useful things of the world are best done by men who are as starkly sober as so many convicts in the death house, but the lovely and useless things, the charming and exhilarating things, are best done by men with, as the phrase is, a few sheets in the wind." Mencken marveled "that no utopian has ever proposed to abolish all the sorrows of the world by the simple device of getting and keeping the whole human race gently stewed." [11]

THE MYTH OF THE HIDDEN ALCOHOLIC

The signs of alcoholism are many, and despite the ability of alcoholics to deceive and camouflage, these signs are visible to those who make the effort to look and want to see them. Nevertheless, the majority of alcoholics are unidentified. It is estimated that our combined approaches to the problem – Alcoholics Anonymous, clinics, hospitals, churches, social agencies, and others – are reaching no more than 15 percent of the alcoholic population.

What about the other 85 percent? We *assume* they are hidden, and alcoholism is frequently described as an iceberg problem with only a small part of it visible while the remainder is beneath the surface. If this means only that most alcoholics are not known to specialized agencies

[10] Rae Jeffs, *Brendan Behan* (Cleveland, Ohio: World Publishing Company, 1968), p. 129.

[11] Bud Johns, *The Ombibulous Mr. Mencken: A Drinking Biography* (San Francisco: Synergistic Press, 1968).

or to Alcoholics Anonymous, there may be some validity to the premise. But if it means that no one is aware of a person's drinking problem, only a small fraction can be classed as unknown. Few practicing alcoholics can successfully hide their alcoholism in all the roles of their lives.

Some may hide it on the job. This is especially true in management circles where there is greater freedom and some may drink in comparative privacy, but sooner or later the alcoholic will expose himself. (Vignette #3)

Alcoholics may be "hidden" in families. A woman who called an alcoholism center said that her husband had been drinking excessively for several years. His health was bad, he seldom ate, and he was repeatedly abusive and violent. The family doctor agreed to see the man if he could be persuaded to make an office visit, but the response to that suggestion was a torrent of obscenities accompanied by the kicking of furniture. Because no one was caring for this man, he was, at least statistically, a hidden alcoholic.

Industry and families are not the only places where alcoholics are unheeded for years. Those who practice in the helping professions see alcoholics every day but seldom do anything about it. The estimate that 15 percent of the alcoholic population is receiving help is probably generous. But, even if it is accurate, it exposes our negligence when related to another estimate – perhaps understated – that as many as 35 percent of the alcoholics are clients or patients somewhere. Those who comprise the vast difference between the two estimates are examined and probed and treated for all sorts of emotional and physical disorders, but not for their alcoholism.

Professional caretakers are almost as culpable as lay persons in their dependence on clichés and stereotypes. Some doctors, for example, cling to the stereotype of an alcoholic as a derelict and are reluctant to even consider that label for those in the higher socio-economic strata. Even when physicians recognize that excessive drinking is associated with physiological disorders among the latter, they seldom pursue the implications of this.

This means two things. One is "that those alcoholics deemed most fit by physicians to receive specialized care for alcoholism are those for whom treatment attempts in the past have been most unpromising." They are, in general, likely to be middle-aged or older with 20 years or more of excessive drinking. The second is that golden opportunities for early detection are missed almost daily in hospitals throughout the country. Blanc *et al* state: "The physician can serve as a case finder of alcoholics; yet until physician attitudes and knowledge about alcoholism undergo change, many alcoholics and prealcoholics will not receive treatment until the disease is so far advanced that treatment becomes highly complicated, therapeutic goals limited, and necessary resources extremely limited and expensive." [12]

The hospital situation is perhaps the most dramatic, but it is possible to examine the complete roster of caretaking settings to discover similar misunderstanding and neglect.

Social agencies see many alcoholics but treat only a few. When this writer began a study of the effect of parental alcoholism on adolescents, he enlisted the cooperation of several agencies. The initial request was for an estimate of the incidence of families in each caseload where there was a drinking problem. Invariably, the estimate was low. One agency, that was devoted primarily to work with adolescents and that had a caseload of 400, suggested that there were no more than a dozen such families. When the caseload was carefully re-examined, using only that knowledge already available to the caseworkers, and without asking any additional questions of the clients, the actual number was closer to seventy-five. The experience in other agencies was comparable.

These alcoholics were not hidden. The caseworkers either knew about them or could have found out through competent history taking or interpretation. Even when parental alcoholism was known there was a tendency to ignore it. This not only left the alcoholics untreated but also limited effective work with the children because the alcoholism remained a dominant and destructive factor in the home.

In one agency some workers insisted that the drinking problems of the parents could not be approached until the clients, usually adolescents, introduced the subject. If they did not, even though clues were available elsewhere, the topic was taboo. Presumably, if the initiative was taken by a caseworker, the therapeutic process would be disrupted. Not all caseworkers accepted that curious philosophy, but there were more than there should have been.

Another setting that provides fertile field for early detection is the courtroom, but again the opportunities are mostly ignored. Alcoholics in court are thought of almost exclusively in terms of the derelicts who crowd the fetid drunk tanks every weekend, but these people are close to the end of the road. There are many defendants, however, whose behavior is related to excessive drinking but in a way that is far less obvious and certainly more difficult to label alcoholic than the person arrested for driving while intoxicated, especially if it happens more than once or twice. This does not imply that every motorist who drives after he has had one or two drinks qualifies as an alcoholic. It does mean

---

[12] H. T. Blanc, W. F. Overton, and M. E. Chafetz, "Social Factors in the Diagnosis of Alcoholism," *Quarterly Journal of Studies on Alcohol,* Vol. 24, No. 2, p. 659.

that if he drives repeatedly while intoxicated his drinking must interfere with normal functioning, and there should be some effort made to determine the extent of his drinking problem with the related responsibility of helping him to do something about it. There is some disagreement about the relationship between alcoholism and automobile accidents, but the statistics from the National Highway Safety Council are impressive.

Drunken driving is not the only clue to the possibility of a drinking problem. Pre-sentence investigations by probation officers are also instruments for early detection of alcoholism that have the potential for much wider use.

The myth of the hidden alcoholic has been one of the major barriers to expanded help because as long as alcoholism is present and untreated it is a formidable barrier against effective treatment of other problems. There is no reason for the alcoholic to remain hidden. The warning signs are there even if the presenting problem is something else. Interested social workers – and social workers employed in all the settings mentioned above – can recognize the presence of problem drinking if they have a knowledge of the warning signals and are willing to apply that knowledge.

Diagnosis is not easy but it is within the competence of any social worker trained to interview and to relate to people. It has to be a judgment based on the analysis of drinking behavior and its impact on the drinker's total life activities. The validity of this judgment depends on the sifting of evidence revealed in interviews conducted by a person with a knowledge of the factors that add up to alcoholism.

Detection requires persistent probing. It means that when Mrs. Y. complains about her marriage and only casually mentions her husband's drinking behavior at parties or his blackouts, that she may dismiss as amusing episodes, the worker is not put off. With these clues, he moves in to elicit more details. It can be done and it is the responsibility of those in professional settings to see that it is done.

VIGNETTE #1

A former woman alcoholic recalled that in her drinking days, when she consistently maintained her position close to the top of the hit-the-bottle parade, she was offered a job as public relations director for a large candy manufacturing company. In an effort to persuade her to accept the position, the president invited her to visit the plant one morning. True to her style, she went on a gargantuan binge the night before the appointment. Equally true to her style, she dragged herself out of bed, camouflaged the telltale signs of a hangover, and kept the date. Outwardly, she was the chic model of a career woman; inwardly, every fibre of her body was on the verge of convulsion. Her host conducted her on a tour which included viewing steaming vats of boiling chocolate. The memory of that experience still caused her to turn green twenty years later. At the time, however, she convinced herself that if she performed so well she was certainly not an alcoholic and then she headed for the nearest bar.

VIGNETTE #2

Rae Jeffs, in her biography of Brendan Behan, has another illustration of the willpower an alcoholic can exert when necessary. On the morning after a monumental binge, the playwright was to meet his parents at a railway station. Mrs. Jeffs was sure his hangover would prevent him from keeping the appointment, but when she arrived he was "standing there in the middle of the room, his body drooping in sort of doomed resignation, his head sagging on his shoulder while his eyes pleaded silently for someone to take care of him. Somehow he had managed to shave and put on a suit, but in the process he had forgotten to take off his pajamas and the cords of the bottom half were hanging down in front of his trousers, while the jacket of his suit did little to hide the fact that the green and white pajama top was a stand-in for his shirt. He was barely articulate, not so much from the drink, but from physical sickness, and the brief efforts he made to be sociable only served to increase the coma in which he was encased. He was not fit to meet his parents . . . but . . . I knew that in his stubborness, he would do so . . ."

Mrs. Jeffs wanted to take Behan to a doctor. "This isn't simply a hangover," she insisted, "you are sick, truly sick." Pathetically, he nodded his head in agreement but replied quietly, "I'm not feeling too bad, not too bad at all." A few moments later, he muttered, "I must see the ould one, I must see the ould one"*

---

*Rae Jeffs, *Brendan Behan* (Cleveland, Ohio: World Publishing Company, 1968).

VIGNETTE #3

Mr. R. was vice-president in charge of production of a large corporation. He was a "hidden" alcoholic for years until his superior was forced to recognize that "something" was wrong. This awakening occurred after Mr. R. attended a two-week executive seminar in another city. During that period, he attended only one of the twenty half-day sessions and then he had a pounding hangover. The remainder of the time was dedicated to continuous drinking interrupted by brief periods of sleep.

Mr. R.'s boss visited an out-patient clinic for alcoholics to ask how he could inform his errant colleague that he was drinking too much. He seemed stunned by the idea that Mr. R. was an alcoholic. How could he be? After all, he had a fine family. He was active in community affairs and in the church. Besides, the boss and Mr. R. belonged to the same country club and their wives travelled in the same social circles. As the interview progressed, it was clear that his reasoning was based on a bundle of *non sequiturs.*

It was obvious that Mr. R. was an alcoholic and his symptoms had been demanding recognition for at least five years. But when Mr. R. complained of constant fatigue he was given extra vacation time because everyone recognized the pressures of the job. Pressure was also used to explain a series of faulty decisions. It also explained why a man who had been gregarious and congenial had become querulous and distant, why it became difficult for him to tolerate even the friendliest criticism, and why his temper flare-ups, aimed especially at subordinates, occurred with increasing frequency.

Of course, everyone knew that Mr. R. drank. Sometimes he was boisterous and offensive at parties. At lunch he had three martinis while his companions had one. And there were blackouts but, as he related his adventures to the fellows in the office, they seemed hilarious.

Mr. R. began to take more and more time away from his job. His lunch hours lengthened and outside appointments kept him "tied up" for many hours. His associates wanted to believe that he was just going through "one of those periods." Unfortunately the period lasted for years. When treatment was finally accepted, it was successful, but earlier action might have avoided years of waste.

The only reason that Mr. R., like thousands of others, was a hidden alcoholic was because those around conspired to hide him. The warning sirens were loud and clear – aberrant drinking patterns, personality changes, absenteeism, deteriorating job performance, blackouts. All were ignored in the hope that some magic would make them disappear.

INTERVIEWING THE ALCOHOLIC AND HIS FAMILY TO IDENTIFY THE DRINKING PROBLEM

Family Adjustment

I usually ask how the patient gets along with his wife when he is drinking, and then, how he gets along with his wife when he is not drinking. This gives us a clue as to what behavior emerges with over-drinking. For example, passive-aggressive people are frequently very hostile and belligerent when they overdrink. It also provides some understanding of the spouse's involvement in the drinking. If the couple is able to get along when the drinker is abstinate it is a favorable prognostic sign. One might anticipate progressively shorter periods of sobriety and compatability frequently leading to separation or divorce. Other questions might include:

Q. "What does your wife (and/or family) say about your drinking?" (This

---

Adopted with permission from Interviewing and Alcoholism," an unpublished paper by Richard Shalvoy, Columbus Area Community Mental Health Center.

allows a defensive client to project and indicates how he and his wife get along. It also provides a clue as to the wife's awareness of a problem.)

The caseworker should listen for and explore changes in drinking pattern over the years. For example:

Q. "When did your drinking begin to cause trouble in your marriage?"

Q. "Do you find yourself drinking more in the past three years?"

or

Q. "Has your overdrinking increased over the past three years?"

Then help the patient to tell you how the change in his pattern occured. Try to be as specific as possible and offer a certain period of time. What may be of further help to the social worker and the patient is to help the patient relive a recent episode with such questions as:

Q. "When did you drink last?"

A. "I drank a little yesterday."

Q. "How much?"

A. "About five beers all day. That's all."

Q. "For how many days preceding that did you drink?"

A. "About one week."

Q. "Do you usually drink for a week or so?"

A. "Yes."

Q. "Has your pattern always been pretty much this way?"

A. "No. I used to drink just one day or two at the most. It's only been the last three years or so that I drank for a week. I can't seem to 'get off' so easy now."

"I used to drink longer than that, but I can't take it anymore. It must be my age."

Another approach with the spouse might be:

Q. "Does your husband's drinking cause problems in your marriage?"

A. "Yes, he promises to stop, and he does for a few days, then he starts right back. I've threatened to divorce him if he doesn't stop, so he stops for a few weeks and each time he starts drinking again."

Q. "What does he say about this?"

or ("How does he defend against recurring problems?")

Q. "How long has this been going on?"

Approaching the marital situation from still another direction one might ask a patient:

Q. "What do you do when your wife complains about your drinking?"

A frequent answer is:

A. "I figure what the hell, I may as well get drunk, she accuses me of it anyway. I can have one drink and she thinks I'm drunk!"

Q. "It must be very difficult to live with a nagging wife. What do you do?" (Be supportive and then see how he protects himself from her, i.e., attacking her or withdrawing.)

A. "I just stay away from home."

Q. "Does that help?"

A. "No, she is usually mad when I get home anyway."

Sometimes we anticipate answers when we should question further, e.g., it may be obvious to us that a man's drinking is presenting a serious problem, however, it is helpful to know specifically what bothers a spouse about her husband's drinking.

For example,

Q. "What about your drinking? Does it make your wife angry with you?"

A. "She doesn't like it when I spend so much money."

or

A. "She says I'm unreasonable when I drink."

A. "She doesn't like it when I drink so much."

The caseworker should work toward developing a history of drinking in the marriage, noting particularly changes in frequency, amount and circumstances, and its gradual interference with the marital relationship. It is also important to determine in what way it interferes with the marriage and the family's attempts to cope with the situation. This is an invaluable aid in helping the patient and the caseworker gain perspective.

Social Adjustment

This area shows how the problem drinker functions in his social environment. It involves a certain progressively social behavior pattern which usually leads to social isolation from the drinker's peer group. Initially considered a social lubricant, alcohol may eventually have the reverse effect. The problem drinker becomes unlike other drinkers in amount and circumstances, and he is increasingly less able to control his behavior while with other people. Drinking to get drunk, not to be sociable, becomes the desired result.

It has been said that people drink for three reasons: (1) to move toward people in a friendly way, (2) to move toward people in a hostile way, and (3) to move away from people. The answers to these questions imply important diagnostic clues and some indication of the type of treatment resources the patient is able to use. For example, a problem drinker of many years recently came to us when he was referred by his probation officer. He was asked:

Q. "Do you prefer to be with other people when you're drinking?"

A. "I always drink alone. If someone in the bar wants to talk, I move away or leave. I don't mean to be snooty – I just want to be alone."

A forty-two year old businessman we recently saw said:

"I can't even call on a client unless I've had a drink."

Q. "Why is that?"

A. "I'm terribly shy and couldn't sell anything to anyone. Over a couple of drinks I do fine."

A youthful appearing man in his early thirties explained it this way:

Q. "What does your wife do when you drink?"

A. "She nags at me but I just walk away. Eventually, though, the little things begin to bother me and I end up getting drunk and telling everyone where to go."

Findings at the Child Welfare Board indicate that there is a large number of female alcoholics. Caseworkers should be attuned to mothers who are employed but not doing their housework. Female problem drinkers are frequently observed where there are unsupervised or untidy looking children poorly cared for. They may also exhibit behavior and standards out of keeping with a previously attained level of functioning. A caseworker recently visited an employed middle-aged divorcee who had shown increasing inability to maintain adequate housekeeping standards. When questioned about this she told the caseworker that she thought she had "more energy" after a few drinks but she utilized the majority of her off-work time to drink and the housework is neglected.

An agitated young woman married only three years told us: "We used to be invited out a lot. We had a group of three or four couples who ran around together. I always had to have two or three drinks before we went out on a party and, usually, I was the first one to get drunk."

Q. "What happened to the relationship you had with these friends?"

A. "Eventually they just began to exclude us because I made such an issue out of drinking. I tried to start a fight with my husband at a party and that sort of ended it. It was horrible."

CHAPTER III

Alcoholism: Theories of Causation

EVERYBODY HAS HAD a go at the causes of alcoholism, and the multi-causation theory has gained the most widespread acceptance. Most authorities view alcoholism as the final consequence of cultural, biological, social, and psychological factors that interact in a complex and only partly understood pattern.

Carl L. Anderson, in the *Encyclopedia of Social Work,* summarized the various approaches:

> Alcoholism is viewed as arising from a complex interplay of physical, psychological, social and other factors, although the extent to which each of them contributes to the alcoholism syndrome is unknown. Psychiatric and psychological approaches concern themselves with alcoholism as a manifestation of a personality disturbance and with the display of emotional factors. Two important questions are: How specific are the emotional bases of alcoholism? Is there a pre-alcoholic

personality? Currently there is lack of agreement as to a single psychological determinant or a group of them.

The sociological approach views alcoholism as significantly influenced by environmental and cultural factors in its onset and development. Among these factors are attitudes toward drinking and drunkenness. Social scientists are active in studies pertaining to the development of alcoholism and to the better understanding of the use or non-use of alcohol in various age, ethnic, social and economic groups.

The physiological approach considers alcoholism primarily as an expression of an altered metabolic or endocrine state that may have a genetic basis. Many interesting data in the biochemistry of the alcoholic are becoming available. Research in this area is proceeding but important questions cannot be answered at this time, such as: Are demonstrable changes in biochemistry a result of or a cause of alcoholism?[1]

Snyder proposes that "the problem of alcohol cannot be understood apart from a consideration of the broader socio-cultural matrix in which drinking occurs." Drinking itself cannot be the exclusive cause of alcoholism, and he cites Orthodox Jews and native Italians as groups in which almost everyone drinks but in which alcoholism is negligible. On the other hand, he says, where drinking prevails and drinking pathologies emerge, exclusively psychological cravings cannot be incriminated and the blaming of mysterious physiological cravings as the sole etiological factor is best avoided.[2]

PHYSIOLOGICAL THEORIES

After alcoholism first attracted widespread attention, largely through the efforts of Alcoholics Anonymous, there were years of determined effort to isolate physiological causes and scientists still spend countless hours in laboratories looking for chemical imbalance or metabolic disorders.

One of the reasons for the popularity of this approach may be our need for simple answers to complex problems. If we find a single biological factor common to all alcoholics (and presumably to no one else), we can then manufacture a pill to prevent and a pill to cure. Recently, a Carnegie-Mellon University biologist found sets and parts of chromosomes missing in the blood cells of over 100 alcoholics. If this means anything, he thinks newborn infants can be tested for potential alcohol-

---

[1] Carl L. Anderson, "Alcoholism," in *Encyclopedia of Social Work* (New York: National Association of Social Workers, 1965), p. 82.

[2] Charles R. Snyder, *Alcohol and the Jews, A Cultural Study of Drinking and Society* (Glencoe, Illinois: The Free Press, 1958), p. 202.

ism and, to make the world an even brighter place, he hopes to find a way for the alcoholic to have a drink or two without losing control by taking a pill to supply missing enzymes. Unfortunately, he doesn't know if alcoholism causes chromosomal defects or if missing chromosomes causes alcoholism.[3]

Despite frustrations and setbacks, physiological theories of causation have been produced in abundance. Some endocrinologists see alcoholism as a metabolic disease because they have found deficiencies of the pituitary-adrenal-gonadal triad in the endocrine glands of many alcoholics. Others blamed the effect of lowered blood chloride levels. Nutritional deficiencies have been seen as a major causative factor by Dr. Roger Williams of the University of Texas. He has declared that "no one could follow the scientific trail I have followed without arriving at the surmise that poor nutrition of brain cells is closely related to alcoholism. This factor is as obvious to me as the psychogenic factors are to most students of alcoholism." [4] He ruefully conceded, however, that it was a surmise and needs to be scrutinized critically. Up to now, the evidence has not been impressive.

Mark Keller, editor of the *Quarterly Journal of Studies on Alcohol,* has declared that "evidence for physiological addiction has never been produced. The evidence for cell metabolism has not been produced. A tough-minded pharmacologist – one who can distinguish between what has been proved and what is said as if it were so for sheer lack of something else to say – has called these notions of altered cell metabolism and physical dependence, 'exercises in semantics, or plain flights of imagination.' " [5]

Surely there are physiological complications found in alcoholics. These include liver cirrhosis, neurological disorders, and gastric and endocrine dysfunctions, all of which require medical attention, but there is no evidence that they were present before the onset of drinking. It is a difficulty common to all physiological theories of causation of alcoholism that they postulate the existence of biological defects *before* excessive drinking develops although this has never been demonstrated.

If one accepts the physiological theory of causation, he must demonstrate that the cell structure of Orthodox Jews is different from that of the Irish because the incidence of alcoholism is quite different. He must also explain what metabolic changes occur in Indians who move from the

---

[3] Denes de Torok, M.D., Quoted in the *UMHS News,* United Mental Health Services of Allegheny County, Inc., Pittsburgh, Pa., Vol. 12, No. 2 (Fall, 1970), p. 6.

[4] Roger Williams, Comment on paper "Alcoholic Prevention and Reality" by Morris E. Chafetz, M.D., *Quarterly Journal of Studies on Alcohol,* Vol. 28, No. 2 (June, 1967), p. 347.

[5] Mark Keller, "Some Views on the Nature of Addiction," E. M. Jellenik Memorial Lecture, presented at the 15th International Institute on the Prevention and Treatment of Alcoholism, Budapest, Hungary, (June, 1969), p. 5.

reservation to urban centers, because their rate of alcoholism then increases. Also, how does the cell structure and metabolism of Orientals, among whom there is little alcoholism, differ from that of Occidentals, among whom alcoholism is rampant?

The physiological theories have always been cherished by alcoholics because it is easier for them to accept their alcoholism if they are different in a way that is beyond their own control. One hears many alcoholics say they are "allergic" to alcohol, although this is a distortion of the meaning of "allergy" because it is used to indicate a craving for rather than inability to accept the substance. This led to the proposition that an alcoholic could never safely take another drink because a single swallow of alcohol would make him break out in a binge.

This theory has never been confirmed. On the contrary, several investigators have administered large quantities of alcohol to alcoholics and found none of the reactions in tissue fluids that characterize allergic phenomena; nor could they induce such responses in laboratory experiments on men or animals where everything was under optimal conditions for their production.

Another theory that has caused trouble is the one suggesting that alcoholics have much greater tissue tolerance for alcohol. Therefore, they can drink more than most of us. Keller sees flaws in this theory, and one of them is the use of the word *tolerance* rather than *adaptation*. Biological organisms adapt, says Keller, and "Every drinker experiences some adaptation to alcohol. The young boy who downs his first 'shot' or 'slug' of liquor may exhibit a bizarre reaction. After having the same drink several times, it may produce hardly any effect. To be affected, he will have to drink more." [6] With alcoholics, the adaptation can be considerable. In Talland's experiments alcoholics were performing skillfully with blood alcohol levels that would render most of us helpless. [7]

Keller says "the high adaptation of alcoholics to alcohol is a side effect or by-product of the fact that they so long and so often drink so much. The essence of the addiction is the fact that they have the need to drink so much so often and for so long that they achieve an extraordinary degree of adaptation. It is not the fact that they have achieved such great adaptation which makes them alcoholics, but the fact that they so urgently and helplessly need the hazy state of affectedness which requires all that drinking and which, coincidentally, results in the observed adaptation." [8]

A physiological interpretation of alcoholism is immensely comforting

[6] *Ibid.*, p. 10.
[7] George Talland, *et al.*, "Tests of Motor Skills," *Quarterly Journal of Studies on Alcohol*, Supplement #2 (May, 1964), pp. 53-73.
[8] Keller, *op. cit.*, p. 11.

to the alcoholic because it absolves him of responsibility for his alcoholism and makes life more tolerable. Parenthetically, it also relieves society from blame, so what it lacks in scientific support it makes up as a social palliative.

The physiological theories of alcoholism definitely contributed to the disease concept of alcoholism, which, when proclaimed by the American Medical Association in 1956, was hailed by many as the greatest revelation since Paul encountered divine guidance on the road to Damascus. However, Dr. Thomas Trotter, who received his medical degree from the University of Edinburgh in 1788, noted in his thesis that he considered "drunkenness, strictly speaking, to be a disease; produced by a remote cause, and giving birth to actions and movements in the living body that disorder the functions of health." And three years earlier in America, Dr. Benjamin Rush had called drunkenness an "odious disease."

Before 1900, the *Quarterly Journal of Alcoholism* published eighty papers referring to alcoholism as a disease, and several additional articles and books appeared in the early 1900s explaining it in terms of physiology, neurophysiology, or genetics. Indeed, one of the psychobiological discussions of alcoholism is in Mary Richmond's *Social Diagnosis,* in which she attributed chronic inebriation to underlying biological disorders although she could not identify them.[9]

In 1946, Jellenik analyzed the data gathered from a questionnaire completed by 158 members of Alcoholics Anonymous and suggested that alcoholism was a disease that progressed from psychological to biological dependency, and the transition occurred when the individual experienced a loss of control of his drinking. As Cahn points out, "the phase concept of alcoholism has become official doctrine for many experts [but] a number of others have questioned the scientific validity of the basic questionnaire as well as the inferences Jellenik made from the data." [10]

Jellenik later abandoned the phase concept and developed a typology of alcoholism involving three basic types: Alpha, which is typified by psychological dependency; Gamma, in which there is increased tissue tolerance to alcohol, adaptive cell metabolism, and physical dependence, and Delta, which encompasses those psychologically or physiologically dependent on alcohol but who persist in deviant drinking patterns. In addition to these three basic types, Jellenik added a Beta species, in which such complications of drinking as liver cirrhosis, polyneuropathy, and gastritis are found, but in which there is neither dependence on alcohol nor withdrawal symptoms.

[9] Mary Richmond, *Social Diagnosis* (New York: Russell Sage Foundation, 1917), pp. 425-433.
[10] Sidney Cahn, *The Treatment of Alcoholism* (New York: Oxford University Press, 1970), p. 11.

It is doubtful that Jellenik intended his taxonomy to be accepted as immutable law throughout eternity, but it has been so regarded by many authorities. Some brave souls have pointed to flaws and Cahn suggests that the main objections are that: "overt behavioral differences and treatment modes are not differentiated into three types; loss of control is inadequately defined and retrospective in nature; and there is no evidence for biological dependency or addiction. Clearly, the disease model is an oversimplification of a complex phenomenon, but one whose acceptance may lead people to believe in both simplistic and unidimensional cure." [11]

The use of the "disease concept" has been defended by some because it may have helped to de-emphasize widely held misconceptions about character weakness, sin, and moral deviation as significant factors in alcoholism. However, it also reinforced the medical model of alcoholism and persuaded the public that its treatment should be primarily in the domain of physicians who, it is assumed, are the persons best equipped to deal with it. That is not true at present, as Plaut points out:

> Two additional aspects of the slogan have bothered me. The first is that if alcoholism is a disease (or illness) then one would assume that physicians would be the persons best equipped to deal with it. Not only is this not true at present but I doubt whether the medical profession can ever be expected to carry the brunt of the care, treatment and rehabilitation of alcoholics. At least this will not occur until medicine shifts its major focus from organic illness to the management of psychological conditions and the control of disordered behavior. Neither alcoholism nor emotional disorders fit the classical models of a medical illness. The management of the acute or chronic effects of excessive alcohol intake is a medical responsibility. But dealing with the underlying drinking problem or addiction may not be. Secondly, we are in the unusual position of insisting that alcoholism is a disease and then turning over much of the responsibility for its treatment to a group that is not only non-medical but also non-professional! In most people's minds diseases are complicated biological processes and require highly technical skills and intervention; if alcoholism is a "disease" in this sense it must be a highly unique one in that the most successful form of "therapy" available so far appears to be that of an untrained group, i.e., the Fellowship of Alcoholics Anonymous! I feel sure that the dual emphasis on the disease concept and on the crucial role of AA carries with it some major problems, of both a logical and an educa-

[11] *Ibid.*

> tional nature. The readiness to rely on AA probably also has reenforced the tendency of many professionals and agencies to shirk their responsibility of working directly with alcoholics themselves. It is easy to say: "Since alcoholics are so hard to work with and since AA does such a good job, why don't we just let AA do the whole job." While a "movement" needs slogans – for internal as well as external purposes – the time has arrived for state and other alcoholism programs to re-examine the usefulness of this particular slogan. [12]

Jellenik himself sharply challenges the medical model of alcoholism. "Research, treatment, and prevention of the various species of alcoholism," he wrote, "are affected not only by the acceptance or rejection of the disease concept but also by the formulation of the nature of such an illness. If the formulation rigidly claims that alcohol addiction or any other species of alcoholism is purely a medical problem, any preventive attempt may be seriously impaired. The usefulness of the idea that alcoholism is a medical and public health problem depends, to a large extent, upon the recognition of social and economic factors in the etiology of all species of alcoholism." [13]

Perhaps the time has come to toss the "disease concept" in the nearest trash can and to view such simple-minded slogans as "Alcoholism is a disease that is beatable and treatable" in proper perspective.

PSYCHOLOGICAL THEORIES– THE ALCOHOLIC PERSONALITY

If alcoholism is not the result of some defective structure or functioning in the physiological system there must be other explanations. Keller speaks for an increasing number of authorities when he says that all he has read and observed in the last 35 years leads him "to see alcoholism as the outcome of a process of adaptation to an addictive lifeway in vulnerable people. Vulnerable people are those who, whether for constitutional reasons or because of being reared in particularly unfortunate ways, or perhaps especially the combination of constitutional and psychic development misfortune, find difficulty in achieving satisfactory adaptations to the way of life that they expect of themselves, and that society expects of them . . ." [14]

How they became vulnerable has been the subject of much study,

[12] Thomas F. A. Plaut, "The State Alcoholism Movement: A Critical Analysis," *Selected Papers,* 15th Annual Meeting of North American Association of Alcoholism Programs, Washington, D.C., (1964), p. 83.

[13] E. M. Jellenik, *The Disease Concept of Alcoholism* (New Brunswick, New Jersey: Hillhouse Press, 1960), p. 158.

[14] Keller, *op. cit.*, p. 1.

especially by the psychoanalytically oriented. The psychoanalytic view does not define addiction in pharmacological terms but sees alcoholism as a substitute for emotionally mature adaptation in dealing with psychic pain. The dependence on chemical substance is seen as the result of developmental failure. "The earlier the developmental stage at which an individual has been arrested," says Eva Maria Blum, "the more infantile his behavior and personality, the more severe his drinking problem if he becomes an alcoholic and the poorer his prognosis. Individuals who have achieved emotional maturity but have regressed under the impact of unfavorable life circumstances may be only temporarily affected. The latter are more likely to return to their previous level of social and personal functioning, whether they have been helped by psychoanalytic or other means." [15]

Since Freud, it has been popular to see the development as arrested at the oral stage. The alcoholic's behavior is interpreted as a regression to an earlier developmental level comparable to the infant with intense oral longings seeking gratification via the bottle. This line of reasoning neatly takes into account the latent homosexual theory, too.

The Adlerian school attributed alcoholism to the individual's desire to eliminate tormenting feelings of inferiority while escaping adult responsibilities. This, they said, was the result of childhood pampering that impaired his ability to face up to the frustrations of adult reality. Menninger has seen alcoholics as having a powerful, albeit unconscious, desire to destroy themselves and to retaliate for betrayal by their parents. [16]

In all theories there are recurrent themes of threats to security, deprivation, and the stunting of emotional and social growth. And, for once, the sociologists have confirmed the facts if not the dynamics. Most of the longitudinal studies, like those of the McCords, show histories of broken homes, economic deprivations, and exposure to heavy drinking. [17]

The significant conclusion is that out of all the conditions come vulnerable personalities and some of them become alcoholics because they do not have the ego strengths to cope with life in a relatively healthy way. To say that they are vulnerable personalities is not the same as identifying them as unique, identifiable, "alcoholic" personalities. Comparative studies of non-alcoholics and alcoholics have failed to isolate personality traits or underlying dynamics that distinguish alcoholics from other deviant groups. Alcohol serves essentially the same function for the alcoholic as other substances or activities do for drug abusers, compul-

---

[15] Eva Maria Blum, "Psychoanalytic Views of Alcoholism," *Quarterly Journal of Studies on Alcohol,* Vol. 27, No. 2 (June, 1966), p. 264.
[16] Karl Menninger, *Man Against Himself* (New York: Harcourt Brace and Company, 1938), pp. 161 ff.
[17] William McCord and Joan McCord, *Origins of Alcoholism* (Stanford, California: Stanford University Press, 1960), pp. 54-72.

sive gamblers, overeaters, compulsive overworkers, credit buyers, and religious fanatics. All the above, incidentally, are exaggerations of reaction patterns found in normal persons.

Several characteristics are common among alcoholics and they seem to play a significant role in personality vulnerability. Not all appear in every alcoholic and the patterns vary, but clinical observation over the decades indicates that excessive drinking is used to compensate and protect.

1. A Sense of Inadequacy and Low Self-Esteem

This is an almost universal characteristic of alcoholics and drinking can frequently effect a quick metamorphosis from a feeling of nothing to a feeling of something. "In the bottle," said Samuel Johnson, "discontent seeks for comfort, cowardice for courage and bashfulness for confidence." One of the co-founders of Alcoholics Anonymous recalled his sense of worthlessness when he lost a job after success seemed certain. He was broke and felt useless, but there was one comforting thought: "With a fifth of gin I could be a millionaire – at least for a while." W. C. Fields, a notable tippler, put it another way: "A man who overindulges lives in a dream. He becomes conceited. He thinks the whole world revolves around him – and it usually does."

A similar feeling of transcending weakness is described by Eugene in Thomas Wolfe's book, *Look Homeward, Angel.* Intoxicated for the first time, he reflects: "In all the earth there was no other like him, no other fitted to be so sublimely and magnificently drunken . . . Why, when it was possible to buy God in a bottle, and drink him off, and become a God oneself, were not men forever drunken?"

Psychological tests indicated that a woman nearing thirty was low in self-esteem and especially low in her concept of her own femininity. Drinking provided "defense and pleasure" and made her friendlier. Men were attracted and, when they gave chase, she slowed down to let them catch her. With enough liquor she saw her femininity approaching that of Sophia Loren.

In a society that places a high premium on masculinity in men, it can be ego-crushing to those who see themselves as failing to measure up. Some find relief in alcohol. A steel worker with an ample supply of muscle felt inferior because he was only 5′4″ tall and had to look up at average men. And he was sure they looked down on him. With several drinks, however, he could match the toughest. His favorite bar was a hangout for minor-league hoodlums who, despite their second-rate status, carried knives and guns. The alcoholic's way of "proving" his manhood was to bolster his courage with liquor and to challenge them by pushing them off bar stools. The therapist always wondered whether he would return for the next appointment. Fortunately, she was able to make him recognize the stupidity of his behavior before he landed in the hospital.

Feelings about inadequate masculinity can appear in many guises. A 26-year-old graduate student drank to provide himself with enough courage to pick up girls. He was a brilliant student, but his academic career was threatened by his binges, which caused him to miss classes and impaired his ability to work up to his potential.

The feeling of inadequancy is found in alcoholics at all socio-economic levels. A successful industrialist is as vulnerable as the poorest slum dweller. (Vignettes #1 & #2)

2. A Sense of Rejection and Alienation

Many alcoholics feel that others will not accept them and this feeling can reach paranoid intensity. This is another facet of their sense of inadequacy, but it creates an inability to meet others on equal terms, individually or in groups, because of fear of rejection. Many say: "I have to have a drink before I can go out and face people" or "I need a few before I can go out on a date." A shy, withdrawn character in an F. Scott Fitzgerald story, perhaps speaking for the author, says: "I found that with a few drinks I got expansive and had the ability to please people. Then I began to take a whole lot of drinks to keep going and have everybody think I was wonderful."

Fallding calls this "facilitation drinking" to ease the person's "integration into society with which he still identifies." Certain individuals, he says, "are unable to surmount internal barriers to participation without a degree of alcoholic anesthesia." Fallding adds that the outcome of drinking to this end is uncertain because it "may well break down one's reserve and coldness or soften one's bereavement or humiliation, or make one feel a man, it does so only very temporarily and it can at the same time release hostile and other impulses which create trouble."[18]

Some of these mechanisms are found in social drinkers and are relatively harmless when kept within bounds. After all, alcohol is a widely used lubricant at parties where people want to let down the bars. But Catanzarro, who sees alcoholism as a destructive habit, points out that if an "abnormal person is repeatedly subjected to stressful stimuli (social gatherings), for example, a very shy or inadequate person, one who is not equipped with the usual array of psychological defenses, or if repeated unusually stressful environmental situations occur, repeated social gatherings where the person knows no one and feels out of place, a prob-

[18] Harold Fallding, "The Sources and Burden of Civilization Illustrated in the Use of Alcohol," *Quarterly Journal of Studies on Alcohol,* Vol. 25, No. 4 (December, 1964), pp. 714-724.

lem habit of excessive drinking occurs." [19]

Most alcoholics are quick to react to any sign of rejection and are hurt by the smallest affront. They are injustice collectors and are ever alert to gather additional evidence of inadequacy and lack of appeal. They find rejection at all levels. In treatment they need indications of realistic appreciation all through the relationship in spite of repeated testing of the therapist.

3. Alcoholics Are Frustrated Perfectionists

Many alcoholics are perfectionists and they cannot tolerate their failure to achieve perfection. This may be one of the paradoxical concomitants of their feelings of inadequacy. When they have to accept compromise, they need the reinforcement of alcohol.

An illustration encountered in almost any out-patient clinic is related to payment of bills. One alcoholic, after a few months of sobriety returned to his daily fifth. He displayed remorse during occasional sober hours and said he wanted help, but unfortunately he owed the clinic one hundred dollars. He declared loudly and righteously that he did not intend to endure the humiliation of facing the staff until his debt had been completely paid. He spurned the family physician on the same pretext.

The suggestion that this man might pay his bills on the installment plan was angrily rejected. It had to be all or nothing. Because he had no money, it was nothing. This did not discourage his continued pathetic efforts to persuade those around him that he was better than other people because of his impeccable virtue in financial matters. This was irrational, but it is the kind of self-deception many alcoholics use.

Alcoholics frequently demand perfection in others that they cannot find in themselves. A man will build inconsequential flaws in his wife into unforgivable character defects. If she fails to clean the ashtrays compulsively, he denounces her as an intolerably sloppy housekeeper. If she is unable to serve expensive roasts and at the same time to save money on his erratic and inadequate earnings, he damns her as a spendthrift. One marriage was described as perfect by both parties, although the disclosure that when the husband drank he shackled his wife and rolled her down the stairs indicated that perfection was not the most accurate description.

The need to show the world that he is superman may impel the alcoholic to set unattainable goals for himself. (Vignettes #3 & #4).

[19] Ronald Catanzarro, M.D., "The Concept of Problem Habits and Their Treatment," Papers Presented at the International Institute on the Prevention and Treatment of Drug Dependence, International Council on Alcohol and Alcohol Addictions, Lausanne, Switzerland.

A variation of this striving for perfection was expressed by Shaw in his play *John Bull's Other Island,* when he has a character named Larry Doyle say: "An Irishman's imagination never lets him alone, never convinces him, never satisfies him; but it makes him feel that he can't face reality nor deal with it nor handle it nor conquer it; he can only sneer at them that do . . . imagination's such a torture that you can't bear it without whiskey."

This is not too far from Vincent Sheean's appraisal of Dorothy Parker's excessive drinking: "I think she drank because of her perceptions. Her vision of life was almost more than she could bear." [20]

4. Alcoholics Are Dependent

Anyone who works with alcoholics knows that most of them are dependent clients. They need support and, if permitted to indulge their dependency, they linger in treatment indefinitely; they want parental figures in their counselors who will protect and nurture them.

Subscribers to the psychoanalytic view have used the dependency of the alcoholic to support their conviction that the alcoholic is an oral personality. Even the social psychiatrists have been unable to resist temptation. According to Chafetz: "Just as the infant seeks through ingestion to quiet the emptiness and sooth the pangs that threaten his security, so does the alcoholic seek this gratification by stimulation of the oral mucosa, by imbibing massive amounts of ethanol and by seeking peaceful oblivion, symbolically attempting to achieve the blissful infantile state . . ." [21]

Well, that's one way of looking at it. Others change the words but essentially they find the genesis of alcoholism in the basic disturbance of the mother-infant relationship in the first year of life, when the infant was unable to develop what Erik Erikson has called "basic trust." Since he never learns to trust anyone else, he regresses to narcissism when his self-esteem is threatened. Clinebell says that "many adult alcoholics respond as though the entire world of relationships were a bad breast, a depriving mother." One must be quite psychoanalytic to put it that way, but there is little doubt that many alcoholics "form impossibly demanding dependencies and then feel angry and rejected when their grandiose demands are not met." [22]

Be that as it may, most students have found a high correlation between alcoholism and dependency. Bacon and her colleagues suggested that "frequent drunkenness or high consumption or both, tend to occur in cul-

---

[20] John Keats, *You Might As Well Live* (New York: Simon and Shuster, 1970), p. 125.
[21] Morris E. Chafetz, M.D., *Frontiers of Alcoholism* (New York: Science House, 1970), p. 9.
[22] Howard J. Clinebell, Jr., "Philosophical-Religious Factors in the Etiology and Treatment of Alcoholism," *Quarterly Journal of Studies on Alcohol,* Vol. 24, No. 3 (September, 1963), p. 481.

tures where needs for dependence are deprived or punished, both in childhood and adult life, and where a high degree of responsible, independent and achieving behavior are required." [23] This accurately describes our own society.

This thesis is supported by the McCords, whose analysis of the data from the Cambridge-Somerville study indicated that alcoholism arises from dependency conflict rather than dependency *per se*. The male who becomes an alcoholic is one who desires maternal care and support but who has repressed this desire because of cultural pressures to conform to the requirements of an adult role. Drinking becomes a solution to his conflict because in American culture it is a masculine act and at the same time it comforts the drinker and makes him feel cared for. [24]

Alcohol is especially rewarding when dependency conflict is acute because it serves a triple function of reducing anxiety, permitting the satisfaction of dependency needs, and facilitating uncritical indulgence of unrealistic achievement fantasies. Besides, when all else fails it is always there. "A bar," said Mr. Jesse B. Simple of the Langston Hughes stories, "is something to lean on." When asked why he leaned on bars so often, he replied: "Because everything else I lean on falls down, including my people, my wife, my boss and me . . . I can lean on this bar but I ain't got another thing in the U.S.A. on which to lean."

Lemert suggests an interesting variation of the dependency conflict. He calls it the "independency conflict" and says it applies "to men who because of commitments to mobile occupations or to other specialized but nonetheless socially acceptable life goals, culturally repudiate the family as a means of sex and emotional gratification. Sex for them is on a 'love 'em and leave 'em basis,' and emotional satisfaction comes from the camaraderie of the work group or from the sense of a job well done. When, for a variety of fortuitous and other factors, such men marry and become immobile, stress arises because the husband-father role conflicts with their image of themselves as mobile and independent or dedicated. Often, for such men, heavy drinking has often been a learned reaction in the mobile work group or occupation and it rather easily changes its function to that of stress reaction with socially invidious rather than socially acceptable cultural associations. This would be consistent with the large number of cases in the present sample in which intoxication was a means of withdrawing from the family situation." [25]

---

[23] Margaret Bacon, *et al*, "A Cross Cultural Study of Drinking," *Quarterly Journal of Studies on Alcohol*, Supplement No. 3 (April, 1965), p. 43.

[24] McCord, *op. cit.*

[25] Edwin Lemert, "Dependency in Married Alcoholics," *Quarterly Journal of Studies on Alcohol*, Vol. 23, No. 24 (December, 1962), pp. 590-609.

5. Other Personality Traits

There are other personality traits. Alcoholics are egocentric and frequently care little about what their behavior does to others. Menninger says that because of their egocentrism it is characteristic that they see their periodic bouts as nothing more than "jolly little affairs which, for all they may end in a rather untidy and tiresome mess, with a few disappointments all round, no one should hold against them. This wish to be treated like a child and to have one's most serious aggressions overlooked is very characteristic of the type of personality which finds excessive indulgence in alcohol so irresistible." [26]

The alcoholic is also a hostile, aggressive person whose aggression can be released only under the influence of alcohol. There was, for example, a passive (when sober) client of this writer who went home drunk one night and, while his terrified wife and two small children watched, completely demolished the lower floor of the house. He smashed the furniture, broke the windows, hurled the dishes, and knocked plaster from the walls. He reduced a comfortable home to a shambles. When his family screamed in protest, he replied with obscenities.

Some feel this aggression is turned inward and that alcoholics are bent on slow suicide. Blane sees it from a different viewpoint:

> Alcoholism is undoubtedly self-destructive, and the alcoholic is the undoubted prey of destructive forces, but neither means that the key to understanding the personality structure of the alcoholic is to be found in aggressive impulses. As I view it, aggression proceeds primarily from the blocking of dependent desires. Aggressive impulses vary in intensity and strength from person to person and, even when strong, are generally subsidiary to conflict over dependent needs. As another observer has put it, Menninger overlooks the deep striving of the alcoholic to be loved and appreciated by society. The alcoholic drinks not because he wants to kill himself; he drinks to preserve himself and to maintain his integrity. That prolonged excessive drinking ultimately destroys rather than preserves, decomposes rather than maintains integrity, that its effects are opposite to those the drinker seeks through it are among the paradoxes of alcoholism. [27]

These and other traits seem to make vulnerable personalities, some of whom become alcoholics as a defensive measure. Two other characteristics are frequently advertised (usually by alcoholics), but until hard evi-

[26] Menninger, *op. cit.*, p. 142.
[27] Howard T. Blane, *The Personality of the Alcoholic* (New York: Harper and Row, 1968).

dence is produced they can be relegated to mythology. These are that alcoholics are exceptionally sensitive people and that they possess a higher intelligence than the general population. The propagandists for this disingenuous thesis can be heard across the land at all times but they are particularly audible during an annual rite called Alcoholism Information Month. During that period, celebrities recovered from alcoholism leave their comfortable eyries to spread the word with a genuinely hard sell.

The rationale for this probably is that more attention will be paid to alcoholism if it can be demonstrated that its victims are a very special breed. That approach must boomerang, however, because counselors, friends, relatives, and many alcoholics know it isn't true. Some are highly sensitive; some are clods. Some are close to genius, others are stupid. In both areas, the vast majority are, like the rest of us, somewhere in between. Alcoholics do not have to be superior to merit help; they just have to be human.

LEARNING THEORY OF ALCOHOLISM CAUSATION

Alcoholism is an adaptive technique, a way of coping with the anxieties and stresses of life. There is mounting support for the theory that the alcoholic learns that alcohol relieves psychic pain and with increasing frequency he uses it as the solution to frustrations, anxieties, depression, and humiliation. He finds out that alcohol works and drinking eventually becomes a way of life because he uses it to achieve personal goals. (Vignette #5)

One of the most irresistible arguments for alcohol is that it works. As Kepner says: "The individual learns that he can avoid these aversive stimuli by reaching for the bottle. Each time he does this and experiences relief or pleasure, the drinking response is reinforced and the tendency to repeat the act is strengthened. Eventually, he may use alcohol to avoid every problem, large and small, and then is a problem drinker or alcoholic." [28]

Conger also emphasizes the importance of reinforcement. He notes that "once a response which satisfies a drive has been made, if only by chance, it tends to become more likely to occur the next time the individual finds himself faced with a similar state of unsatisfied need." Conger illustrates this thesis with the case of a salesman who finds "he can reduce fear of the prospective client by a quick drink or two ahead of time. If he is then successful in selling the client, he may tend to repeat the drinking

---

[28] Elaine Kepner, "Application of Learning Theory to the Etiology and Treatment of Alcoholism," *Quarterly Journal of Studies on Alcohol*, Vol. 25, No. 2 (June, 1964), pp. 280-281.

the next time he is faced with a similar situation, not only because the drinking is rewarding in that it reduces painful feelings of anxiety, but also because other motives – perhaps those for security, prestige, or recognition – are satisfied if he is successful in placing an order." The net result might be favorable or unfavorable. If "this initial experience of success is sufficiently reassuring to the salesman, he may not feel under as much tension when faced by similar situations in the future and may not have as much need for his bracer. If this is not the case, however, and he again feels genuinely anxious and apprehensive, he may easily resort to the previously effective response of drinking – eventually becoming dependent on alcohol to help him through all such situations." [29]

Alcohol not only works, it works quickly. On an empty stomach it is promptly absorbed into the blood and carried to the brain where it produces an anesthetic effect and reduces anxiety. For many people, this is extremely rewarding. Anthropologist David Horton once said that "the strength of the drinking response in any society tends to vary directly with the anxiety level in that society." His studies were confined to preliterate societies and the statement may be an oversimplification, but there is no doubt that alcohol is a magic fluid for the tormented.

Psychologist Dan Anderson, in an unpublished lecture, has said the components of learning are motivation, action, consequences, and drill. They can combine to make an alcoholic. Anxiety provides one powerful source of motivation. The action is drinking and the consequence is not only relief from pain but, for many, an enhancement of pleasure. The drill involves the repetitive use of alcohol to achieve the desired effect.

Some contend that learning principles, especially reinforcement, cannot account for alcoholism because the devastating social and physical consequences invariably outweigh temporary relief values. After each binge the alcoholic may wind up sick and broke. However, behavior is likely to be motivated by immediate rather than delayed consequences. Rewards come to the alcoholic quickly; punishment is remote.

The process is, in the long run, inevitably self-defeating. The alcoholic has learned to use alcohol to cope with personal problems and a hostile environment, but he has failed to develop more constructive and socially acceptable defenses. Unfortunately, alcohol has worked as nothing else would. Adelstein points out, "the reinforcement [relief] is immediate in contrast with delayed reinforcement of other, alternative adaptive maneuvers for handling the anxiety. The progressive reflex progressively preempts the field of response choices which narrows down rapidly to

---

[29] J. J. Conger, "Reinforcement Theory and the Dynamics of Alcoholism," *Quarterly Journal of Studies on Alcohol,* Vol. 17 (1956), pp. 296-305.

virtually this one response for the widest range of stimuli." [30]

Sooner or later, of course, the benefits will decline and the payments will increase. Pain will transcend pleasure; defeat will come more frequently than triumph. In the end, alcohol solves nothing. All it actually does is obliterate feelings of conflict and permit a person to feel good for a short time, but actually the problems increase so that more and more alcohol are needed in order to reduce increased feelings of anxiety. "The difficulty is," wrote Oliver Wendell Holmes in *The Autocrat at the Breakfast Table,* "that the alcoholic virtues don't wash; but until the water takes their colors out, the tints are very much like those of the true celestial stuff."

There is no permanent escape. "We can kid the world," says the alcoholic Tyrone to his lover in O'Neill's play *A Moon for the Misbegotten,* "but we can't fool ourselves .. nor escape ourselves no matter where we run away. Whether it's the bottom of a bottle, or a South Sea Island, we'd find our own ghosts there waiting to greet us – 'sleepless with pale commemorative eyes,' as Rosetti wrote . . ."

Coming off a binge, the alcoholic does find his own ghost – guilt – waiting for him. The only way to solve that problem is to turn again to alcoholism. His other defenses are gone and he is bankrupt. He now drinks to defend himself – not against the world but against himself. He is actually drinking to solve the problem of alcoholism. He feels despair about his drinking and the only way he can exorcise painful feelings is to take more alcohol.

The alcoholic has learned to depend on alcohol so completely that, if he is to recover, he must find new ways of coping with life's problems. That is difficult, but before he can succeed he must unlearn a form of behavior he has overlearned through the years. It is a formidable task but essential to treatment.

CULTURAL ROLE IN CAUSATION

People have a wide choice of coping mechanisms so why do they choose alcohol? Why not drugs, gambling, cultism, or schizophrenia? Or, why not sleep? One man stayed in bed through an entire summer although he had not a trace of physical illness, but he did have a need to escape from the world around him. Jellenik observed that, rather than seeking a specific substance, the alcoholic seeks intoxicating effects and another substance might be just as satisfactory.

The answer must be found at least in part in cultural patterns. An

[30] Joseph Adelstein, M.D., "Clinical and Social-Psychiatric Aspects of Alcoholism," Lecture at the 1963 Rutgers University Summer School of Alcohol Studies. Reprinted by National Council on Alcoholism, New York, N.Y., p. 4.

Orthodox Jew may have all the problems mentioned in the foregoing pages, but the chances are remote that he will turn to alcoholism. He might resort to compulsive gambling or narcotic addiction or wind up in a mental hospital, but he will avoid alcoholism because the Jewish culture has strong sanctions against drunkenness. Since the in-group ties of the Jewish community are strong, the sanctioning power on the individual is also strong. One writer noted that "to be a drunkard is to cease being a Jew." The rate of drinking among Jews is extremely high, especially in the ceremonial use of wine. But the incidence of drunkenness is negligible. To use wine in excess is to abuse something sacred.

As Jews depart from orthodoxy, however, they are integrated into the larger culture and the picture changes. There is more intoxication and there is a higher incidence of alcoholism. Snyder found that intoxication experience among Jewish college students claiming Reform or no religious affiliation matched the experience of Irish Catholic or British Protestant background. [31]

The situation with the Irish has been the antithesis of the Jewish condition. For centuries misery and the uncertainty of living made drinking acceptable, and alcoholic excesses in the first generation of Irish immigrants were notorious. In Ireland, according to Tony Gray, "drunkenness is regarded as a good man's fault." [32] Playwright Brendan Behan viewed drinking in Ireland as an accomplishment and said the Irishman has to go around telling the world he is drunk. Thus, when the Irish were unable to handle problems it was natural to resort to alcohol. George Potter, in *To The Golden Door,* wrote: "The temporary victory in drink over frustration, insecurity and the sense of inferiority which constantly dogged him, probably accounted as much for the Irishman's intemperance as any of a score of other factors."

These influences are apparent in all societies. In Chinese culture the demand for repression of aggressive behavior and maintenance of composure may dictate the choice of gambling or narcotics.

In some cultures there is great pressure to drink. Interview material from several hundred Navaho alcoholics indicated that they were weary of the high cost in physical pain and social dysfunctioning and had tried to abstain. However, any attempt to refuse a drink from a member of the fellowship was countered by a concerted, unrelenting pressure to drink. They were accused of rejecting the drinking companion by rejecting his wine. Sometimes members of the group would point out that on the basis of the man's past performance he would eventually give in and drink anyway, so why didn't he cut out the nonsense and take a drink without

[31] Snyder, *op. cit.*
[32] Tony Gray, *The Irish Answer* (Boston: Little, Brown and Company, 1966), p. 324.

so much delay and fuss. [33]

The choice of alcohol as a defense is not likely to be popular in an abstinent society where the cultural attitude is negative and prohibitive toward the use of alcoholic beverages as it is where Islam, Hindu, and Ascetic Protestant traditions prevail. Alcoholism does occur, but most people choose other substances.

A permissive or at least ambivalent attitude seems necessary. Because of the strong temperance crusades of the nineteenth century that culminated in the Volstead Act of 1920, the United States has generally been viewed as ambivalent and even today it is estimated that about one-third of the adult population is abstinent. But prohibition failed because the majority insisted on their right to drink.

The drinking of alcoholic beverages is part of the American heritage. Gerald Carson wrote: "The transit of English civilization to the shores of New England included the conception held firmly in the mother country and later at both Plymouth and Massachusetts Bay that beer, ale, wine, cordials, and spiritous liquors were pleasant drinks, necessary to a good life and the preservation of good health. The *Mayflower* was stocked with what Governor John Winthrop quaintly described as *hot waters*. The first Indian got drunk in 1621. And when the Reverend Francis Higginson went out to the plantations in the *Talbot* in 1629 his catalogue of things needful in the New World included forty-five tons of beer and twenty gallons of brandy." [34]

Visitors to the United States noticed the ubiquitous presence of liquor. William Cobbett discovered in 1818 that he could hardly enter any man's house without being offered wine or spirits. Frances Trollope, an Englishwoman, said in 1831 that "the use of . . . [alcohol] among the men, with more or less discretion according to the character, is universal." Six years later novelist and naval officer Frederick Marryat reported the drinking customs of Americans: "They say that the English cannot settle anything without a dinner. I am sure Americans can fix nothing without a drink. If you meet you drink, if you part you drink; if you make an acquaintance you drink. They quarrel in their drink, and they make it up with a drink."[35]

In general, drinking of alcoholic beverages is part of the American heritage. Drinking was a part of life on the frontier and the saloon was a legitimate descendant of the colonial saloon. "The frontiersmen," wrote

---

[33] Robert J. Savard, "Effects of Disulfram Therapy on Relationship within the Nahavo Drinking Group," *Quarterly Journal of Studies on Alcohol,* Vol. 29, No. 4 (December, 1968), pp. 909-916.

[34] Gerald Carson, "Rum and Reform in Old New England" (Sturbridge, Mass.: Old Sturbridge Village Booklet Series, 1966), p. 3.

[35] Allan M. Winkler, "Drinking on the American Frontier," *Quarterly Journal of Studies on Alcohol,* Vol. 29, No. 2 (June, 1968), p. 419.

Max Lerner, "prided themselves on their drinking excesses: the isolation of life, along with its rigors, led to a plentiful consumption of homemade spirits. For the plantation leisure class of the Old South, heavy drinking was at once an antidote to boredom and the mark of hospitality for the landed gentry. Among the miners and cattle ranchers of the Far West, the frontier saloon was an outlet for the turbulence of new and lawless settlements. All these strands of social inheritance may still be found in American drinking, yet while the old reasons for heavy drinking no longer apply in the urbanized indoor society, the drinking remains. The new reasons for drinking are probably more closely connected with the driving tempo of life in America and the anxieties, frustrations, and aggressions it engenders." [36]

All of this may help to explain why alcohol is the defense of choice for those vulnerable personalities who fail to develop sturdier and more constructive defenses. Drinking is an acceptable custom and alcohol is readily available, so the vulnerable personality can take it from there. That does not imply any merit in efforts to change that situation. If drinking were less popular and alcohol were more difficult to obtain, there might be a reduction in alcoholism, but unless other social factors were altered, those who now become alcoholics would only make another choice.

[36] Max Lerner, *America as a Civilization* (New York: Simon and Schuster, 1957), p. 661.

ALCOHOL, CATS AND PEOPLE

(An Illustration of Learning Theory) by E. M. Jellinek

Likely you have never seen a drunken dog or cat or horse, for in the lives of animals alcoholic beverages play no role at all. Yet there are some facts about inebriety, or drunkenness, which may be illustrated best through experiments with animals.

While dogs are expected to learn a variety of tricks, cats are usually exempt from the ambitions of amateur animal trainers. With a little patience, however, and a knowledge of animal psychology, cats too may be taught to perform quite elaborate tricks.

A noted psychiatrist, Dr. Jules Massermann, once taught sixteen cats to open a box and take food from it whenever an electric bulb in their cage flashed for a second or so. These cats came to watch eagerly for this signal, as it meant the satisfaction of a need – of their hunger drive.

After they had learned their lesson well the experimenter taught them to operate a light switch, a rather large button which was placed on he floor of the cage. Whenever the cats wanted food they would press this button with a paw, watch for the light and then go to the food box. Later the electric switch was placed on the wall of the experimental cage. The

Reprinted with permission from *The Allied Youth*, Vol. 17, No. 6 (March, 1948).

cats had to stand on their hind legs and press the button on the wall with their forepaws. Since this meant food for them, they learned this somewhat difficult trick, too.

Dr. Massermann wanted to know how alcohol would influence this behavior which the cats had learned. But the cats would not drink alcoholic milk voluntarily, and so the alcohol had to be given by stomach tube or by injection. They got enough alcohol to make them drunk.

When the cats were mildly intoxicated they forgot how to operate the light switch on the wall, although that had been the last performance which they had learned. But they still operated the switch on the floor, a performance which they had learned at an earlier stage. Then as intoxication progressed they were no longer able to operate the floor switch, but they still responded to the flashing of the electric light when it was operated by the experimenter. Finally at the most severe stage of their intoxication the signal lost all meaning for them.

From this experiment it is easy to see that alcoholic intoxication interfered with the learned behaviors in the reverse order of learning. What was learned last was forgotten first, and what was learned first was forgotten last. Such is also the effect of alcohol on men and women. The conduct and habit patterns learned latest in life are affected first and the experiences and simplest functions learned earliest in life are affected last.

After the cats had properly learned their tricks and had become educated, the experimenter made life rather difficult for them. When they went to their food box in response to the light signal, they got a slight electric shock or were exposed to a sharp air blast. After this had happened four or five times the cats would neither operate the light switch nor respond to the signal when operated by the experimenter. They would not even take food outside the cage. They showed signs of distress, they went through all kinds of contortions, and they seemed to have lost all interest in the outside world. They would not even take notice of a mouse.

Strange as it may sound, these cats were victims of a conflict – of a conflict between the hunger drive and the drive to avoid pain. And this conflict paralyzed their entire behavior.

At this point Dr. Massermann again gave the cats some alcohol by injection, much less alcohol than in the first part of the experiment – just enough to make them mildly intoxicated. When the cats were "under the influence" they suddenly began operating the light switch again and taking their food from the box. As soon as this mild intoxication wore off, they lapsed into their apathetic behavior and the effects of the conflict again became evident.

After this experience Dr. Massermann placed two containers in the experimental cage, one containing pure milk and the other, milk with up to 10 per cent alcohol. The cats now drank the alcoholic milk voluntarily. As a matter of fact they could not be gotten away from it. They didn't even look at the pure milk. As long as they were mildly intoxicated they overcame their difficulties.

In other words, these cats had become dependent upon alcoholic intoxication; they had become addicted. When they were re-trained so as not to be afraid of the air blast or the electric shock – that is, when their conflict was solved – they did not touch the alcoholic milk any more. They were rehabilitated from their alcohol addiction.

Men and women too are subject to conflicts in their personality, to conflicts of opposite drives. When these conflicts are strong they are called neuroses. In such conflict situations men and women frequently seek artificial solutions of their problems, and one of the artificial ways out is alcoholic intoxication.

Cats, of course, have no means of figuring out their difficulty, or of making an intellectual or emotional effort to adjust their difficulties. Recourse to intoxication may be quite appropriate for cats, particularly since their drunken behavior does not cause them to lose their jobs, or to distress their families, and they are not going to get into trouble with the law.

Human beings, however, have intellectual and spiritual assets which they can use in order to overcome their conflicts. And if, instead, they do have recourse to intoxication, they do get into serious trouble with their families, with their employers, and with their friends.

One of the finest ways of preventing inebriety is to develop the spiritual and intellectual assets of one's personality and to learn how to utilize them. In these days in which all of us are beset by the anxieties caused by the so-called Atomic Age, it is particularly important that we should not rely on crutches, that we should not look for artificial escapes – but that we should make a conscious and conscientious effort to deal with the difficult situations.

VIGNETTE #1

Mrs. G. let everyone know how she felt about herself. At the age of 25 she was fat and slovenly and looked at least ten years older. With a little care she could have been quite attractive, but when first seen at the alcoholism center she seemed determined to confirm the low opinion she held of herself.

It wasn't difficult to understand how she had arrived at this point. She was born into squalor and confusion and she had lived for a quarter of a century with this double burden. Both parents were alcoholics and were divorced when she was six and remarried to each other when she was eleven. A psychiatric evaluation reported that there "were no family relationships at any time."

She had sex play with her brother and several other boys at the age of twelve and at sixteen became pregnant and had to leave high school. She was sent to a detention home, where the baby was delivered. Later she married and had two children by her husband and two children by other men while she was still married. After four years she was divorced. She continued her promiscuous behavior, contracted gonorrhea, which made her feel "dirty and no good," went on county relief, and felt that she coud never accomplish anything worthwhile.

Her life was complicated by the fact that she, a white Catholic, had married a black man and almost all other men in her life were black. Prejudice dies slowly at all levels of society but most slowly perhaps in marginal socioeconomic groups where the struggle for survival is toughest and scapegoats are necessary. Illusions of the inferiority of others based on race is a tenacious stereotype and she heard it all. A white girl with black men, in her social milieu, must be a whore or worse.

The situation was made even more bitter by the fact that she wasn't really accepted in black society. She never belonged to either white or black groups, and wherever she went she was lost amid the alien corn.

Her escape was liquor. It was a natural for her. She wasn't sure when she had her first drink but she said she virtually nursed whiskey and was given paregoric for colic when she was a baby. She was given hot toddies to keep her warm in houses and flats that were often cold. She sipped her parents' beer from infancy and was drinking steadily by the time she was thirteen.

She drank to escape many things and one was that she was nothing – not a wife, not a mother, not a woman. In her promiscuity, she invariably consorted with men who were her inferiors regardless of color because that made her feel she was superior to somebody. But this only reinforced the image she had of herself as a slut. She drank to make the most sordid escapades seem romantic, to see herself temporarily as a seductive sexual object, a desired woman. Perhaps she might one day again be someone's wife. She drank because, in an alcoholic haze, she could imagine that she was a loving devoted mother.

VIGNETTE #2

Mr. H. was the vice-president of a large corporation and in charge of branch operations in the Bahamas. From outward appearances, he was a model success story with all the trappings of authority, social prestige, financial security, two expensive cars, and a home with the finest address.

That was Mr. H. to business associates and friends. But it all fell away at home because he felt he was nothing. He perceived himself as an industrial executive but not as a man. Except for the fact that he provided money to keep the family going, he regarded himself as a failure in traditional male roles. These nagging doubts about his masculinity were emphasized by his wife, whom he described as "a person of strong will." She had to have things her way and was a "take-charge woman." When she taught school, she was in constant conflict with other teachers and the principal. Her controlling personality so raised the hackles of others that she was repeatedly voted out of organizations and squeezed out of positions of authority. Not so at home, however, where she could not tolerate this but neither could he fight back. His recourse was in the bottle. Alcohol, he said, erased all problems.

VIGNETTE #3

Mr. W. had been encouraged as far back as grade school days to believe he was a genius. His I.Q., admittedly an unreliable measure of almost anything, was reported as being 170. A doting mother was naturally delighted and teachers beamed fondly. Through high school and college, as the boy grew into a man, he was convinced that he was, indeed, a genius. Apparently he also persuaded himself that he should accept only such employment as would fully utilize that titanic gift. However, if one decides to work exclusively at the genius level, job opportunities are limited, so Mr. W. was almost continuously unemployed. His drinking became alcoholism and he finally sought clinical help.

The therapist recognized his superior intelligence but thought it missed the genius level by a wide margin. He decided to give the patient another intelligence test despite its limitations. This time the score was around 130. This seemed closer to reality. Also, it enabled the therapist to point out to Mr. W. that he was highly intelligent but hardly a threat to the reputation of Leonardo Da Vinci. The patient was persuaded to abandon striving for Olympus and to seek employment at a realistic level. He eventually found a position as a school teacher and was quite successful.

This change was not accomplished easily or quickly. There were many facets in the therapy but the beginning was the need of the patient to see himself and his potential realistically. This meant the establishment of attainable goals and avoidance of the self-punishing despair that follows inevitable failure when one tries for the impossible.

VIGNETTE #4

Mr. K. was a milk route driver and earned a comfortable living. His excessive drinking interfered with many areas of his life but not with his job performance. However, with the grandiose ideas common to alcoholics, he decided, at the age of 53, to turn to journalism despite an education limited to the eighth grade and considerable difficulty in writing a simple declarative sentence. To make the transition from route salesman to journalist, he thought, would require at most a six to eight-week training course.

Mr. K. knew what he wanted. He not only wanted to be a reporter; he had also decided to aim for a job as political commentator because he had heard that Walter Lippman was getting along in years and a replacement would be in order.

This patient was fairly well-oriented in most aspects of his life but his insatiable need to conquer his feelings of failure and to achieve prestige badly distorted his thinking and the realities of his ambition. Treatment had to focus partly on the fact that he really had succeeded and that there can be more genuine satisfaction in being good at a job one can do than being a failure at something for which one is in no way qualified. He needed the security of knowing that he could be a success as a *person*.

VIGNETTE #5

D. L., a personable young man of 25, had several conflicts about his drinking. He admitted that he liked to drink and was reluctant to give it up. On the other hand, when he started he seldom stopped until he passed out and this frightened him. Also, he was worried that it might get worse.

In the initial interviews he was ill-at-ease and he betrayed his nervousness by rapid talk, inability to sit still, and forced laughter. As he talked, his poor self-image became apparent. He brooded about the aimlessness of his life, his feeling that he could never complete anything he started, and depression about his sexual failure with women which he recognized as totally psychological.

He had used alcohol as early as the seventh grade because it made him feel so good. "I really enjoyed it, felt different, it gave me a great feeling." As he grew up, he discovered that he could do many things with alcohol. If he didn't drink too much, he could even make it with women. He also felt socially equal. "I drink now," he said, "because it makes me feel like a big shot."

It wasn't all positive. Drinking interfered with his academic performance both in high school and college, so he dropped out of the latter in his junior year. When he married, he didn't really want the responsibilities and alcohol helped to minimize them. When sober, he realized this was another failure so he drank to forget that.

As with others, the major thrust of treatment with this man was to make him feel worthwile through activities that would provide success. There were many ups and downs, but with encouragement he returned to college and completed his senior year with three A's. His marriage improved and his wife proved to be a source of considerable strength. When he terminated treatment, he was about to enter law school.

CHAPTER IV

Motivating the Alcoholic to Accept Treatment

THE INITIAL PROBLEM in the care of an alcoholic is to persuade him to seek treatment. This can be accomplished only through motivation, and, as Sterne and Pittman have observed, there is probably no other illness in which so much verbal concern is expressed for the patient's motivation to recover as in alcoholism. It is emphasized by lay organizations such as Alcoholics Anonymous and is "a frequently recurring theme among health and welfare personnel."[1]

In evaluating the readiness of alcoholics to accept treatment, there is strong feeling among helping persons—professional and non-professional—that motivation is an all-or-nothing phenomenon. The alcoholic either has it or he doesn't. If he has it, he is a good candidate for treatment; if he doesn't, there is little anyone can or should do for him except wait until he is ready.

[1] Muriel W. Sterne and David J. Pittman, "The Concept of Motivation: A Source of Institutional and Professional Blockage in the Treatment of Alcoholics," *Quarterly Journal of Studies on Alcohol,* Vol. 26, No. 1 (March, 1965), pp. 41-57.

The judgment that an alcoholic cannot be helped until he wants to be helped is derived in large measure from the early catechism of Alcoholics Anonymous, whose members were convinced that it was useless to attempt rehabilitation until the alcoholic asked for help on his own initiative. In recent years they have applied that principle with greater flexibility, but even today many AA groups insist that the alcoholic himself must make the initial contact. Referrals or telephone calls from spouses, parents, employers, and others are not acceptable. It must be the alcoholic because that, they say, is the only evidence he is sincere.

This approach makes motivation the sole responsibility of the alcoholic, which is absurd in view of the nature of alcoholism. If it is true that the alcoholic has developed a strong denial mechanism to protect his drinking, it is ostrich-like to insist that he must be the first to demonstrate his treatability. Denial creates resistance to treatment that is seldom surrendered by the alcoholic without help.

The alcoholic, imprisoned by his illness, must be *enabled* to seek and accept treatment and this usually requires the intervention, prodding, and support of so-called "significant others." But this will be an exercise in frustration unless he finds, when he reaches the point of readiness to accept help, community resources motivated to treat him and even to reach out to him. The latter is as vital as his own motivation. When the doors of agencies, hospitals, and clinics are closed to him, the nearest liquor store or tavern is the only sanctuary. Motivation is a multiple process that is best understood in the context of the 'systems view of alcoholism.' [2]

In most cases the alcoholic must first be helped to want help. Even when he knows he should stop drinking he is prey to conflict. "Every alcoholic," said Vogel, "has some drive to move in the direction of sobriety and become an accepted, constructive, functioning member of society. Another part of him is driven in the opposite direction, to a life revolving around alcohol."[3]

Alcohol is the alcoholic's agony and ecstasy. The ecstasy is that it works miracles. It allays fears, anxieties, and stresses. It is the magic elixir that transforms the pain of inadequacy into the exhilaration of well-being. "The sway of alcohol over mankind," wrote William James, "is unquestionably due to its power to stimulate the mystical facilities of human nature, usually crushed to earth by the cold facts and dry criticism of the sober hour. Sobriety diminishes, discriminates and says no; drunk-

---

[2] Robert F. Ward and Louis A. Faillace, "The Alcoholic and His Helpers; A Systems View," *Quarterly Journal of Studies on Alcohol,* Vol. 31, No. 3 (September, 1970), Part A, pp. 684-691.

[3] Sidney Vogel, "Psychiatric Treatment of Alcoholism," *The Annals of the American Academy of Political and Social Science* (January, 1958), p. 104.

enness expands, unites and says yes. Not through mere perversity do men run after it. . . ."

The agony is that the miracles are transient and the return to reality is inevitable. Alcoholism has only made worse what it seemed to cure.

Ambivalence can plague the alcoholic even after he decides to seek help. Catherine Peltenberg, a social worker who has had long experience with alcoholics, observed that "the majority of alcoholics coming for help, even though coming voluntarily, are ambivalently motivated. Many genuinely want sobriety but they are too afraid, too depressed, too overwhelmed by inferiority feelings, too convinced that they can't make it, too 'driven' to dare to make a wholehearted attempt to do so. After all, one doesn't usually give up one's sedative until the pain has subsided. Too little attention is usually paid to what crutch or what sedative alcohol signifies in the particular case, too little attention is paid to what alcohol does *for* a person since what it does *to* him is so flagrant."[4]

As Horace wrote centuries ago:

> What wonders does not wine! It discloses secrets; ratifies and confirms our hopes; thrusts the coward forth to battle; instructs in art. Whom has not a cheerful glass made eloquent; who not quite free and easy from pinching poverty.

Those around the alcoholic see and emphasize the negative consequences of his drinking and plead with him to give it up. The alcoholic knows the negatives, but he also *feels* the positive effects and as time passes he rejects the former and embraces the latter.

Friends, relatives, and employers cannot understand why an alcoholic stubbornly refuses to "learn his lesson" from benders that end in excruciating misery; why he deliberately repeats the experience within months, weeks, or days. It is because he represses memory of the pain; when he starts to drink he recalls only the euphoria and liberation. Besides, he seldom intends to go on another binge; he seeks only relief but in the process loses control.

The fact that alcohol works, despite its disadvantages, forces the alcoholic to protect his need to drink against the pressures to give it up. As his behavior becomes increasingly unacceptable and his grasp on the management of his life weakens, he must find refuge in denial.

This does not mean, contrary to the oft-repeated cliché, that the alcoholic is necessarily the last to recognize his alcoholism. Indeed, he may have been the first, but with the passing years alcohol has become a primary defense against what seems to him the intolerable clutch of cir-

[4] Catherine M. Peltenberg, "Accessibility of the Problem Drinker," Paper presented at the Institute on Alcoholism, sponsored by Alameda County Tuberculosis and Health Association and the Council of Community Services, Mills College, Oakland, California June, 1960.

cumstance, whether it be an oppressive social situation, marriage tantamount to a state of war, job harrassment, wracking physical pain, or a combination of these things. He knows he is drinking too much but cannot admit it to himself or to others because the thought of being stripped of his armor terrifies him. Such is the paranoid, or, in the words of AA members, the "stinking thinking" of the alcoholic.

As his fear increases so must his denial, until he convinces himself that there is nothing excessive about his drinking or, if there is, it is just for the time being. As soon as current pressures are alleviated he will return to normal drinking. He remembers the pleasures of drinking. Some recovered alcoholics recall many years when even excessive drinking was a lark. There was pain but also exhilaration. There was melancholy but also joy. One man described his drinking as the "fun beginning" of what later became almost a matter of life and death.

This iron-clad denial prevents alcoholics from seeking help on their own even when the pain has become acute and the pleasure negligible. The first order of the enabling business, then, is to penetrate the denial. That isn't easy. Friends, relatives, family, and even employers are likely to make their first assault with such useless weapons as exhortation, ridicule, denunciation. If they do, they underestimate the alcoholic's skill in rationalization. He has to defend himself not only to protect his drinking but to protect his self-image. Swift said:

> Nearly every alcoholic moves around the circle of his life busily patching up his battered self-image in a continuous effort. When that image is wounded by some new criticism of his ways, he tries to cut the critic out of his circle and hastens to cover the scar with a new tissue of rationalization.
>
> Doctors who diagnose liver damage and issue warnings are not consulted again. Fellow workers who (without the backing of an enlightened company policy) suggest he better cut down a little are written off as prudes or busybodies. And the wife's harangues about the drinking go easily unheeded as long as they aren't echoed by any of his peers, most notably his drinking companions, his friends (if he has any left who aren't drinking companions) and his other relatives, if they are the distant and tolerant kind.
>
> Only rarely is the alibi structure brought down by a lucky shot or a glancing blow. Usually it takes a barrage.[5]

In most instances, the social worker's initial contact with a problem of alcoholism is through a member of the family, and, since most alco-

[5] R. Michael Swift, "How to Help an Alcoholic Who Insists He Doesn't Need Any Help," Fairfield Plan Publication No. 1, Fairfield County Conn. Council on Alcoholism, Inc., p. 9.

holics are men, it is likely to be a wife. When she calls, she is at wit's end. Her husband has guzzled himself into a stupor and she can't budge him. She is afraid to live with him because of real or threatened violence. Last night, for example, he accused her of assorted acts of infidelity and other scandalous behavior. When she protested, he hit her. She says she has tried everything. She has emptied bottles down the drain, although she may confide this sheepishly because most people know it is the most futile of gestures. In desperation and anger, however, they continue to do it. Through fifteen years of marriage she has threatened to leave him more than twenty times. Has she ever left? Of course not, because he is such a nice person when sober.

She usually responds with surprise or indignation when the worker tells her that what she has been doing may enable the alcoholic to continue drinking but will not enable him to seek help. Why should he stop drinking as long as he is protected? With slight variations, employer or parent can be substituted for wife and, of course, the same principles apply to a husband when the woman is the alcoholic.

The first interview may be educational—helping the wife to understand what alcoholism is and how she can avoid playing into her husband's drinking. She will have to resist buying peace at any price, meaning that she will not go to the liquor store to replenish the supply no matter how pugnacious her husband becomes. She will not call his employer on Monday mornings to excuse his absence, as she must recognize that he got himself into this predicament and has to accept responsibility for getting out. She will not cover his bad checks written during his binges but will insist that he make restitution. (Vignettes #1 & #2)

When the woman is alcoholic, she frequently uses sex as a weapon and rejects all advances unless her husband supplies her with alcohol. There are obvious discomforts in taking a firm stand, but if he surrenders to her blackmail she will probably increase the ransom and the drinking.

The alcoholic will be enabled to accept help only when he is released to take responsibility, which in the family situation means that he must be released emotionally and in all situations means giving up attempts to control the drinking and to provide protection from its consequences. If, for example, the family has capitulated to the alcoholic's every whim and need during his drinking, the social worker can support a change in strategy. Two simple illustrations are:

1. The family plans to go to the movies after dinner and the father does not appear. Everyone knows he is touring the bars. In the past they have abandoned their plans and waited anxiously for him to come home. They should be helped to learn that it is far better to

go to the movies without him. When he gets home he can fend for himself, thus accepting the consequences of his behavior.

2. A picnic is planned for Sunday morning. The alcoholic goes on a bender Saturday night and wakes up with a pounding hangover. He wants to cancel the picnic and he may alternately demand and plead for tender loving care but this should not be permitted to spoil the day for everyone else. There is no reason why he should not be left to sweat it out for himself.

These measures may seem punitive, but they are actually realistic. They free the alcoholic to decide if he wants to be part of the family. If he does, he will have to do something about his alcoholism because it no longer gives him special privileges.

The family is helped to reject excuses and empty promises because, as Swift pointed out, motivation is partly a process of collapsing the alibi structure in order to get the alcoholic to accept the need for treatment. Logically, it is a task to be undertaken by those closest to the alcoholic —his family, friends, and working associates for whose benefit the alibi structure was erected in the first place.[6] (Vignette #3)

If this is to be done effectively, those involved, especially spouses, should be helped to avoid supporting the alcoholic's denial, projection, and rationalization. The alcoholic must face the truth of his condition and that is accomplished by opposing rationalizations with realities. (Vignette #4)

This does not mean that a person should be held responsible for becoming an alcoholic, but he can and must be held accountable for doing something about his illness or he must accept the consequences. Continued protection renders him impotent to make a choice because his initiative is atrophied. When, however, the straightjacket of protectiveness is removed, he is free to decide if he will continue to drink with the prospect of destroying his life or if he will take steps to achieve the sobriety that may offer the only possibility of salvaging the future.

The incentive to make this choice depends on the creation, enhancement, and maintenance of a high level of concern about one's behavior and the clinical problem, says Finlay, "is one of shifting one or more aspects of the patient's (or prospective patient's) situation to an acute and chronic stage."[7] (Vignette #5)

Others have written in terms of utilizing a recent crisis or creating a more effective one. The decision comes, said Tiebout, "when the individual senses the utter futility of the path he has been pursuing and realizes that hopes once held high have been dashed causing him to sink

---

[6] *Ibid.*, p. 5.

[7] Donald G. Finlay, "Effect of Role Network Pressure on an Alcoholic's Approach to Treatment," *Social Work*, Vol. 11, No. 4 (October, 1966).

ever lower until he finally hits a bottom which makes him feel 'this is the end.'"[8] It is a point at which he is convinced the future will inevitably be disasterous if he continues to drink.

The crisis that motivates a change in behavior occurs at different levels for different people. For some it is the loss of a first job, for others it is the loss of the tenth job. For some it is the time at which they realize their children are afraid to invite friends into the home because they are ashamed of the behavior of an alcoholic parent. Others are motivated by the first arrest for drunken driving while some need the jolt of a wife and children leaving the home.

It is impossible to predict the event that will mark the turning point. One young woman, in retrospect, thought it should have happened in her life when she was raped by two men during a blackout related to drinking, but it didn't. She returned to the bottle within 24 hours and postponed the search for help until she had been dismissed from three jobs.

Most clinicians would agree with Finlay's conclusion from his study in Toronto that the two persons who are most influential in promoting a patient's approach to treatment are his spouse and his employer. Employers are frequently in the most strategic position to persuade the alcoholic to make a choice. This need not and should not be done punitively. The employer tells the employee that he is a valuable worker and the company hopes to retain him. However, he is an asset only when sober and free of disabling hangovers. If he wants to keep his job, he will have to get help with his drinking problem. If his efforts are sincere and ultimately productive, his job is secure; if he refuses to seek help and continues his drinking pattern, the company will dismiss him. This approach does not interfere with the employees' freedom of choice; it simply makes sobriety a condition of employment.

Crisis can be employed in many situations. A man arraigned in court for a second or third or fourth offense associated with excessive drinking can be given a choice between a jail sentence and probation with the provision that he applies for help. The indiscriminate use of judicial muscle has been rightly viewed with suspicion because of the potential for violation of civil rights. The courts are crowded with alcoholics and some can be directed to sources of help. This is legitimate as long as there is free choice, however unpalatable, between incarceration (if indicated) and treatment.

Duress can be a motivating technique. For some alcoholics, the requirement to undergo treatment, after a careful evaluation, means that at long

---

[8] Harry M. Tiebout, "Intervention in Psychotherapy," *The American Journal of Psychoanalysis* (May, 1962), p. 75.

last someone is interested in them. Offers of treatment on a take-it-or-leave-it basis can be interpreted as rejection.

Research has indicated that pressure does not diminish the potential effectiveness of treatment. A study by Lemere, O'Hallaren, and Maxwell at Shadel Hospital in Seattle revealed that few of the 1,038 patients in the group studied would have sought help unless pressure had been exerted. Some of the patients who were initially involved in treatment under protest relapsed, but they later returned under their own volition for successful therapy. The significant conclusion was that those patients who came to the clinic under duress did just as well in treatment as those who came voluntarily.[9]

Some therapists question the wisdom of crisis, especially when created, but most agree that it is the only device likely to penetrate the narcissism of the alcoholic. This, said one writer, "may even involve disintegration but disintegration may be positive. A crisis in the life of any individual may serve to dislodge him from a maladaptive fixed position which, in the case of an alcoholic, is destructive drinking as a defense mechanism. . . ."[10]

Tiebout recognized the risks in the strategy of crisis but concluded the results were worth it. He saw "a great danger of arousing a hornet's nest of trouble but I am also mindful of the unhappy and somewhat bitter voice of the patient who said, 'I am through with hand-holding psychiatrists!' I thought he had a point. . . ."[11]

Crisis, as we have pointed out, has the built-in merit of discomfort which can spur action. Discomfort alone is not enough; it must be combined with hope. The two, as Helen Harris Perlman says, "must hold for the sustainment of responsible willingness to work at problem solving. . . ."[12]

That is certainly true for the alcoholic. In addition to his concern about the potential disaster in continued drinking, he must see in sobriety satisfactions superior to those provided by alcohol. Otherwise, why give up drinking?

COMMUNITY ATTITUDES

Enabling the alcoholic to accept help would present formidable difficulties if the hangups in his personality were the only barrier to success, but they aren't. The attitudes of society can sometimes defeat the best

[9] Frederick Lemere *et al.*, "Motivation in the Treatment of Alcoholism," *Quarterly Journal of Studies on Alcohol,* Vol. 19, No. 3 (September, 1958), pp. 428-431.

[10] Harry M. Tiebout, "Crisis and Surrender in Treating Alcoholism," quoted from "Positive Disintegration" by Kazimirex Dabrowski, *Quarterly Journal of Studies on Alcohol,* Vol. 26, No. 3 (September, 1965), p. 496.

[11] *Ibid.*

[12] Helen Harris Perlman, *Social Casework* (Chicago: University of Chicago Press, 1957).

efforts. Unless the alcoholic can cope with these attitudes, he may not be able to mobilize the emotional fortitude to ask for help.

The stigma that society attaches to alcoholism, although considerably diminished in recent years, still arouses a sense of shame in many and a reluctance to expose themselves as alcoholics. Non-alcoholic members of the family are similarly affected and they do not want anyone to know about the alcoholic in their midst because relatives and neighbors might not understand. This may explain why one authority estimated that the average family does not admit a member is an alcoholic until the illness has been critical for seven years, and, once admitted, the family waits two more years to ask for help.

Alcoholics are also keenly aware of the general attitude that asking for help is a sign of weakness. Because they are almost universally victims of eroded self-esteem, they are constantly struggling to achieve some triumph on their own. The idea of asking for help only reinforces their sense of failure, and potential clients are convinced that "it won't be any good if I don't do it myself." This feeling is fortified by society's attitude that the individual who can do for himself and is master of his own fate is far more commendable than one who has to depend on others. This vestige of the puritan ethic that emphasizes the nobility of self-control and strength of character makes the alcoholic appear spineless and deficient in will power. Unfortunately, that false premise suggests to many guardians of community funds that alcoholics are not worth helping. If they really wanted to stop drinking they could.

The alcoholic who bangs his head against this wall of public attitudes —especially when his friends, neighbors, and fellow employees are part of that public—needs to be convinced that using help is a sign of strength rather than weakness.

UNMOTIVATED AGENCIES

In relation to alcoholics, too many helping agencies and their personnel are equally negative and erect barriers that can discourage the best motivated alcoholic. Nothing is gained—indeed, much is lost—if alcoholics and their families seek help and find the doors of agencies and clinics closed to them. We have been quick to condemn the alcoholic or his family for resistance to treatment but slow to recognize that the fault may not be only with alcoholics but also with ourselves.

In many cases, professionals tend to reject those whom they view as inadequately motivated, and with alcoholics they act as if motivation were an all or nothing phenomenon. This is not true of alcoholics or any other group. This attitude may be accompanied by moral judgments that divide alcoholics into two categories: those who express enthusiasm for help are worthwhile; those who seem indifferent are not.

According to Pittman and Stern, this attitude is widespread: [13] They interviewed or sent questionnaires to 177 employees of health and welfare agencies in St. Louis. One of the items read: "Alcoholics can be divided into two classes: those who have the motivation to recover and those who don't." Almost half the respondents (48 percent) agreed. Another 25 percent were undecided and only 27 percent disagreed. Also, 25 percent said that "any changes in behavior which the alcoholic makes under an enforced regimen of treatment are unlikely to persist when he is no longer in treatment."

The investigators found that among the helping professionals motivation for sobriety "is often implicitly equated with conformity to the specifications for treatment set by the therapist, such as willingness to keep regular appointments; to undergo a specific form of treatment for instance psychotherapy; or to see alcoholism as a symptom of an underlying psychiatric condition rather than as a ramifying problem to be addressed directly. Yet research has not shown that any of these are actually prerequisites to sobriety."

They encountered such reactions as the respondent who wrote:

> There would be some reaching out by the worker to the alcoholic but this is not our primary focus. The man might have withdrawn from the clinic because he didn't show too much motivation in coming in, in the first place. There is not much need with the shortage of manpower to solicit business with someone you think isn't motivated in the first place.

Another wrote about a walk-in for whom he found a job although the alcoholic located a residence on his own. "I put him in touch with the AA chapter. In the course of ten days he had disappeared. Well, he didn't have enough motivation to deal with the problem. I don't determine this, they do."

The theme that motivation is either present and therapy succeeds, or it is lacking and nothing will work ran all through the study. The more dynamic concept "in which the alcoholic's decision to work toward sobriety is dependent upon a complex interaction of internal and external influences converging upon him at a point in time" was rejected by 75 percent.

Professional training made little difference in the ideas held about alcoholism and motivation. The professionals tended to take a less static view, but there was no significant difference in rating the primacy of

---

[13] Sterne and Pittman, *op. cit.*

motivation to recovery. One consoling note is that of all the professionals, the social workers were the least moralistic.

Responsibility for such failures cannot be assigned to individual professionals but more to the system factors (mentioned in the beginning of this section) which are multiple and which influence a practitioner's willingness to be involved with alcoholics. Ward and Faillace illustrate this in a hospital setting.

> Most physicians' knowledge about alcoholism is inadequate, due, in part, to the generally poor teaching about it in medical schools. This usually results in the young physician being ill-prepared to treat the alcoholic patient or realize his own feelings concerning alcoholism. His inadequate training, reinforced by his and society's prejudices, leads to feelings of helplessness and hopelessness. The young physician, compensating for these feelings, often has an unpleasant rescue or forgiveness interaction. Like the adolescent child, his efforts to rescue are usually unsuccessful, not only because of the alcoholic's pathological reaction in such a situation, but also because the hospital system is often so constructed as to reject the alcoholic either overtly or covertly. For example, if the physician wants to hospitalize the alcoholic only for "drying out," he frequently encounters hostility from the rest of the hospital staff. He soon learns that it is easier to stay uninvolved. In addition, if the hospital can avoid becoming involved one of the legal or social agency systems will. This rejection results in further drinking by the alcoholic and reinforcing of the myth about his being unmotivated. In order to comprehend the situation the whole sequence of complex events must be observed and an attempt made to enlighten the medical personnel about how their feelings and attitudes affect the patient.[14]

The structure and archaic routines of an agency or hospital can thwart the motivated patient, but Chafetz and his colleagues demonstrated that changes can be dramatically effective. At Massachusetts General Hospital they discovered that less than one percent of the alcoholics seen in the emergency service ever went to the alcohol clinic for treatment although theoretically all such patients were referred. It was assumed the 99 percent did not want help, i.e., were not sufficiently motivated.[15]

A study of the situation convinced Chafetz that, on the contrary, some

---

[14] Ward and Faillace, *op. cit.*
[15] Morris E. Chafetz, *et al.*, "Establishing Treatment Relations with Alcoholics," *The Journal of Nervous and Mental Disease*, Vol. 134, No. 5 (May, 1962), pp. 395-409.

may have wanted help but could not survive the obstacle course from initial contact to the alcohol clinic. A patient entering the emergency service was seen by the following: an admitting clerk, chief medical officer, a specialist if there were any complications, a financial officer, a nurse, a social worker, and assorted physicians and paramedical personnel who might be called in.

If the patient made it that far and still wanted to go to the clinic he had to go to an admitting officer in the out-patient clinic, be seen by another financial officer, go upstairs to the clinic where he would be seen by the clinic secretary, a psychiatric social worker, and possibly the psychiatric resident on call that day. An appointment was then made for the patient to see a psychiatric resident for evaluation. If he kept that appointment, his name was placed on the waiting list for treatment. Then, if he appeared when called–usually four to six weeks later–he was assigned to a permanent therapist who was invariably someone he never saw before. Little wonder that the 99 percent of the patients didn't think it was worth the trouble.

The Chafez group saw a golden opportunity ignored. "The situation at the time of admission to an emergency service finds the alcoholic vulnerable to the beginning of a rehabilitative relationship. To maximize this motivation, it is essential to constructively utilize the patient's dependency needs which means "treating him with respect and consideration, reducing the frequency of frustrating situations, and gratifying his requests." This does not mean indiscriminate giving, "but gratification that serves to establish and further the patient's trust and confidence in the caretaker."

The result was a pilot study involving 200 male alcoholics. One hundred were in an experimental group, received special consideration, and were unhampered by red tape, and each member was promptly assigned to one of the treatment teams. The second 100 patients formed a control group and received no special treatment other than the usual emergency service.[16]

With the barriers removed, 65 percent of the experimental group made initial visits to the alcohol clinic as opposed to 5.4 percent of the control group. An impressive 42 percent of the experimental group returned to the clinic five or more times in contrast to 1.1 percent of the control group.

Acceptance and interest can be basic ingredients of motivation. The manner in which a referral is made is important. Trice studied readiness to affiliate with Alcoholics Anonymous as related to factors contributing

---

[16] *Ibid.*

to and militating against affiliation. The quality of the referrals made a considerable difference.[17]

In one of its former locations, the Cleveland Center on Alcoholism was in the same complex of buildings as the medical service of a major hospital. The distance apart was less than half a block. In a single year, more than 100 patients were referred to the Center, but only one made it. Inquiry revealed that referrals were usually made by physicians who brusquely told alcoholics they had better get to the Center before drinking destroyed them. Most went to the closest bar.

Arrangements were then made to have a doctor call at the time of referral and a caseworker visited the patient in the hospital to discuss the problem and explain the treatment offered at the Center. With that change from the impersonal to the personal, more than 30 percent of the patients followed through on the referrals and there is reason to believe that percentage could have been increased if more staff time had been available.

The importance of the accessibility of agencies in enabling alcoholics to seek treatment cannot be overemphasized. Accessibility may mean reaching out and this applies with special pertinence to poverty populations. Failure to recognize this has left some agencies vulnerable to the charge that the evaluation of the client's motivation as a screening process can be used to exclude clients from variant cultural backgrounds, particularly from lower socio-economic classes, who may not be comfortable in a middle-class clinic's style of operation.

We cannot assume that alcoholics and their families from the slums are unmotivated because they do not march on agencies in droves. We might instead consider the possibility that agencies and clinics are inaccessible. A report from the Cleveland Center on Alcoholism illustrates the need to reach out.

Like most private agencies, the caseload was primarily middle-class for many years although there were a few clients at both extremes of the socio-economic spectrum. The staff of the agency became increasingly aware of the void in its services as they met with workers in agencies and churches in depressed and marginal neighborhoods.

> Invariably, alcoholism was a problem among clients and congregations. Social workers and clergymen welcomed the description of the center with its open intake policy and little or no delay in accepting applicants for treatment. Our listeners could hardly wait to refer alcoholics and their families.
>
> Unfortunately, those referred seldom appeared. Many

[17] Harrison A. Trice, quoted in Sterne and Pittman, *op. cit.*

seemed to want help but they just couldn't make it. Distances in Cleveland, as in most large cities, can be long; transportation costs high for families who have to count pennies; care for small children must be arranged. It just didn't seem to be worth that much effort to many people and others did not have the bus fare.

We went out to them.

The first group was composed of wives of alcoholics and met in an inner-city church. Lack of staff compelled us to limit this initial test to four meetings and we did not expect nor achieve any miracles. But we did reach eight families who might never have been helped if we had waited for them to come to us.

One mother, for example, had been harassed for six months by an alcoholic husband who had deserted and fled to Chicago. Drunk and sober, he cajoled and threatened by telephone and said he could not stop drinking without his wife and children with him. With the support of the group, she was able to reject the seductive pleas to which families of alcoholics are so vulnerable. She insisted that he do something about his drinking first. Faced with this firm choice, he did get help and returned to Cleveland.

Several months after the enforced termination of the program, one of the women from the group visited the Center with a staff person from the church and asked that it be reactivated. It was and has been in continuous operation on an open-ended basis for nearly two years.

At first, we did not have much success in reaching the alcoholics themselves. Occasionally, curious husbands wandered into the group to find out what it was all about. After a year, we received a request from the alcoholics to start a group with them.[18]

Many social agencies are well-equipped to work with alcoholics and their families, but instead they seem to be primarily interested in getting rid of them. A team of social workers in Columbus, Ohio, concluded that "it appears we expend more energy in skillfully (and not so skillfully) referring a client to another 'more appropriate' agency than in developing skills and techniques toward helping the client find direction in more productive and satisfying patterns of living.[19]

---

[18] Herman E. Krimmel, "Reaching the Unreached Alcoholic," paper presented at the National Council on Alcoholism, pp. 6-7.

[19] J. G. Pantalos, *et. al.*, "A Review of Policies and Practices of Selected Community Resources in Regard to Problem Drinking Situations" (Columbus, Ohio: The Coumbus Area Council on Alcoholism, Inc. 1960), p. 12.

Pittman and Sterne reported: "The attitude that agencies other than the one in which the interviewer works are more appropriate treatment resources for the alcoholic is prevalent. In general, agencies not providing intensive professional casework tend to see this service as pertinent. Casework agencies, in turn, typically though not exclusively, view alcoholism as a psychiatric problem and tend either to refer the person to psychiatric facilities or to work in a circumscribed area in which they feel competent and to encourage further psychiatric assistance and/or affiliation with Alcoholics Anonymous. Few psychiatric clinics, in turn, see their role as one in which alcoholism in and of itself is treated; several refer to Alcoholics Anonymous. *This makes for a merry-go-round of referrals.*[20]

Little wonder that many alcoholics lose their enthusiasm for help. Motivation is important but we should ask, "Whose motivation is deficient?" To write off large numbers of alcoholics as unmotivated is an abdication of professional responsibility. It may underline flaws in professional techniques. If so, it is a social work responsibility to develop new techniques.

[20] David J. Pittman and Muriel W. Sterne, "Report on Alcoholism: Community Agency Attitudes and Their Impact on Treatment Services" (Washington, D.C.: U.S. Department of Health, Education, and Welfare, 1963, Public Health Service Publication No. 1273), p. 18.

VIGNETTE #1

Mr. Q. admits alcohol was a problem. He describes himself as a "hopeless victim of alcohol" and when he is drinking seriously he consumes a fifth of bourbon in three hours. He has been a drinker so long he could not give it up.

He rejects any suggestion that he should give up drinking. After all, he had a severe heart attack, gall bladder surgery, a bad bronchial congestive cough, and two back injuries involving a possible ruptured disc. "Alcohol is the only thing that relieves the back pain and the cough." He rationalized that alcohol is better for physical discomfort than drugs because "drugs are 'dope' and, therefore, a hazard."

His main concern is that his capacity for liquor has declined. Also, he has hangovers and gets sicker than he ever did and needs a few drinks in the morning to steady him. His only reason for being at the agency seems to be that he wants help so he could drink without these unpleasant consequences.

This man did maintain sobriety for a period of three years, but after his wife had a nervous breakdown he was so "disgusted" that she would do this to him that he figured "the hell with it." He renewed his affair with alcohol by drinking almost without interruption for four days.

All through this his wife made gestures. She threatened divorce several times but never went through with it. She went to an attorney but dropped the suit when her husband convinced her that understanding and affection would be more effective than any drastic action which "drives me to drink."

Mrs. Q. also emphasizes the good things in the marriage that deterred her from action. When questioned, the only good thing she could think of was that the relationship is sexually compatible despite the drinking.

The worker spent several weeks attempting to support Mrs. Q. in taking some decisive action. She made her see that her choice was clear if not ideal. She could do nothing but endure her husband's drinking and hope that some other factors might motivate him to get help, or she could face him with a choice of losing his family or doing something about his drinking if he wanted the family to stay together.

At first he laughed because he had heard meaningless threats many times. But this time she obtained a separation, and when Mr. Q. realized that she meant to save the futures of herself and the children, he decided that the family was important to him and he would have to do something about it.

VIGNETTE #2

Mrs. A. called requesting help concerning her husband's drinking, which had been going on for fourteen years. She felt that she was reaching the breaking point and was unable to mobilize herself constructively.

During the first interview she said she had tried everything: "I have cried, nagged, begged, and threatened but he just goes on drinking and denying that there is anything wrong." She was worried because their two oldest sons recognized a problem and had tried to reach their father without success.

Mr. A. is a salesman but his wife is distressed because each time he is in line for a promotion he decides to change jobs. This causes financial difficulty because going to a new job requires a period of time before he can create productive contacts with potential buyers. Savings are depleted and she thinks he has borrowed on insurance policies. He has never assumed responsibility for the bills although in recent months she tried to explain the financial condition to him but he didn't seem to care.

Drinking has apparently affected their sex life of which there is very little. For the past year he has been staying away from home for a few days at a time but she doesn't think other women are involved. She repeatedly returned to her conviction that he is a basically good family man and much interested in the children.

Their social life has diminished because of his drinking. At parties he becomes sloppy and belligerent until he passes out. He has to be put into the car when it is time to go home. If he does wake up, he insists on driving.

When he drinks at home, he makes life miserable for everybody. If she says anything he replies irritably that she has faults too and no one is perfect. But, she added, she still loves him and wishes she could reach him. "I want so much for him to change and when I am pointing out how his drinking is causing family problems, he sees this as being critical of him for his faults and turns around and criticizes me."

Wanting to change the situation, even with help, is sometimes not enough.

The worker wrote: "During the active phase of treatment, casework efforts were largely educational in nature around alcoholism. This was done to help her see that she could not control her husband's drinking and also to alleviate the guilt she felt about having caused it. I also focused on helping her to stop nagging and engaging in other behavior that could only provoke and frustrate him more."

As Mrs. A. came to understand the problem of alcoholism she was able to share some of this understanding with the children. One joint interview was held with the child experiencing the most difficulty and this served to support Mrs. A. in her interpretation.

She had phone contacts with Al-Anon and was encouraged to attend meetings. Her husband sullenly opposed this but, with the worker's help, she realized that she had her welfare and that of her children to manage so she attended meetings and found them helpful.

As the contacts continued she took an increasingly firm stand in view of her husband's recalcitrance and eventually took a job. Faced with this change, Mr. A. decided to come in for an interview but he steadfastly denied that his drinking was a problem and could not see that it had any relationship to family disturbances. He declared he would not "give in" to his wife.

This left only two alternatives in his wife's mind – that he get help with his drinking or they would have to separate. He chose the latter. He accepted a job in another city but visits his family frequently and contributes financial support more reliably than he did in the past.

VIGNETTE #3

Mr. Z. was told by the medical director of his company to get help from an agency with his drinking. He was described by the agency worker as resistant, evasive, and determined to minimize his drinking. He presented "the picture of a man who feels persecuted by the company and insisted that his drinking does not merit and does not warrant the threat of dismissal."

He was a supervisor of more than fifty employees and defended his drinking at lunch – no less than three martinis – as necessary because his companions enabled him "to learn things about the business" and, because they drank, he also had to drink.

Under some questioning, he conceded that noontime martinis affected him differently than they did the others. He added that he invariably took a third, knowing he shouldn't, but after the first two the third came so easily. On his return to the office after lunch, his drinking was obvious because in the morning he was quiet, almost withdrawn, but in the afternoon he was boisterous and jolly until someone crossed him. Then his temper exploded and he made life miserable for his subordinates.

Mr. Z. first denied any significant drinking outside working hours, but in the second interview he admitted that he did drink beer at night. It turned out that he drank a lot of beer, and it just might be the reason he felt sluggish the next morning. His nocturnal drinking lasts four or five hours and his wife "does not care for this at all."

Were there any more difficulties related to drinking? Well, come to think of it, he had been a little high driving home one night and he turned the car over. He wasn't hurt but he was arrested for driving while intoxicated and fined $150.

During the third session the worker asked Mr. Z. to pretend that his wife and the company physician were both in the office and to say what he thought they would say if they were actually present. This was the beginning of a realistic appraisal of his problem and an awareness that drinking was interfering in most of the significant areas of his life rather than in just small segments of it. He agreed that his drinking was characterized by lack of control and unpredictability and that total sobriety was necessary for him.

After that he wasted no time. He worked hard despite several moments of crisis; there were no relapses. He was surprised to notice that few of his luncheon companions had more than one drink and some abstained. And he was able to learn about "things in the business" without alcohol.

Meals at home tasted good for a change and he had more time for his family. At the end of a year, he was still sober and terminated contacts at the agency but continued to see the company physician.

VIGNETTE #4

Mr. L. wanted to be a writer. As a young man he had been elated when his play was accepted for Broadway production. The elation was short-lived because the press reviews unanimously echoed the sentiments of one critic who wrote that he knew of better dramas written by members of a Hoboken sewing circle. The play closed after two performances in which the cast outnumbered the audience.

The struggling writer took this in his stride, however, and accepted a job writing technical publications for a large corporation. The salary was good but the frustrations were many because he wanted to write *literature,* not instructional manuals. He began to drink, and as the drinking increased, the quality of his work deteriorated. Finally, he was fired. Despite a wife and four children to support, in addition to a mortgage and car payments, he was not discouraged. On the contrary, he rejoiced at the termination of steady, well-paying employment. This was the opportunity of his dreams. He had never had the guts to quit but now he was freed from the daily rigors of a routine job in the prison of a faceless corporation. He could devote his talents to the novel that had been struggling for birth in his tormented being but which through the dreary years, could not be brought forth.

Mr. L. had accumulated modest savings and persuaded his wife that with this freedom and her encouragement, his genius was ready to burst into full bloom. He even persuaded her that it would make things easier if she got a job. She swallowed the bait and shared his enthusiasm. As the weeks and months passed he discussed his progress in glowing terms. However, the accumulation of empty pints and fifths suggested that he was hitting the bottle more consistently than the typewriter keys.

Meanwhile, the bank balance dwindled. He overdrew the joint checking account several times but his working wife covered the bad checks. When she tried to talk with him about unpaid bills, allowances for the children, and other financial matters, he told her: "It makes me nervous! I don't want to hear it. Do whatever you want to do." If Mrs. L. persisted, he accused her of trying to start an argument.

Through all this she had faith. Or, more accurately, she wore emotional blinders to shut out reality. He said he was creating literature and she wanted to believe him. Actually, he wasn't even writing a fifth-rate magazine story. He was drinking, enjoying grandiose illusions, and she was supporting them. She was partly afraid of losing what she had – a home and family – and he played on those fears. If she complained, he angrily threatened to leave. Had not Gaughan left an unappreciative wife and children to pursue his inevitable destiny in Tahiti?

Reality has a way of puncturing illusion and eventually the situation became so intolerable that Mrs. L. went to a family agency "just to talk it over." Of course her husband was not an alcoholic. How could he be? He was such a decent man.

The caseworker reviewed almost step by step the relationship between drinking and Mr. L.'s loss of his job, between drinking and his financial irresponsibility, between drinking and his mood cycles. Whatever it was called, alcohol was a problem.

These thoughts had occurred to Mrs. L., who was intelligent, but maybe alcohol wasn't the problem. Maybe she was doing things that made her husband drink and blocked the fulfillment of his potential. The caseworker patiently convinced her that she could not be the cause of her husband's alcoholism although, in the interaction of marriage, she undoubtedly did things that triggered drinking episodes. This, however, might be the result, not the cause of alcoholism.

When the guilt feelings were assuaged, the worker supported Mrs. L. in the essential job of confronting Mr. L. with his responsibilities. It was his job to support the family. He could write at night and she would give him all possible encouragement, but he had to understand that until his writing provided adequate income, it would be necessary to accept remunerative employment and to function as father and husband. It was also pointed out that he couldn't do this unless he stopped drinking. If he needed help she had a right to expect him to apply for it. There were to be no idle threats – just firmness blended with understanding.

Mrs. L. was perceptive and quick to understand intellectually. It took longer to cope with her conflicting emotions and to mobilize the strength to take action that would, at best, involve calculated risk. After several interviews, she was convinced she had to do something. The confrontation was effective. Mr. L. did agree to visit the agency with her, although at first he was hostile and contemptuously dismissed the social worker and psychiatrist as insensitive, semi-literate clods.

Gradually, he conceded that he wanted to save his family life because that was the only way he could save himself. He stopped drinking, and with sobriety, was able to make constructive choices. He obtained a job an an editorial associate on a trade publication. Also, sobriety enabled him to use the literary skills he had and he sold a few stories.

Mr. L. might never have started on the road back if his wife had not been helped first. Incidentally, he later admitted that if he had been confronted with the facts of life earlier, he might have saved a few wasted years.

VIGNETTE #5

A 25-year-old alcoholic finally reached the Cleveland Center on Alcoholism after five years of sodden weekends. He lived with his parents in a small community about 25 miles from Cleveland. He had started to drink while in college, and he became an alcoholic who plunged into disabling drunkenness every time he took one drink.

He was a weekend drinker. Every Saturday night, the police found him in a comatose heap in one of the town's unsanitary alleys and they invariably took him to the local jail. Just as invariably, his father appeared with bail so that his well-bred, middle-class son would not have to spend the night in the depraved companionship of other prisoners.

The parents did set one limit. They refused to finance their son's binges. So he helped himself to $600 from a roll of cash carried by the family maid who did not trust banks. The father promptly hushed this potential scandal by replacing the money.

Predictably, the situation deteriorated. One day, in desperation, the parents came to the Center. The worker told them that they were providing an ideal excuse for their son to continue drinking. After all, what could be the motive to stop as long as he could depend on them to provide an escape hatch from the consequences of every escapade?

He suggested that they set limits – not punitively, but realistically. Either their son had to get help or face the consequences. This might mean he could not continue to live in his parents' home or it might even mean a jail sentence if the arrests were repeated. If he earnestly wanted to do something about his problem, he could expect the family to mobilize to help him. If he refused, however, he definitely would be on his own.

The parents agreed to set the suggested limits and their son came to the Center. In effect he was confronted with a crisis and the necessity for making a choice.

CHAPTER V

Alcoholism and the Family

ALCOHOLISM IS WIDELY labeled a family illness because it sucks into its vortex not only the alcoholic but also those around him and inflicts severe damage on spouses and children. Dr. Ruth Fox, a psychiatrist who has worked with alcoholics for many years, wrote that "probably no marriage with an alcoholic can be considered a happy one. There may be periods of relative harmony, but there is such a basic inadequacy in the one who drinks (and surprisingly enough often in his partner too) and lack of faith in human beings that the mutual trust and sharing necessary for a good relationship are absent . . ." [1]

The causes of breakdown in families where alcoholism is present have been examined under a variety of sociological and psychological microscopes and in the past much of the emphasis has been on personality flaws. There has been the appearance, at least, of attempting to lay the

[1] Ruth Fox, M.D., "The Alcoholic Spouse," included in *Neurotic Interaction in Marriage*. Edited by Victor W. Eisenstein, M.D. (New York: Basic Books, Inc., 1956), p. 7.

blame on someone.

The most visible target is the alcoholic because his behavior frequently creates chaos and his personality characteristics make the odds against a successful marriage almost prohibitive. As indicated previously, there is no single personality type among those who become alcoholics, but there are common traits that appear in various combinations. Among them are irresponsibility, excessive dependency needs, self-indulgence, hostility to authority, feelings of inadequacy, and inability to cope realistically with the problems of daily living. Many students found enough of these traits in most alcoholics to stamp them as "character disorders." That is an ambiguous label, but there is little doubt that the profile of the average alcoholic is the antithesis of the ideal marriage partner.

But what of the spouse? This usually means a wife, because the majority of alcoholics are male. With the alcoholic as the principle culprit, she was seen as the tragic, helpless victim of circumstances, but that image has been vigorously challenged. At a meeting to discuss the focus of this chapter, a psychiatrist with a penchant for analogy suggested: "Before we blame everything on the wifebeater, let's take a look at the wifebeater's wife. Maybe she had something to do with it."

Many have been doing just that with the wives of alcoholics. One writer held the wife "equally responsible for the making of the marriage and the participant in the creation of all the pain and unhappiness that follows."[2] Some went even further. For several years, there seemed to be a backlash of opinion and a relentless determination to indict wives for all the troubles of alcoholic marriages. Investigators, mostly mesmerized by the teachings of psychoanalysis, explored the psyches of women who married alcoholics and saw a collection of disturbed, poorly integrated females who, they concluded, had unconscious needs for weak and dependent husbands. (Vignette #1) Whalen called alcoholism a red herring that merely obscures the basic marital pathology and assigned the wives to four categories: Suffering Susan, Controlling Catherine, Wavering Winifred, and Punitive Polly.[3]

Undoubtedly, there are wives who match these stereotypes. Doc's pathetic mate in William Inge's play, *Come Back, Little Sheba*, is archetypical of those who enjoy martyrdom. There are misguided souls with an unshakeable faith in the power of the love of a good woman to alter character and behavior and they get married to prove it. Also, there are controlling and punitive women who find convenient victims

---

[2] Ruth M. J. Segall, "Social Work Approach to Problems of the Alcoholic and His Family," NAACP, Selected Papers, Detroit, 1958.
[3] Thelma Whalen, "Wives of Alcoholics: Four Types Observed in a Family Service Agency," *Quarterly Journal of Studies on Alcohol*, Vol. 14, No. 4 (December, 1953), p. 635.

in dependent alcoholic men.

Inevitably, there are dangers in generalization and the question has been raised whether or not such women are more likely to be involved in alcoholic marriages than in any other kind. Kogan and Jackson found the conclusions of writers like Whalen fallible in their assumption that the personality disorders detected in wives of alcoholics must have existed prior to the marriage. They suggested that identifiable personality types associated with these women might be the result of their common experiences with alcoholic husbands.[4]

Bailey does not dismiss the possibility of personality shortcomings before marriages and sees it as a "reasonable hypothesis that a woman who marries a full-blown alcoholic is more disturbed than one whose husband's premarital drinking is still within socially acceptable limits. The point to be emphasized, however, is that marital choice *is probably less related to the specifics of drinking behavior* (italics mine) than to the unconscious attraction of personality characteristics. Thus, a woman with a need to dominate or to mother or a woman with great sexual anxiety may marry a present or future alcoholic, but she is just as likely to select a non-alcoholic of similar personality structure."[5]

In most families alcoholism appears after many years of marriage. Personality difficulties have been accepted or tolerated and resentments sublimated or repressed. Then something happens to disrupt the organization of the famly and the underlying stresses and tensions come to the surface. It may be a series of events, each one in itself seemingly unimportant, but the accumulation creates intolerable crisis. The crisis can be born of the eventual recognition that the marriage did not, as the partners had hoped, solve their individual problems, nor did it meet the expectation they anticipated in a life together and the repeated disappointments are too much for their psychic resources.[6]

DENIAL

The initial reaction of most families to the awareness of alcoholism is denial. The refusal to face the fact is primarily a reaction to the existence of the family in a society with pejorative attitudes that impose feelings of shame and guilt. Despite public education through the mass media and other channels, the stigma of alcoholism remains. A wife,

---

[4] Kate Kogan and Joan K. Jackson, "Stress, Personality and Emotional Disturbances in Wives of Alcoholics," *Quarterly Journal of Studies on Alcohol*, Vol. 26, No. 3 (September, 1965) pp. 468-495.

[5] Margaret B. Bailey, *Alcoholism and Family Casework* (New York: The Community Council of New York, 1968), p. 63.

[6] Samuel C. Bullock, M.D. and Emily H. Mudd, "The Interaction of Alcoholic Husbands and Their Non-Alcoholic Wives During Counselling," American Journal of Orthopsychiatry, Vol. 29, No. 3 (July, 1959), pp. 519-527. Copyright The American Orthopsychiatric Association Inc. Reproduced by permission.

ashamed of her alcoholic husband's gross behavior, makes excuses. A young executive is apprehensive lest his superiors discover he has an alcoholic wife. Children are ashamed of their parents.

Shame is especially difficult for children to tolerate. George Bernard Shaw remembered when he first realized his father drank too much. "Mama," he cried. "I think papa is drunk!" In recounting this episode, biographer St. John Ervine observed that "the disillusionment of a child is a bitter experience and is never forgotten." Decades later, when sentimentalists accused Shaw of disrespect for his father's memory, the dramatist angrily recalled the anguish that had been created in the home and how the elder Shaw's repeated drunkenness made Dublin a desert for the family. His behavior severed ties with the numerous Shaw clan as well as with friends and acquaintances. There was the stigma of alcoholism and they were ostracized.[7]

The pattern is familiar; it has been repeated countless thousands of time. Despite some understanding through education, the feeling is still pervasive that alcoholism is shameful and should not happen. It is scant comfort for a child to be told the professional party line that alcoholism is an illness rather than sin or moral turpitude. He is far more sensitive to the scorn of classmates than to the reassurances of psychiatrists and social workers. (Vignette #2)

An adolescent who, several times a month, had to haul his father from the tavern, take him home, and put him to bed, told of the anger and nausea that assailed him each time it happened. He was afraid to face his friends after each episode and equally afraid to abandon his father.

Children do not like to have parents who are "different," especially if that difference is given public exposure. One alcoholic man chased his wife into the street with a whip when he was drunk and angry. The neighbors and their children watched. The busybodies clucked their disapproval and the insensitive laughed. The children of the alcoholic cringed and withdrew.

A second explanation of denial is that it helps a spouse protect her own self-esteem. "If I admit he has a problem," a wife may rationalize, "I will have to wonder whether I am contributing to this problem and whether there is something wrong with me. If he has no problem I am without guilt." Similar dynamics operate in children who, if they admit a parent is alcoholic, may feel, "I must be doing something to make him this way," or "Maybe he drinks because he doesn't love me and I don't deserve his love."

In Patricia Dizenzo's bittersweet novel, *An American Girl,* the narra-

[7] St. John Ervine, *Bernard Shaw* (New York: William Morrow and Company, 1956), p. 5.

tor writes in her diary about her alcoholic mother:

> Mom was in a terrible mood. She found my entry to the Rinso contest in my room and made fun of me for entering, saying I lived in another world. She said I had no sense of humor and depressed the hell out of her. It was the old story of how her drinking was my fault. Sometimes when Mom criticized me I thought about being different—always smiling and polite, treating Mom and Dad with respect no matter how drunk they were, and acting like the loving daughter—but I was never in the right mood when I got into conversations with her.

A third compelling reason for family members to deny is their illusory hope that if they refuse to concede the existence of alcoholism long enough it will disappear. They will wake up some morning to find that it was just a ghastly nightmare. Despite their discomfort, therefore, they postpone any action to alter the *status quo* because they are afraid that any threat to the family equilibrium might produce even more intolerable stress, so they ignore warning signals. (Vignette #3)

Actually, denial reinforces the alcoholic's drinking. He thinks he has to continue to drink to live, and he exploits the family's vulnerability by using his considerable powers of persuasion to convince them he is not an alcoholic so there is no reason for concern; he is quite capable of handling his drinking.

THE FAMILY SYSTEM

Examination of the personalities of alcoholics and the personalities of their spouses was used by many to assign blame to one or the other. That approach was never effective. The family is a system and within it the members act on and react to each other. Ward and Fallaice are among those who see alcoholism as a symptom of a complex process that makes the behavior of the alcoholic dependent on various interacactions in the family.

> For example, if a family member has had a long history of heavy drinking there were many interactions within the family which occurred in response to his drinking, some of which may come to provide positive reinforcement of drinking. Some of these family responses fall into patterns showing powerful reinforcing effect on drinking behavior. Human systems (e.g., a family or an employee-employer relationship) function through the communication occurring in complex information networks in which varying levels of integrity (goal-directed behavior) and homeostasis (lack of strain and stress) in the

> system are maintained through feedback mechanisms. The "information" may be any kind of verbal or behavioral message from one to another member of the system (employee is absent from work on Monday morning, husband is 'drunk again' etc.). The response prompted in the receiver in turn influences the sender in a continuous process of feedback which tends to move the system to a level of homeostasis in which there is least strain; that is, least anxiey and greatest gratification of needs of each system member, but which in the case of alcoholics may maintain drinking behavior.[8]

The authors illustrate this in a variety of ways including what they call the "morning after syndrome."

> The alcoholic's disruptive drunken behavior has provoked intense feeling which must be resolved before the family can operate as a unit, but only a certain limited number of ways of dealing with these feelings are available to the family. Early in alcoholism the wife responds to her husband's plea of physical illness, shame, guilt or remorse with either sympathy and forgiveness, or anger and punishment. Such a process temporarily fulfills the psychological needs of both the alcoholic and the spouse, reducing the strain between them, and the family unit is maintained. If the wife is forgiving, the husband has learned that forgiveness for being drunk can be obtained, provided he is appropriately remorseful and very sick. If she punishes him for his behavior by criticizing him, his guilt and shame are relieved and he feels considerably less anxious. In either case the pattern cannot be understood except in terms of the total sequence, as if it were designed to produce forgiveness or punishment or comfortable emotional distance. This is an example of a pathological "complementary relationship" in which partner A's behavior provokes and presupposes B's response, and vice versa. Several things are important to note about this "complementarity." It has a "circular" quality. Thus, attempts to break the chain at some arbitrary point, in order to determine cause or blame, are essentially irrelevant, if not impossible. Another aspect of a complementary relationship is that it tends to become increasingly rigid, with fewer alternative patterns available to the partners. The spouse may derive considerable gratification from the opportunity to be the forgiver or the punisher. The conscious wish is to rescue or

---

[8] Robert F. Ward and Louis A. Faillace, "The Alcoholic and His Helpers," *Quarterly Journal of Studies on Alcohol,* Vol. 31, No. 3 (September, 1970), p. 685.

> help, yet these very behaviors contribute to the perpetuation of the problem by the above reinforcing characteristics of a complementary relationship.[9]

Steiner, a disciple of Eric Berne, sees alcoholism as a game played by those who "willfully engage in repetitive, interpersonal behavior sequences involving alcohol, with the production of an interpersonal payoff as the covert motive." This may happen in many situations but the family is, for many, the most convenient playground. Steiner's view is a transactional one which considers alcoholism as the end result, or effect, of alcoholic behavior and "implies that addiction and illness will subside when the alcoholic no longer engages in these games" and "can no longer elicit certain necessary transactional responses from others." This has profound implications, especially for treatment because it must always involve others. The transactional analyst "would predict that an alcoholic stranded on a desert island with a large supply of alcohol will stop drinking because drinking is only part of a transactional situation; and without persons to transact with, the need for alcohol will disappear. The traditional view might predict that, since his need for alcohol is due to an illness, the alcoholic would continue to drink, probably to his eventual death."[10]

The games played by alcoholics are varied. Steiner calls one of them "Drunk and Proud of It" and it includes many of the components of guilt and punishment mentioned previously. The players are the alcoholic and another person who alternates between Persecutor and Patsy.

> The fact that there is usually no rescuer in this game is one of its key characteristics. A D&P player is basically interested in getting persecuting parents so angry that they show their impotence and foolishness. This game is often played by salesmen and executives with their wives, and for them the aim of the game is to punish the wife for her dominating and possessive attitudes. Under the influence of alcohol, a D&P player can engage in extra-curricular activities with his secretary, can lose large sums of money at the poker table, and can stay out with the boys until all hours of the night, with complete impunity. When his wife reproaches him the morning after, he apologizes, saying, "Boy, I feel terrible about this, honey. I'll try to be good from now on." The wife, until now the Persecutor, has two alternatives. Either she accepts the apology, putting herself in the role of Patsy; or she rejects the apology and continues as Persecutor which, since "It" is contrite and rueful,

[9] *Ibid.*, p. 686.
[10] Claude M. Steiner, "The Alcoholic Game,"*Quarterly Journal of Studies on Alcohol*, Vol. 30, No. 4 (December, 1969), pp. 920-938.

> now becomes quite untenable and makes her seem merciless and bitchy. Since "It" doesn't miss any work (not more, in any event, than anyone else in the office), and manages to keep everything going fairly well, he is not interested in a Rescuer and would certainly not allow one to enter the game. Occasionally, the wife plays Patsy when she agrees to go to an office party and then is forced to witness her husband "under the influence" behaving naughtily.[11]

It is not surprising that Steiner's paper drew hostile fire; it challenges the disease concept as well as the progressive and chronic characteristics of alcoholism. However, as Machover points out, it focuses sharply "on the interpersonal contexts of current behavior and on the complementary and mutually supporting 'scripts', 'positions' and 'roles' of the people comprising the transactional unit. It is recognized that, in a sense, the participants in transactional patterns share, to a greater or lesser extent, joint authorship for the 'play' in which they are engaged. There is surely much merit, too, in the related notion that a major alteration of any significant role in the transactional pattern must have the effect of altering roles complementary to it."[12]

Machover feels there are limits to the transactional approach and one is that it does not take sufficient cognizance of personality structure. Even when the emphasis is on personality, however, there is always interaction rather than a one-way process. Consider the dependency factor. Many wives of alcoholics say: "I don't really have a husband, just another child who requires attention and care." The reactions to this situation vary. Some women try to goad their spouses into resuming the normal roles of husband and father, but the tactics of nagging and ridicule may only drive them to increased drinking. Some women find that they enjoy the mothering, controlling role and encourage dependency even while complaining about it. (Vignette #4)

In Clifford Odets' play, *The Country Girl,* we see how each person feeds the neurotic needs of the other. The alcoholic, being immature, craves mothering. The wife, a dominant, protecting personality falls naturally into the mothering role. The more she accepts responsibility for running the family, the more dependent and irresponsible he becomes, although this is accompanied by resentment. The cycle can be endless.

One of the most disruptive phenomenon in an alcoholic family is that of changing roles. As long as a family system is relatively smooth in its operation, the various members play their roles predictably and accord-

---

[11] *Ibid.,* p. 925.
[12] Solomon Machover, "Comment on 'The Alcoholic Game,'" *Quarterly Journal of Studies on Alcohol,* Vol. 30, No. 4 (December, 1969), p. 942.

ing to the expectations of the others. "Everyone," as Joan Jackson has pointed out, "is aware of where he fits, what he is expected to do, and what he can expect from others in the family. When this organization is disrupted, repercussions are felt by each family member. A crisis is under way."[13]

Changing roles is most apparent when the man is the alcoholic. If he neglects his financial responsibilities, for example, his wife may have to take over by default. There is little choice when he is like the man who told a social worker that he could not tolerate having to worry about the family finances so he left all of the decisions about money to his wife. When his wife wanted to talk with him about unpaid bills, allowances for the children, or any other financial matters, he would evade the problem by telling her, "It makes me nervous. I don't want to hear it. Do whatever you want to do." If his wife persisted, he accused her of trying to start an argument.[14]

Sometimes the alcoholic decreases the household money he allots his wife as his need for alcohol increases. Whatever the fluctuations in income, the funds for drinking are withheld. In dire circumstances the alcoholic pawns the family valuables, writes bad checks, borrows far beyond his ability to repay, and, if necessary, steals. One writer tells of a case "in which the father failed to overcome his drinking and hence finances were always a source of trouble. The son (twelve years) became a newspaper boy. At the end of each month when the boy would make collections and bring the money home, the father would steal from his son's collection. Mother and son were frantic in efforts at trying to find a hiding place from the father."[15]

Many women obtain jobs, at first to supplement dwindling family incomes, but later some become the sole support of the family. The man who lost job after job was relieved when his wife received a modest inheritance. "I've supported you and the kids for twenty years," he declared. "Now you can support me." Except for regular trips to the liquor store, he spent his day sitting in a rocking chair drinking until he became sick enough to be hospitalized.

The shift in roles invariably fuels marital conflict. The alcoholic tends to drift into more dependency and this meets some of his needs. Nevertheless, he is angry because it emphasizes his inadequacy. Unless the process is halted, he tries to retaliate. In one way or another he must dominate (as opposed to accepting responsibility for) the family. Keller-

[13] Joan K. Jackson, "Alcoholism and the Family," *The Annals of the American Academy of Political and Social Science,* Vol. 315 (January, 1958), p. 93.
[14] Shober A. Ellis, "Effects of the Alcoholic on the Family," *Professional,* Vol. 2, No. 4 (September-October, 1965), Published by Florida State Alcoholic Rehabilitation Program.
[15] Edward M. Scott, *Struggles in an Alcoholic Family* (Springfield, Illinois: Charles C. Thomas, 1970), p. 149.

man has said: "It is appalling how the alcoholic controls the family, especially his wife, husband or mother. The alcoholic drinks again and again. The family screams, cries, yells, begs, pleads, prays, threatens to practice the silent treatment . . ."[16]

The ways in which the alcoholic, especially the man, tries to assert himself can result in some of the ugliest and most devastating manifestations of alcoholism. One is violence, which may enable the alcoholic to feel that he is showing everyone who is the *man* of the house. A study of *The Effect of Parental Alcoholism on Adolescents* made at the Cleveland Center on Alcoholism revealed that violence was frequent in families with an alcoholic regardless of socio-economic status. A man whose wife described him as "sweet and loving" most of the time staggered home one night and virtually demolished the lower floor of their home while she and their two children watched in paralyzing terror. He smashed furniture, broke windows, knocked plaster from the ceiling, and hurled dishes against the wall.[17]

The scars of violence can last a lifetime. Actress Ethel Waters was raised in a home that included two aunts whose drunkenness was intolerable. In her autobiography, *His Eye was on The Sparrow,* Miss Waters recalls that their drinking and the related violence and quarreling was something she could never accept. On an unforgettable Christmas Eve, one of the women came home riotously intoxicated. Ethel vigorously objected. The aunt cursed her and threw a hatchet which fortunately missed its target, but the act itself left emotional cuts that were deep and lasting.

The dependent male alcoholic may attempt to re-establish his place as the dominant in the sexual area. He likes to view himself as one of history's great lovers, but there are complications. One is that alcohol is a depressant. Imbibed moderately it may release inhibitions and seem to act as a stimulant, but when consumed excessively, it depresses all human functions, including the sexual one. The male alcoholic, frightened by what seems to be waning virility, drinks more and more in the hope of recovering his masculinity. It only gets worse. In the marital relationship the difficulties are compounded because he may not only be impotent when drunk but also sloppy and repulsive. Repeated incidents have a cumulative effect and carry over into periods of sobriety when the man may be physically able but his wife, unable to forget, does not respond.

---

[16] Joseph Kellerman, "Guide for the Family of an Alcoholic," Kemper Insurance Company, Chicago, Illinois.

[17] Herman E. Krimmel and Helen Spears, "The Effect of Parental Alcoholism on Adolescents," Paper presented at National Conference on Social Welfare, Los Angeles, 1964, Published by the Cleveland Center on Alcoholism, Cleveland, Ohio.

One enraged husband kicked the furniture and made belligerent gestures with his fists. "I'm pretty goddamned fed up," he roared. "I've told you a thousand times I want a wife, not a walking frigidaire. I'm a man and I'm human but there hasn't been any sex around this house for the last six months. I always thought that was part of marriage until I got trapped with you."

The man's wife stared at him coldly. "That's right," she replied, "there hasn't been any for the last six months and there isn't going to be any for the next six unless you stop drinking. My idea of romance doesn't include some slob coming home loaded at three in the morning yelling that he wants to make love—if that's what you call it."

That dialogue was recorded from the report of a couple seen at the Cleveland Center on Alcoholism. With only slight variations, it can be heard every day in the homes of thousands of alcoholics. The havoc alcoholism creates in sexual relationships may have repercussions in the total life of the family.

The alcoholic blames his wife—never the drinking. She is frigid or she doesn't like him or is unfaithful. There are episodes of unreasonable jealousy as he accuses his wife of daily infidelities. "She must be giving it to somebody because she isn't giving it to me". Some men call their wives fifteen or twenty times a day and have tantrums if the women take a few extra minutes for shopping. One man employed a detective to watch his wife. She, in retaliation, refused to leave the house and he raged because she didn't buy groceries.

Some who fail in the marital relationship try to reaffirm their virility with other women, but success, if it comes at all, is usually fleeting. "When I'm drinking," confessed a would-be Lothario, "I'm a lousy lover with any woman."

One of the pitfalls for alcoholics who stray in search of the magic elixir of potency is that they are frequently attracted to socially and intellectually inferior women. The lower the better, it seems, because it enables them to feel superior for the moment, but they are later plagued by remorse and guilt which makes the situation worse than ever.

When the woman is the alcoholic in the family, the sexual problem is likely to be different in that she can usually perform and she may barter sex for alcohol. One young wife said: "I just told him—no liquor, no sex." As long as her husband thought it might help, she usually got the liquor, but as her drinking increased he realized he was being used. Conflict replaced compatability.

The demoralization invades every area of family life including recreation. The alcoholic deserts and finds himself on the outside. When he tries to return, it may be too late. An alcoholic father may nurse fond hopes for a son to become an athlete. The boy, neglected or shunted aside in childhood, may lose interest before he becomes old enough to participate in high school or sandlot sports and his father takes it as a personal affront. But, as Scott points out, with the change in family structure, "the father has not been a good identification figure and the son has lost interest or turned to more feminine interests or no interest at all."[18] Like all phenomena in alcoholic families, this one is not universal but it is one of many variations.

As the situation worsens, the family recognizes that it has an alcoholic in its midst. Denial has failed. Repressed conflicts may erupt into a full-scale marital combat. The chief aim of the drinker is to continue drinking and that of the spouse is to prevent it. This is the period when the non-alcoholic tries to control or eliminate the drinking. It is a period of hiding bottles, nagging, pleading, and setting curfews that are never observed.

It is also a period when children are mercilessly exploited by both parents. They are weapons in the war between the alcoholic and non-alcoholic and the struggle for their allegiance is unrelenting and destructive. "Sometimes parents realize what they are doing and are shocked by the realization," reported the authors of the Cleveland study.

> One mother told of enlisting the aid of her children in what she called the 'ceaseless war against their father.' They defended her in arguments, supported her efforts to foil her husband's demands for liquor and helped hunt bottles he hid in the basement.
>
> If, in his sober periods, they expressed affection for him, she was resentful. Finally, she saw how 'this constant war resulted in a pitiful sense of insecurity for them and made them noticeably nervous and unstable.' What they developed, she added, was 'a feeling for their father far worse than good clean hate. They developed a patronizing pity for him that was in reality no pity at all. They regarded him as a combination of clown and idiot.'[19]

Almost all the adolescents interviewed for that study emphasized the demands made on them to take sides. This happens in other families, too, but where alcoholism is involved the lines are more likely to be clearly drawn between the 'good' and the 'bad' and this can intensify rather than alleviate conflicts.

The conspiratorial maneuvers can only make things worse. They are not only damaging to the children, but the alcoholic drinks more to

[18] Scott, *op. cit.*, p. 149.
[19] Krimmel and Spears, *op. cit.*

drown his feelings of rejection. There is a strong temptation to say that he becomes paranoid in reaction to the conspiracy, but unfortunately the feelings are rooted in reality and he drinks to cope with them. And the more he drinks, the greater is the need of the non-alcoholic members of the family to unite in common defense.

Attempts to control the drinking are equally self-defeating because it can't be done. Indeed, a wife cuts the power her alcoholic husband had over her by no longer needing or attempting to control him. This is not easy because the alcoholic has a variety of weapons to perpetuate the emotional ties, however unhealthy they may be. The games described earlier by Steiner and played so skillfully by the alcoholic may be among these weapons.

One of the weapons is the ability to arouse anxiety in the family by threatening to desert, to quit a job, or to inflict violence. Unless those around him take a stand, he will continue his behavior, secure in the knowledge they are not going to let him suffer the consequences. They cannot let go emotionally.

A second weapon is the ability to arouse anger or to provoke loss of temper. A wife's nerves are frayed to breaking so she screams incoherently and hurls a vase at her husband. She usually misses, so he laughs, taunts her, and makes her angrier. If the non-alcoholic loses control, she also loses the ability to help the alcoholic. "Consciously or unconsciously," says Kellerman, "the alcoholic is projecting the image of self-hatred against the other person. If it is met by hostile attacks, it is thereby verified and the alcoholic in his own mind justifies the former drinking and also now has an additional excuse to drink in the future."[20]

Once the cycle is in motion, it may be impossible to determine precisely when the drinking created the conflicts that in turn provoked the drinking. But one thing is certain–unless the actions and reactions are interrupted, there will come a point of no return when the family is so shattered physically and/or emotionally that, like all the king's men, the helping professions will not be able to put the pieces together again. The need is for help before that point is reached–not only for the alcoholic but for the family.

The foregoing text concentrates on the alcoholic husband and the non-alcoholic wife, partly because of the preponderance of male alcoholics. There are, however, alcoholic housewives but little has been written about their husbands who may also need help. In the absence of research, clinicians have reported from observation that they tend to be more punitive and impatient for results. This writer recalls a

[20] Kellerman, *op. cit.*

scientist of international reputation who had little time for the antics of his alcoholic mate. He almost dragged her to the clinic and, in effect, told the therapist to let him know when she had recovered. Needless to say, the therapist insisted on the husband's participation in the treatment.

Dr. Bailey has noted that "husbands of alcoholic women are quicker to terminate their marriages and less likely to seek help than wives of alcoholic men. Because of the greater stigma associated with female alcoholism, these husbands will often ignore or cover up the drinking for a considerable time, but then may abruptly leave. Some of these husbands are extremely punitive and lacking in capacity for understanding, so that clinicians have generally reported difficulty in working with them. Problems of economic support for herself and the children may decisively influence a wife to remain with an alcoholic husband, but in addition the maternal qualities of many of these women make them more accepting of sick husbands than men are toward sick wives. In addition, the maintenance of an intact home, at least in its outward appearance, is probably more important to women than to most men."[21]

For a while, there was so much enthusiasm for classifying the wives of alcoholic men that it threatened to become a parlor game among professionals. Little attention was paid to the reverse situation. Fox made one of the few attempts and delineated the following types: "the long-suffering martyr who mothers and spoils his child-wife, the husband who leaves furiously but comes running back, the unforgiving and self-righteous husband, and the punishing, sadistic variety. There is also the dependent male who expected to find another mother in his wife and who is hurt and bewildered at finding that the woman he married—the one who put up such a show of self-confidence—has become just as dependent as he through her alcoholism. Then, of course, there is the 'normal' man who wakes up in dismay to find himself with an alcoholic wife."[22]

There are also the ultimate in family disasters, the alcoholic couples. They, too, have been neglected in research. Dr. Fox saw a variety of patterns in these marriages. "When one is sober, the other may drink out of retaliation or relief when the partner sobers up. Both partners may start drinking together socially and end up in bitter quarreling. Not infrequently, a spouse becomes alcoholic in an attempt to keep his alcoholic partner company."[23]

She also noted some of the difficulties in treatment of the alcoholic

---

[21] Bailey, *op. cit.*, p. 64.
[22] Fox, *op. cit.*
[23] *Ibid.*

couple because "one may recover and find himself just as intolerant of the other's drinking as those who had never been alcoholic."[24]

CHILDREN OF THE ALCOHOLIC MARRIAGE

"The most deadly of all possible sins," Erik Erikson has written, "is the mutilation of a child's spirit." That sin is committed every day in families where there is an alcoholic parent or parents. Although some of the difficulties encountered by children in these families have been described in the foregoing text, additional emphasis seems appropriate.

If we are interested in prevention–and who among us would deny such interest?–the fate of the children of alcoholics is important. This does not imply simply prevention of future alcoholics although there is some evidence that many alcoholics are from families in which one or both parents were alcoholic. The greater significance is the risk of children growing up in a domestic climate of bitter conflict and learning to cope by the use of neurotic, destructive behavior which may not include alcohol but may produce miserable alienated adults.

This seems almost inevitable in families where, as Cork says, there is practically no sensitivity to the needs of children, communication is hostile and negative, and overall security and encouragement is absent.[25] It is not that such parents wish to hurt their children, but their own self-interest makes the intrusion of children a source of irritation.

Perhaps basic to all difficulties imposed on children of alcoholic parents is inconsistency. They seldom know what to expect. Some of these conditions affect children in other families but Ruth Fox has described the difference:

> The more subtle implications of the alcoholic father differs qualitatively from those of the father who is just rough and unkind. In his periods of sobriety, the alcoholic father frequently is charming, affectionate, understanding and penitent. He inspires the natural love of his offspring who build therefrom an ideal father image of omnipotence and loving kindness. The disillusionment of a drunken episode is shattering to the frail superego structure of the child. He is forthwith subjected to alternating experiences of exalted hopes and blighted disappointments. He may be compared to the hungry experimental animal which is tempted with food and frustrated by sudden barriers, such a process may produce convulsions or 'nervous breakdown' in the animal. It is surely dangerous to the highly organized human creature who, in the formative

[24] *Ibid.*
[25] Margaret R. Cork, *The Forgotten Children* (Ontario, Canada: Alcoholism and Drug Addiction Research Foundation, 1969), p. 11.

period of childhood, is just becoming aware of social and cultural standards, as well as of the interpersonal relationships of his home. It is not surprising that a child thus exposed presents a bewildering array of ambivalence, inconsistencies, antagonisms and touching overtures of affection.[26]

Dr. Fox also feels that the alcoholic mother may have more potential for damaging children than an alcoholic father because she is usually drinking at home and her physical presence while intoxicated cannot be avoided. The children, therefore, have to bear the brunt of her behavior.[27] When the father is alcoholic, there is greater opportunity for the mother to protect the children from his behavior.

In the atmosphere of inconsistency and instability, periods of sobriety may provide interludes of peace or even a measure of happiness for the family. But they are only interludes. For children, there may be scarcely time to readjust their thinking before the alcoholic parent is off and running again. The violence is repeated, the promises with their hopes of joy are unfulfilled, cherished goals are abandoned, and the sharing of pleasure in the family is impossible. Children become bitter and hostile when they are repeatedly let down. A few items from the Cleveland study are illustrative:

A seventeen-year-old boy, seen at a private agency because of truancy and school failure, finally revealed his brooding resentment about the numerous parental separations that resulted from his father's excessive drinking. For him, however, it wasn't any better when they were together because conflict erupted every time the father got drunk. When the father was not drinking, he was passive, ineffectual and removed from the mainstream of the daily functioning of the family.

This boy had never known an example of mature love and the constancy of a healthy parental relationship. He never knew what to expect so he withdrew. He was afraid to test relationships because he had been bruised by adults and was uneasy with his peers. Although he was an attractive young man, he was inhibited with girls and doubted that he could ever achieve an easy comfortable relationship with them.

Another boy became dejected and hopeless about his situation at home and while he refused to leave physically, he withdrew emotionally. The school described him as an "isolate" although quite dependable and hard working. He had no

---

[26] Ruth Fox, M.D., "The Effect of Alcoholism on Children," *Progressive Child Psychiatry*, (New York: Karger-Basel, 1963), pp. 55-65. Distributed in reprint by National Council on Alcoholism.
[27] *Ibid.*

friends because he was suspicious of the motives of people and could not accept anyone who was not "perfect in every way."

The insecurity, which is a barrier to relationships, is often increased in alcoholic families by the almost inevitable war between the parents which compels them to devote most of themselves to warfare instead of to total family living. There is seldom genuine peace—just truces. Children, being resilient organisms, may strive again and again, for healthy relationships but just as achievement seems close, it is blocked by the appearance of an alcoholic parent on another binge.

How many times can they try, how many times can they accept frustration without giving up? The position of the child of an alcoholic marriage is like that of a ballplayer on the bench who is never called into the game and cannot, therefore, develop his skills. The ability to develop healthy relationships comes only with practice.[28]

The importance of family therapy may be reinforced by the fact that the authors of that study found that the emotional health of the children had a direct relationship to the emotional health of the non-alcoholic parent. Even if the alcoholic could not be reached for treatment, there was much benefit in treating the spouse.

[28] Krimmel and Spears, *op. cit.*

VIGNETTE #1

Mrs. S. came to the office because her 45-year-old husband had been hospitalized following an acute alcoholic episode. She opened the interview by informing the caseworker that she had been furious when the patient telephoned to tell her she would have a weekly appointment. Since she is a graduate student, seemingly more interested in the pursuit of a degree than in her husband's recovery it did not help when he suggested that she might have to give less time to her studies and more time to understanding him. There was little doubt about her hostility. She saw no reason for these interviews because she had seen two doctors and read extensively in psychology and she understood her husband and their relationship. She just didn't like what she understood.

As she saw it, the patient blamed her for everything because she was a mother symbol and there were all sorts of guilt feelings and resentments. He also hid behind his father although he was not averse to using the latter as a scapegoat for his actions when that seemed convenient. Knowing all this, she gave her husband Erikson's *Childhood and Society* to enable him to

Adapted with permission from a case provided by the Hartford office of the Connecticut Commission on Alcoholism.

understand the wellsprings of his behavior.

Mrs. S. described herself as an impatient woman, adding that her patience with her husband was just about exhausted. When he is frustrated he responds with temper tantrums which are just another expression of his general childishness. She said she knew the patient for nearly three years before they were married but was never aware of the *real* Mr. S. That didn't become visible until she became ill two months after the marriage when his drinking increased sharply and he virtually abdicated responsibility. She feels he will not stop drinking unless he knows it will kill him because he does not want to face any problems.

For that reason, the patient never wanted children. Their only child, a boy, now nine years old, was a source of constant irritation to him and he became angry if the youngster was noisy or active.

Second Appointment

Mrs. S., oozing hostility, had an abnormal psychology book with her and read passages to the worker. They were supposed to describe her husband. She said she had read parts of the book to Mr. S., especially those pertaining to neurotic-behavior and egocentricity. The worker commented on the futility of this approach which only caused Mrs. S. to look at the former as if he were a backward child.

Third Appointment

Mrs. S. wanted to know what was happening during the patient's treatment in the hospital. She indicated the therapist was wasting time if he wasn't reaching the unconscious and being taught how to "control his frustration level." She also wanted to know whether he would see a psychologist or social worker after discharge. She was merely told the patient was getting the help he needed at this time.

Mrs. S. talked about her son and how he rebels against her standards. But it is all for his own good because she doesn't want him to grow up to be like his father. She tried to persuade him to accept criticism as being constructive because this is something her husband cannot do.

The worker told her the patient would be going home in a few days which caused Mrs. S. to comment that her troubles would certainly increase from that time on.

Fourth Interview

Mrs. S. began by saying it depressed her when the patient is home because he demands her constant approval and has a need to tell her every move he makes. She told him he drives her up the wall. He replied that she should talk to me about it. She compared the patient emotionally with their nine-year-old son although she is sure the son is more mature than his father will ever be.

Mr. S., complained his wife, has never used his brain creatively although he has permitted others to use it for their benefit. Friends of her husband presumably confirmed his limitations in conversations with her and they are as pessimistic about the possibility for change as she is. There has been some improvement but "he'll go right back because his ego is weak and his superego is strong."

Following that curious comment, she said she had doubts when she married him because he had been quite a boozer in his youth and she was afraid he might revert to drink. A priest told her she would have to make up her own mind. She decided to marry him and bewailed the fact that she has grown but he has stagnated. They quarrel about almost everything, including money. She admits being stingy but needs the security of savings. He can be wildly extravagant.

Fifth Interview

Mrs. S. said her husband was home for a visit prior to discharge and she found him most disagreeable. They were invited to dinner with friends and she volunteered to make canapes but Mr. S. objected because it would divert attention from him. My impression is that she finds fault with everything he does.

She telephoned two days later to suggest a separation because her husband refuses to accept any responsibility. She added that psychiatrists told her years ago that the marriage was hopeless. She speculated that the patient likes the hospital with its freedom from burdens but she can't stand it when he brings his complacency home.

Mrs. S. is thinking of talking with an attorney about a separation. Since it is our impression that she seeks counsel only from those who will tell her what she wants to hear, I told her any decision about a separation would have to be her own. It is my feeling that Mrs. S. cannot accept the patient taking a stand about anything or suggesting in any way that he is resisting control.

She requested that future interviews be by telephone because she is "terribly busy" and can get out only when the cleaning woman is there. Even that day is devoted to marketing and other chores.

Mrs. S. called again about a week after the patient had been discharged. She complained that he cannot decide whether he wants to stay home with "all the hurly burly" or whether he can risk the loneliness of living alone. She added that in her opinion (the only one worth anything), he has never developed inner resources and has not learned self-control. Nevertheless, she conceded grudgingly that his attitude has improved and he is open to criticism and she might give him another chance.

VIGNETTE #2

Judy could not understand why her father drank when it made him so terribly sick. "If I have an allergy to strawberries," she said, "I just stop eating strawberries."

She also spoke of her shame. "When I was ten years old, I was walking with a girl-friend and saw him lying on the grass. He was sick and dirty and covered with vomit. I was torn between helping him and just getting away. Anyway, I told my friends to go and I tried to help him but he just wanted to be left alone. I was scared and ashamed."

When her friends went home with her, she always asked them to wait outside. "I could never never tell them he was an alcoholic because they wouldn't have understood. They might just think he was horrible and I didn't want that. Sometimes I would make up stories about him. I don't know why. But I'd tell people we had a great big house in the country where I'd go to spend the weekend and have my own room, beautiful clothes, and that he gave me lots of spending money."

Once she saw him in an attack of delirium tremens and it was terrifying. "He was a most wonderful person when sober," she said, "but then he'd leave home saying he was going to look for a job. He wouldn't come back for three or four days. Sometimes he was brought in by the police." She gulped hard and said quietly: "Things could have been so different."

VIGNETTE #3

Mr. and Mrs. A were 26 and 27 years old, respectively. They were married eight years and had three children aged three months to seven years. There were no prior marriages. They were living together in a rented home. Mrs. A had telephoned the agency twice before during the past two years but had never been seen. On the present occasion an appointment was scheduled immediately because a drinking problem was mentioned in the telephone application. Both came to be interviewed.

Mr. A was reported to have just returned from a five-day "binge." He had lost his job that day. Mr. and Mrs. A were an attractive, handsome couple of at least average intelligence. Mrs. A was not sure what she wanted or what her problem was. Her greatest concern was in relation to her husband's recent absence from the home and his preference for beer and playing baseball to herself. She manifested considerable guilt over problems in the marriage and in her husband's behavior. Mr. A appeared concerned and cooperative but was guarded, speaking in a friendly, joking, barroom fashion. He tentatively questioned whether he was an alcoholic but immediately denied this on the grounds that he kept beer at home that he never drank and that he experienced situations in which he could have drunk but had not.

An exploration of the drinking problem indicated that Mr. A had been drinking somewhat regularly since the age of 15 but more severely in the last two years. It was not possible to elicit a specific description of how much he drank. He played baseball with a group from a tavern. As he described it after a brisk baseball game, he looked forward to a glass of beer at the tavern. He stated that he usually would drink the first beer quickly. He would have five or six and at that time a point came at which he would either quit drinking or he would "close the bar." He described becoming sick when he drank distilled beverages. He denied experiencing blackouts; he admitted some loss of recall after a night of heavy drinking but claimed eventual recall. He described eating with a good appetite but not during the recent five-day "binge." He avoided specific discussion of those five days.

Mrs. A, when questioned about her husband's drinking behavior, immediately denied that he was an alcoholic because he kept beer at home which he rarely drank. However, she described him as drinking rapidly and in a gulping fashion. When they went out socially, he always had a bottle of beer in his hand, never whisky. She recounted instances when he "passed out" or fell asleep in a sitting position. He became verbose and silly when drunk. He did not seem to suffer from hangovers but did crave water the following morning. He would drink and drive, but she reported no accidents. When the family automobile had been damaged on two occasions, Mrs. A did not doubt her husband's accounts that he had been hit by a "drunk" in one instance and that a friend had been driving the other time. Mrs. A described occasions when they would argue about where he had been and with whom. She felt that he denied recall or made up stories that were contradictory. She felt that he was not so drunk as to be unable to remember.

Mr. A was seen once and Mrs. A twice; they failed to appear for further appointments. The indications of early-phase alcoholism were the 11-year drinking history which had only become marked in the last two years; gulping; possible loss of control after the fifth beer; possible but vague evidence of blackouts (Mr. A's statement of some loss or recall); possible automobile accidents as a result of drinking; and some indication of failure to eat while drinking. The reference to a "binge" was interpreted as a casual usage of the word. Mrs. A was unable to provide any evidence of characteristic post-bout behavior. In addition, the couple had a sex problem suggesting an extra-marital relationship. Though the family was intermittently dependent on relatives, it was nevertheless a functioning family unit. Mr. A, though he had just lost his job as a salesman, obtained another quickly. Neither spouse appeared interested in the drinking behavior. In the essentially educational approach used, both appeared to deny the alcoholic symptoms.

VIGNETTE #4

There was no question about Mr. Y.'s alcoholism and he freely conceded this. His troubles began at the age of nineteen and since that time he had been arrested as a public drunk, for driving while intoxicated, and for indecent exposure during a drinking episode because he decided to urinate in the street. He was discharged from the Army because of alcoholism and has lost several jobs.

He explained his present drinking as being caused by his angry reaction to the fact that his wife "orders him around too much." He sees her as a powerful and controlling person and is resentful.

Mrs. Y. says she is frightened when he does any drinking, fearing the times when he gets roaring drunk and "becomes practically insane." She has gone through the period when she poured out his whisky and is aware that this never solved anything. She still pours it out at home so that he won't get drunk there and demand the car keys.

The caseworker asked Mrs. Y. if she knew about the problem at the time of their marriage. She did but thought she could change his drinking habits and has been continuously frustrated in her efforts. She cannot see why her husband does not want to please her. He knows how much religion means to her and promises to attend mass. Then he gets drunk on Saturday night and is hardly a candidate for a church pew the following morning. He growls that it wouldn't do him any good feeling the way he does anyway. She thinks if he doesn't go for his own sake he ought to go for hers. To her this would be a form of giving.

After being told by social workers and doctors that she should manage the money, Mrs. Y. discussed this with her husband and he agreed. Now he uses this as a weapon. He spends money, incurs debts, and demands that she find a way out of the difficulty.

Mrs. Y. attributed some of the problems to the fact that she and her husband came from different backgrounds. She was the third of nine children and always had considerable responsibility for the younger ones.

Mr. Y. was the oldest of two children in a family completely dominated by his mother. His father was described as little more than a puppet with his wife pulling the strings. Mrs. Y. insisted she didn't want her husband to be like his father; she wanted him to stand up and be a man. But she never really gave him a chance and he never really seemed to want it.

The caseworker wrote that the interaction "seemed to be one of ambivalence over struggles between dependence and independence. Mr. Y. constantly expressed resentment at his wife's dominance (described as just like his mother's) but in every way he demonstrated his wish for this dominance and the opportunity it gave him to outwit those who dominated him. Mrs. Y., on the other hand, was content as long as her husband behaved as 'a good boy.' "

CHAPTER VI

Alcoholism and Poverty

IN 1968, THE National Advisory Committee on Alcoholism declared that "the problems of alcohol abuse are a particularly malignant component of poverty. The conditions of poverty and alcoholism interact with mutually perpetuating reinforcement . . ." [1]

In the same year, the U.S. Labor Department put a new emphasis on alcoholism as a major cause of ghetto unemployment and stressed its importance as a factor in placing participants in national manpower training and development programs. Later, a bulletin from the Office of Economic Opportunity stated: "Alcoholism has a particularly heavy impact on persons and families already burdened with multiple conditions of poverty."[2]

When the State of Iowa applied for a grant from the Office of Eco-

[1] National Advisory Committee on Alcoholism, "Interim Report to the Secretary of the Department of Health, Education and Welfare," (December, 1968), p. 10.
[2] Office of Economic Opportunity, OEO Guidance Issuance, Number 6136, July 21, 1969.

nomic Opportunity, Harold Hughes, who was then governor, supported the request with the statement: "Poverty and alcoholism go hand in hand in Iowa."[3]

We noted in Chapter One that many welfare departments report a high incidence of alcohol problems. Other writers have described excessive drinking in ethnic and minority groups who for decades have been condemned to live in the demoralizing squalor of the urban ghettos. Alcohol provides a way for the disadvantaged to cope with the intolerable conditions of living and there is abundant evidence that blacks in our society bear the greatest burden of poverty and carry the added miseries of ethnic rejection. Certainly, it is an oversimplification to say that poverty is *the* cause of alcoholism–even in the ghetto–but it is difficult to shut our eyes to some of the more recent and carefully controlled studies showing that the alcoholism rates among black people are two to four times greater than those among white.[4] A three-year study at Harlem Hospital revealed that the increasing use of alcohol was a crucial factor in the lives of male patients defeated by society.[5]

Race adds to the problem, but the basic problems are those of poverty. In the heart of Chicago's uptown area one writer saw run-down tenements with broken windows and smelled urine in the hallways. He saw drunks "folded in grotesque shapes in the doorways. The garbage is uncollected, and whiskey bottles wrapped in paper bags seem to grow in every front yard. . . ."[6]

Dozier found the problem of alcoholism among American Indians even more severe. The proportion of Indians arrested for all alcohol-related crimes is the highest in the nation–twelve times the national average. He attributes Indian problems with alcohol to historical, social, and cultural circumstances that have eroded the dignity and independence of the Indian plus the fact that American Indians share, with other minorities of low economic status, the burdens of discrimination, poverty, wretched housing, and lack of education. Alcoholic beverages, he concluded, have been the easiest way to deaden the senses and to forget the feeling of inadequacy.[7]

Arrest rates may not be conclusive evidence because police seem to

[3] Gerald E. Klonglan, *et al., Agency Interaction Patterns and Community Alcoholism Services, Sociology Report,* No. 73, Iowa State University, (1969), p. 12.

[4] Muriel W. Sterne, "Drinking Patterns and Alcoholism Among American Negroes," in *Alcoholism,* David J. Pittman, ed. (New York: Harper and Row, 1967), p. 71.

[5] Fred T. Davis, Jr., and Henry Lipscomb, "The Para-Professional; An Essential Component in a Multi-Discipline Team Approach to the Treatment of Ghetto Alcoholism," unpublished paper presented at Annual Conference of North American Association of Alcoholism Programs, San Antonio, Texas, (September, 1970), pp. 1-2.

[6] Jack A. Newfield, *Prophetic Minority* (New York: New American Library, Signet Books, 1966), p. 130.

[7] E. P. Dozier, "Problem Drinking Among American Indians, The Role of Sociocultural Deprivation," *Quarterly Journal of Studies on Alcohol,* Vol. 19 (1966), pp. 292-304.

show greater enthusiasm for arresting those in minority groups, especially if they are poor. Some officers will pick up a well-dressed businessman who is sleeping it off in a public place and escort him home. This discrimination is, perhaps, inevitable in a society where equal justice under the law is an unachieved goal rather than a current reality. The well-to-do seldom get to the drunk tank. Nevertheless, the Division of Indian Health of the United States Public Health Service and the Navajo Health and Navajo Alcoholism Committees consider alcoholism to be the number one health problem of American Indians, even though it is ranked as fourth in the general population.[8]

Statistics–especially comparative statistics–are limited but there is no need to play the numbers game to know that alcoholism is a major problem of poverty. Nor do we have to prove the point by decades of research translated into a series of chi squares and other cabalistic formulae cherished by statisticians. There may be opposition to efforts to debunk the myth of the hidden alcoholic but few talk about hidden alcoholics in the ghetto. They are the most visible of all. In the taverns and on the streetcorners of Harlem and Hough, of Watts and the Washington slums, desperate men drain the last drop of their fifths and pints of Thunderbird as they try to wash from their consciousness the misery of days without hope.

Alcoholism has always been a major problem of those with a low socio-economic status, but it was–and still is, for the most part–ignored. Those working in the field of alcoholism have long insisted that alcoholism strikes indiscriminately and is evenly distributed throughout the population. This thesis was probably devised to make alcoholism "respectable." In our society, one way to make something respectable is to show, without fear of favor, that it victimizes physicians, lawyers, teachers, business executives, and other upstanding members of the establishment.

Alcoholism *is* found at every level of society but it seems likely that it should be more prevalent at lower socio-economic levels. If it is true that alcohol for the alcoholic is a defense against what for him are intolerable conditions of living, it follows that the poor have much more to defend against and fewer defenses to command than their economic superiors.

The poor feel helpless and hopeless, and without the power to act and the hope that action will effect a better life, men must find escape. Hagstrom said it this way:

> The situation of poverty, then . . . is the situation of en-

---

[8] Fred R. and Ladonna Harris, *Indian Health Sources — A Blue Cross Report on the Health Problems of the Poor* (Chicago: Blue Cross, 1968).

> forced dependency, giving the poor very little scope for action, in the sense of behavior under their own control which is central to their needs and values. This scope for action is supposed to be furnished by society to any person in either of two ways. First, confidence, hope, motivation, and skills for action may be provided through childhood socialization and continue as a relatively permanent aspect of the personality. Second, social positions are provided which make it easy for their occupants to act, which make it possible for decisions of their occupants to be implemented in their futures. Middle class socialization and middle class social positions customarily both provide bases for effective action; lower class socialization and lower class social positions usually both fail to make it possible for the poor to act.[9]

Even youth is no protection against hopelessness. McKay found it virtually impossible to reach alcoholic juvenile delinquents on the basis of appealing to them to think of their futures. Their attitude was that "there is no tomorrow" and "why worry, I could walk out of here and get killed by a car on the street." One could misinterpret this behavior as a display of bravado, said McKay, but he saw it as "a clear demonstration of their feeling that they had little or no ability to exert self-control nor did they think they had much to say about the future direction of their lives."[10]

DEFINITION OF ALCOHOLISM

It may be necessary in working with poverty groups to reconsider the definition of alcoholism. Most of us define alcoholism in terms of impaired functioning in the family, job, or health on a continuous basis due to drinking. If we think of it at all we are inclined to give less emphasis to that part of the definition that mentions continuous drinking in excess of community standard, but this is not important.

Excessive drinking in Winnetka or Shaker Heights might not be considered excessive in Harlem or Hough. Even drunkenness does not have the same impact. In the Establishment, we tolerate or encourage drinking but we have little patience with drunkenness, especially if it is loud, boisterous, aggressive, or messy. When his behavior is flagrant, the alcoholic is ostracized and his family may be socially isolated.

There is much greater acceptance of this behavior in the ghetto.

[9] Warren C. Hagstrom, "The Power of the Poor," in *Mental Health and the Poor,* Frank Riessman, Jerome Cohen, and Arthur Pearl, eds. (New York: Free Press of Glencoe, 1964), pp. 205-223.

[10] James R. McKay, "Drinking and Delinquency," in *Alcohol, Alcoholism and Crime,* Report of Conference at Chatham, Mass., June, 1962, p. 53.

Sterne reported that this acceptance extends to those arrested for alcohol related offenses. A study of male inmates of the District of Columbia Workhouse reflected greater social integration of the black than of the white public intoxication offender. The former were "functioning members of their consanguine groups and participants in a broader interactional network not limited to a 'skid-row type' sub-society." They saw their families as less opposed to drinking, even during the heaviest alcohol use, and less likely to have lost friends due to drinking.[11]

Littman reported that many Indians drink more openly, "frequently on the street even in Chicago, which is an indication that there is little or no shame in being drunk. Most studies point to the absence of negative sanctions against drunkenness. . . ."[12]

All alcoholics use alcohol to escape or to cope with crisis but for many it seems to be the one magic substance that enables them to go on from day to day. Sterne cited the case of a teenage girl who went with friends to a carnival and got "really high" on vodka. At the same time her mother was out with a boy friend and became "running drunk." When the mother came home at 4:30 a.m. she was so drunk she had to be dragged to bed by the children. This episode was not unusual and the repetitions created some difficulties, but as the mother described it, she was "smiling, grinning and very happy." The family had lived in the depths of poverty for nineteen years and had a monthly income of $202 for nine people. Alcohol was frequently used in excess to "escape the boundaries."[13]

People in desperate circumstances can ignore the disabling effects of alcohol because it promotes psychological and social integration in a culture that does not provide constructive substitutes. It dispels gloom, provides instantaneous pleasure, and occasionally permits a feeling of omnipotence. This may be true at other levels of society, also, but the degree is much greater in the poverty population. Combined with gambling and sex, it is for many a way of life and alcohol is probably more important than the other two. This, it should be emphasized, is not an indictment of people but of a society that offers them few choices.

The impact of excessive drinking on family functioning shows many variations at different socio-economic levels. It was observed in one study that wives in the ghetto are generally passive about the drinking behavior of their husbands. Sometimes they bring wine or beer to them. If a suburban man thinks it is his masculine prerogative to get bombed

---

[11] Sterne, *op. cit.*, p. 76.

[12] Gerald Littman, "Alcoholism, Illness, and Social Pathology Among American Indians in Transition," *American Journal of Public Health,* Vol. 60, No. 9 (September, 1970), p. 1776.

[13] Muriel W. Sterne, "Drinking Patterns in the Negro Ghetto," North American Association of Alcoholism Program, Report #35, p. 11.

every weekend and slap his wife around, he may soon find himself without a wife because she is probably capable of supporting herself. In many poverty families, women are designed to this behavior. They may not like it any more than their suburban sisters, but their alternatives are limited and they may prefer to endure the known miseries of their marriages rather than risk the unknown perils of life on their own. Consequently, where the families do stay together, excessive drinking seems to be less disruptive of domestic life.

The word "seems" is used because the dynamics have been interpreted in different ways. Hollingshead and Redlich, in their study *Social Class and Mental Illness,* concluded that persons in the lower social strata—and especially the lowest one—tolerate more abnormal behavior.[14] Mechanic argues that the symptoms (he referred to mental illness, but it might well apply to excessive drinking) are disruptive but "the wife attempts to explain or justify them within the context of normality." She mobilizes her defenses in various ways to handle the disruptive behavior. "One should not imply," he adds, "that there are no significant differences in people's tolerance for a wide variety of deviance, but there is little real evidence for the claim that these differences occur on a systematic basis."[15]

A significant fact of ghetto life is that it is a drinking culture that is a more intensive and extensive version of the drinking culture of the larger society. There are not only taverns and bars but bootlegging stations as well. Children, especially adolescents, are vulnerable to the impact.

Research has indicated that most of those who drink have their first exposure to alcoholic beverages at the age of 13 or 14. This has aroused alarmists, but for most boys and girls in middle and upper social classes, it is a wary testing of adult behavior that is part of the growing-up process. Rarely does it lead to excessive drinking in adolescence. The ghetto is different. Childhood is not the prolonged and protected stage in the life cycle that it is at other levels of society. There is early initiation into drinking and probably into sex and these behavior patterns are quickly woven into the life style. Boys must become men and they drink like men. In one project, with the "hard-core unemployed" in the IMPACT program of the Office of Economic Opportunity, there were more than 100 men and all drank heavily before they were 19, most before they were 16, and some had started fairly regular drinking by the

---

[14] August B. Hollingshead and Frederick C. Redlich, *Social Class and Mental Illness* (New York: John Wiley and Sons, 1958).

[15] David Mechanic, "Illness and Cure," in *Poverty and Health,* John Kosa, Aaron Antonovsky, and Irving Kenneth Zola, eds. (Cambridge, Mass.: Harvard University Press, 1969), p. 207.

time they were 12.[16]

Similar data emerged from a study of adolescents in an urban, all-black housing project population characterized by poverty, economic dependency, and marital instability.

> Children in the project grow up in an atmosphere communicating the great salience of drinking through the ubiquitous presence of discarded alcoholic beverage containers around buildings and in children's play areas, the ecological concentration near the project of well-patronized taverns and liquor stores, and a wide array of human role models for consumption of alcohol. Opportunities for project youth to make repeated observations of drinking by adults in their social world, not infrequently their next-of-kin, abound. The public nature of much of this drinking and its consequences makes it possible for children from homes in which there is little or no alcohol use to be almost as familiar as those from homes where alcohol is used liberally with the phenomena of frequent, heavy consumption of alcohol, intoxication, and the association of both enjoyment and trouble with alcohol.
>
> These youth manifest pronounced ease of entry into adult drinking patterns and other behavior ordinarily the prerogative of adults. The relatively low impact of common agents of adults. The relatively low impact of common agents of childhood socialization—family, school, church, and youth organizations—in either guiding toward specific goals or in diverting or restraining from others, as well as the accelerated entry of lower-class Negro youths into adult status and their participation in informal recreation at times with persons many years their senior, appears to be related to early involvement in drinking that cannot be characterized as merely experimental.[17]

REACHING THE ALCOHOLIC IN THE POVERTY POPULATION

It is generally conceded, as it has been in other sections of this volume, that crisis motivates alcoholics to seek help, but the crisis or "bottom" is different for different people. The inhabitants of the ghetto live each day of their lives in the shadow of crises that would pulverize the neatly attired junior executives who take the 5:15 p.m. to their homes in Connecticut. It is not surprising that they may not respond in quite the same way.

[16] Herman E. Krimmel, "Alcoholism and the Poverty Population," unpublished paper presented at National Conference on Social Welfare, New York, May 27, 1969.
[17] Sterne, *op. cit.*

Even so, it may not be as different as many seem to think. Parents can be motivated to help because of family problems. One man realized that his drinking left him without funds to buy toys for his children at Christmas; another could no longer communicate with his older son. Another man had his thumb shattered by a falling garage door and, being drunk, he didn't realize it for three days. By that time it was so bad that amputation was considered. If drinking did that, he decided, he had to cut down. (Vignette #1)

In many cases, crisis may not be enough because there are many barriers between the poor and the helping professionals. One is the deep-rooted suspicion of the former toward the latter and this is frequently expressed with undisguised hostility. "What's your racket?" they ask. "What are you getting out of this?" Their contacts with social workers have often been painful and futile. They have asked for bread and been offered insight. They have wanted to know how to cope with violence inflicted by alcoholic husbands and been given lessons on the dynamics of alcoholism.

The wife of an alcoholic in a group of Appalachian migrants told us she had left an interview with a worker in a family agency so tearful and semi-hysterical that she walked the long distance home to avoid the curious stares of strangers on public transportation. She had gone to the agency to seek help in relieving the strains on the family caused by her husband's drinking. She was told brusquely by the caseworker that she was the cause of her husband's alcoholism and she had better mend her ways. No explanation, no offer to help.

Another woman, after years of violence, humiliation, and destitution summoned the courage to separate from her husband. When she applied for public assistance for herself and four children who had suffered shocking abuse at the hand of their father, she was told to take her husband back solely because of his financial contribution.

Some people have been rejected because of their appearance and many professionals are caught in what psychiatrist William Schofield calls the YAVIS syndrome. They prefer clients who are Young, Attractive, Vigorous, Intelligent, Sophisticated. The poor, unfortunately, do not look as good as the rich, but that hardly justifies refusing their petitions for help. One man had been drinking a half to a full gallon of wine every day. His health was poor and his body odors were less than an olfactory delight. His thick speech was difficult to understand and contributed to the impression of low intelligence. He had been arrested frequently and prognosis seemed dim to at least three agencies that kept their doors closed. A probation officer referred him to an alcoholism center where he was finally accepted into a group therapy program. He agreed to take Antabuse which, as long as he took it, would prevent him from drinking. This was a long shot in his mind and he frankly admitted he didn't know whether he would stay with it. The world without alcohol did not look too promising, but things changed for the better fairly quickly and sobriety had its rewards. His health improved dramatically and he obtained a job. Three months later his appearance had undergone almost complete metamorphosis. He was well-groomed and he bathed regularly. He spoke clearly and interestingly, and, to the astonishment of those who had been ready to write him off, his intelligence was unmistakably normal or slightly above.

These are not universal incidents but neither are they isolated. They happen over and over again and the suspicion they arouse has an epidemic quality. Too often the clinicians' judgment is based on external manifestations of pathology and the concurrent economic and domestic problems. As a Toronto study on *Social Class and the Treatment of Alcoholism* suggested, "If the characteristics of these patients were evaluated against the conditions of life in the lower socio-economic groups of society, they might assume different meanings."[18]

The negative feelings of the poor might be diluted if they were convinced that their needs were the primary consideration, but that isn't always the way it is. The needs of professional "helpers" sometimes interfere. If any success is expected, it is essential to find out why *they* want to change, not why we *think* they should want to change.

Effective help may require different goals and different techniques. For example, the goal of total abstinence for life has long been regarded as the *sine qua non* of working with alcoholics but in the poverty areas it is frequently unrealistic. The experience of a two-year project in Cleveland is instructive.

> Throughout the years of our existence as an agency, we have been unbending in one principle—that the first order of business in treating alcoholics is to insist that they give up alcohol completely. This is necessary to enable alcoholics to face their problems and soberly explore options for future behavior. This approach, however, depended on the many resources available to middle-class people. When such resources are almost non-existent, as in the poverty areas, our expectations must be altered.
>
> The lesson was learned slowly. We embarked on our new adventure with the zeal of crusaders determined to impose the

[18] Wolfgang Schmidt, Reginald G. Smart, and Marcia K. Moss, *Social Class and the Treatment of Alcoholism* (Toronto, Canada: University of Toronto Press, 1968), p. 95.

good life–at least our conception of it–on the dispossessed. It didn't work even in those situations where we had the most authority.

For example, the hard-core unemployed from the IMPACT program were, to put it mildly, unenthusiastic about our service but they were told that unless they participated they could not be placed in jobs at the end of the 90-day training period. This was the motivation. The reward of a job was concrete and important to men who had never had anything.

At first, total abstinence was made part of the price for a job. They were not willing to pay that price. Then, like many professionals who are baffled and frustrated by failure, we stiffened our resolve. Those clients who failed to show genuine promise of abstinence at the end of 30 days were told they would have to take Antabuse (a drug that blocks the oxidation of alcohol and induces severe physical distress) to help them stop drinking and as evidence of the commitment. Otherwise, their cases would be made inactive. Most refused to take the medication and those who did failed to continue.

This was not simple defiance although that element may have been present. One man did say in a group meeting: "Don't ever take Antabuse 'cause man that's like swallowing authority." Much more important was the fact that these men and others like them could not afford a commitment to abstinence. Alcohol, as we said before, is sometimes the only thing that permits them to function and makes existence possible. Few outside the ghetto can or want to understand this desperation. In their situation, the idea of completely giving up the one thing that sometimes sustains them is a prospect too terrifying to contemplate.

In one group of women alcoholics which met in a private home, there was drinking during the sessions for a few weeks. Any effort by the therapist to stop this would have been futile so the discussions were about children, sex, money and the like. The confrontation around drinking had to wait.

People who have had nothing must find something before they can shed their major or only defense. And this approach did work. The men in IMPACT who obtained and kept jobs no longer had to drink as much. The job provided satisfaction, some independence and was evidence of manhood. Few, however, have given up alcoholic beverages completely. The slums around them are a constant reminder that they may again need an emergency escape and there is still a social life that has drinking at its center.[19]

More than at other levels, alcohol is vital to help men in the ghetto to momentarily salvage their self-esteem. Ulf Hannerz points out that, as an expression of masculinity, "it is considered 'natural' for men to like liquor, and the opinion may be expressed on occasion that it is an index of masculine strength not to want to dilute liquor with too much soda. A noteworthy corresponding folk belief which appears common among men is that 'liquor makes hair grow on your chest.' This is taken literally; beard growth is allegedly also affected."[20]

One factor that motivates ghetto alcoholics to seek help and is seldom applicable to men in higher socio-economic groups is fear of physical deterioration. Physical health is precious and they fear any disability which might diminish masculine prowess. One professional prize fighter never took a drink before the age of twenty-six when he injured his back. Then he started and was soon an alcoholic. It was bad enough that his boxing career was ended, but even worse was the dread feeling that "I was no longer a man." If these men can be persuaded that drinking increases their vulnerability, they are frequently accessible to help.

The lack of self-esteem and the empty feeling of inadequacy is almost universal among alcoholics but is far more difficult to work with among the poor because it is compounded by the poverty. A businessman may feel inadequate for many reasons but usually there are tangible compensations. The ghetto dweller has few or none. The alcoholism and the poverty reinforce each other in an endless process.

In this setting, the combination can immobilize men. Not everyone will leap at the opportunity for a job and sometimes we fail to recognize the real problems. As Liebow explains, a "man's low self-esteem generates a fear of being tested and prevents him from accepting a job with responsibilities or, once on the job, from staying with it if responsibilities are thrust on him, even if wages are commensurately higher. Richard refuses such a job, Leroy leaves one and another man, given more responsibility and more pay knows he will fail, and proceeds to do so, proving he was right about himself all along. The self-fulfilling prophecy is everywhere at work. In a hallway, Stanton, Tonk, and Boley are passing a bottle around. Stanton recalls the time he was in the service. Everything was fine until he attained the rank of corporal. He worried about everything he did then. Was he doing the right thing? Was he doing it well? When would they discover their mistake and take away his stripes (and extra pay) away? When he finally lost his stripes,

[19] Krimmel, *op. cit.*
[20] Ulf Hannerz, *Soulside* (New York: Columbia University Press, 1969), p. 84.

everything was all right again."[21]

Such men cannot be expected to abruptly give up the tavern or street-corner that are centers of their social life, the places where they are accepted. There they can rap and in rapping they can rationalize and hide their failures. They can, like the customers of Harry Hope's saloon in Eugene O'Neill's *The Iceman Cometh,* "keep up the appearances of life with a few harmless pipe dreams about their yesterdays and tomorrows. . . ." The tavern groups may be their only source of self-esteem and security. The quality of friendships are exaggerated but for a while everything seems better and, in the short-term hedonism of the tavern, there is the possibility of spontaneity and enjoyment. Without alcohol they are men hobbled with despair and with no visible possibility of help.

Traditional casework, especially the species with a psychoanalytic emphasis, has never been a smash hit with the poor. The question has been raised whether the one-to-one technique has failed because it is not appropriate to this population or because therapists have refused to adopt it to the special needs of the low socio-economic group. The range and content of the life experiences and the value systems of those who have been coruscated by the rot and grime of decades are quite different from those of the middle-class professional. The "here and now" orientation of low-income clients limits the effectiveness of the "talking therapies," at least in individual treatment. They want tangible help. (Vignette #2)

Their needs are immediate and relief from anguish cannot wait for the therapist to complete an exploration of the psyche. *Action Now* is essential, but, to the middle-class therapist, this attitude may imply a "present-time orientation" and an inability to defer gratification. The future of the middle-class presumes a surplus of resources to be invested. Those in poverty, however, like the men who congregate at Tally's Corner, live in a sea of want. "Gratification of hunger and the desire for simple creature comforts cannot be deferred. Neither can support of one's flagging self-esteem. Living on the edge of both economic and psychological subsistence, the streetcorner man is obliged to expend all his resources on maintaining himself from moment to moment."[22] There is the fairly common pattern of a man who squanders his week's pay on a two-day binge and points out that, when this is done, it is not because he is " 'present-time' oriented, unaware of or unconcerned with the future. He does so precisely because the man is aware of the future and the hopelessness of it all."[23] Freud recognized this need a long time ago when he suggested that "the poor are even less

[21] Elliott Liebow, *Tally's Corner* (Boston: Little Brown and Company, 1966), pp. 55-56.

ready to part with their neuroses than the rich, because the life that awaits them when they recover has no attraction."

The major problem of the middle-class alcoholic may be alcoholism. The major problem of the poor alcoholic is not simply alcoholism, severe as that may be. (Vignette #3) It is poverty, and most men cannot change unless that condition is changed. At the very least, wrote one social worker of therapy with the poor:

> A coordinative effort between psychologic intervention and social change must be mounted to help the individual establish identity and self-awareness. This seems so obvious! Yet, where classical therapy has erred time and again, is in forgetting that identity is not forged in a vacuum. It is not sufficient just to know oneself; a person doesn't even have the desire to know himself unless he is proud of what he is and what he stands for.
>
> Suppose our mythical therapist has somehow managed, without involving his patient in social action, to develop a man who thinks well of himself. What happens then? The patient leaves the therapist's office and realizes that the symbols of success are the possession of money and things, education, or belonging to an influential social group. He regards himself and sees that he lacks these attributes. The fact that his therapist approves of him is a thin shield against the eroding realities of deprivation. His therapist cannot change his status. What can? Social action. . . . [24]

The above applies to alcoholics as well as to others in poverty areas.

Unfortunately, providing immediate action is rendered less likely in the ghetto, because where service is needed most, it is least available. Hollingshead and Redlich reported that the quantity, characteristics, and kinds of service available to people with mental illness is in inverse ratio to class position.[25] The same is true of those with alcohol problems. The Office of Economic Opportunity charged that not only do the poor have less access to community services but "the alcoholic and his family have frequently been excluded from service simply because of the fact of alcoholism; in effect, they are punished rather than treated for illness."[26]

Skid Row and The Chronic Court Offender

The poverty population described in the foregoing pages is com-

[22] *Ibid.*, p. 65.
[23] *Ibid.*, p. 66
[24] Reuben Bitensky, "Social Action — the Therapy of Poor Folk," *Mental Hygiene*, Vol. 53, No. 4 (October, 1969), pp. 506-507.
[25] Hollingshead and Redlich, *op. cit.*
[26] OEO Guidance Issue, *op. cit.*, p. 1.

prised mostly of people struggling to function within life patterns that characterize the general population. Despite staggering social odds against them, they try to maintain family groups, find and keep jobs, and climb a few rungs on the economic ladder, although this does not necessarily mean escape from the ghetto.

We have not discussed the inhabitants of Skid Row who frequently exist at the lowest levels of poverty. They present a special problem to the community because their descent to the lower depths has made them part of a subculture that requires a different approach and different facilities if they are to be helped. They are mostly homeless men who have no other place to go. The number of women on Skid Row is negligible.

Here we are concerned only with the alcoholics on Skid Row and surveys in Philadelphia, Minneapolis, and Chicago indicate that they are only about one-third of the total. Surprisingly, an equal number are teetotalers and the remainder are described as moderate drinkers.[27] But the alcoholics are a major problem and provide most of the chronic drunkenness offenders who pass in endless parade before the benches of dingy municipal courts throughout the country.

Emphasis in the last few decades has been on minimizing the Skid Row problem because alcoholism could be accepted as a "respectable" illness only if divorced from the stereotype of the derelict. Few statistics have been so often repeated as the one that claims, that only three to five percent of the alcoholic population ever reaches Skid Row. That may be true, although statistics are unreliable. It may also be true that Skid Row populations are dwindling but, when all that is said, the fact remains that the majority of the two million arrests annually for chronic drunkenness comes from Skid Row. Not all, of course. These arrests include obstreperous conventioneers, rowdy collegians celebrating victory in the big game, and a few weekend inebriates, but they are a small minority.

Most are revolving-door offenders who are in and out of the courts ten or twenty or a hundred times. The number of individuals does not match the number of arrests. In a typical year, for example, about one-fifth of all persons arrested in Los Angeles for drunkenness accounted for two-thirds of the total arrests. Six chronic offenders in the District of Columbia had, over a period of years, been arrested for drunkenness a total of 1,409 times and had served a total of 125 years in penal institutions. They were still drinking. The presidential commission that reported these statistics also noted that the majority of repeaters live on

[27] Earl Rubington, "Getting off Skid Row," Fourth Annual Conference of Association of Halfway House Alcoholism Programs, Tulsa, Oklahoma, 1969, p. 50.

Skid Row.[28]

Aside from clogging the court dockets, the Skid Row alcoholic "presents serious problems, not only to himself, but also to people who live and work in the surrounding neighborhoods. Although overt violence by Bowery men against outsiders is rare, they do rob and attack each other, especially on 'check days' – those days when Social Security and other pension and benefit checks arrive. Destitute alcoholics also harass the community in countless small ways. They panhandle. They lie semi-dressed in doorways and on sidewalks, where they obstruct passersby. They wander into traffic. They carry vermin and communicable diseases such as tuberculosis, influenza and pneumonia. They urinate and vomit in the street. Left unchecked, they are a source of constant irritation as well as a health menace to their neighbors."[29]

Regardless of numbers, this is a major social problem and demands the attention of social workers. The drain on financial and human resources is staggering. The men of Skid Row are the alcoholics who require the most help and receive the least. At best, the treatment is inadequate; at worst it is barbaric. One reporter wrote:

> Although he may have been picked up for his own protection, the offender is placed in a cell which may frequently hold as many as 40 to 50 men where there is no room to sit or lie down, where sanitary facilities are inadequate and a stench of vomit and urine is prevalent.
>
> The drunken behavior of some of the inmates is an added hazard. It is questionable whether greater safety is achieved for the individual who is arrested for his safekeeping.[30]

Chronic drunks are arrested, convicted, sentenced, jailed and released only to be re-arrested and to go through the same futile routine within a few days or weeks or months – sometimes within a few hours. Whatever strengths they may have can be destroyed and their values brutalized by this life.

"Although being clubbed or smashed against a wall symbolically reminds a man that his body, the most intimate dimension of his self-concept, is vulnerable," says James Spradley, "it also has another important meaning. Like a rehearsal before a dramatic performance, it forcefully instructs the tramp to play the part of a dependent and passive actor within the bucket. The longer a man has been in the

[28] *The Challenge of Crime in a Free Society,* A Report by the President's Commission on Law Enforcement and the Administration of Justice, (New York: Avon Books, 1968), p. 535.
[29] First Annual Report of the Manhattan Bowery Project, p. 9.
[30] *Challenge of Crime in Free Society, op. cit.* p. 533.

world of tramps, the more he learns to respond as if he were an animal whose master had broken his will. Labels, threats, physical abuse and thefts of property in themselves are hard for a man to take, but more significant is the implicit message in these actions: they clearly identify for the tramp those who hold power over his life then and during the coming months he may spend in jail. . . ."[31]

Pittman and Gordon have described the chronic drunkenness offender as a "man who has never attained more than a minimum of integration in society. He is and always has been at the bottom of the social and economic ladder; he is isolated, uprooted, unattached, disorganized, demoralized and homeless, and it is in this context that he drinks to excess. As such, admittedly through his own behavior, he is the least respected member of the community and his treatment by the community has at best been negative and expedient. He has never attained, or has lost, the necessary respect and sense of human dignity on which any successful program of treatment and rehabilitation must be based. He is captive in a sequence of lack or loss of self-esteem producing behavior which causes him to be further disesteemed. Unless this cycle is partially reversed, positive results in treatment will be difficult to attain."[32]

The most formidable barrier to reaching these men is that they can find solace and comfort on Skid Row. They are accepted there as they are nowhere else. The bars "function as churches and clubs; employment agencies and dating centers, begging places, drinking and eating places and flops. Most of all they are a place to find friendship, even if it is only of a fleeting nature. In a Skid Row bar one is not restricted in his behavior; he can perform in ways appropriate to this subculture and know he will be accepted; he can find out important information about jail and court and employment which other tramps will freely give him. . . ."[33]

"They are," commented one writer, "a group without a future. Most of them have no idea where they will go when their shabby rooms and the tavern itself fall to the bulldozer."[34] Perhaps the most cynical comment about the companionship of squalor was made by Larry, a character in *The Iceman Cometh.* There is calm, he comments, because "it's the last harbor. No one here has to worry about where they're going next, because there is no further they can go. It's a great comfort to them. . . ." There is little point, he adds, to wasting your pity. "They

---

[31] James P. Spradley, "The Moral Career of a Bum," *Transaction,* Vol. 7, No. 7 (May, 1970), p. 19.
[32] David J. Pittman and C. Wayne Gordon, "The Chronic Drunkenness Offender," in *Alcoholism,* David J. Pittman, ed. (New York: Harper and Row, 1967), p. 105.
[33] Spradley, *op. cit.,* p. 26.

wouldn't thank you for it. They manage to get drunk by hook or crook, and they keep their pipe dreams, and that's all they ask of life. I've never known more contented men. It isn't often that men attain the true goal of their heart's desire." (Vignette #4)

Eugene O'Neill, who wrote *The Iceman Cometh,* told an interviewer "the philosophy is that there is always one dream left, one final dream, no matter how low you have fallen, down there at the bottom of the bottle. I know because I saw it."[35]

That philosophy may not be universal on Skid Row, but it exists. Attempts to solve the problems of these men have frequently been misguided. Sometimes they reflect the customary gambit of trying to find something quick and easy, like rehabilitation classes for alcoholics conducted in courtrooms. Hannerz pointed out that most of the street-corner men see them as a farce and quoted one man as saying, "Those classes are a lot of bullshit." The men "Bring their bottles right into the class, and there's one of these fellows standing up there telling you about how he stopped drinking, and you can see he's half drunk right up there, and he's gonna get more drunk as soon as he gets out of there."[36]

Even the Alcoholic Treatment Centers seem to misunderstand the real needs. One articulate man wrote a letter: ". . . The alcoholic treatment center kills you with kindness and boredom. This place is a pressure chamber and then some audio system plays some taped melancholic crap either so low you can't hear the news or so loud you can't hear each other or think – a sort of brainwashing – torture. . . . The circle continues, where she stops, no one knows. . . ."[37]

This part of the alcoholic population may be the most difficult to help, but it is not hopeless. Projects in Philadelphia, Los Angeles, and Boston have demonstrated some success but it requires the mobilization of many resources and techniques suited to the needs of the clients.[38] The magnitude of the problem is belied by the relatively small number of people involved and its solution may depend to a great extent on the use of social work skills.

---

[34] Matthew Dumont, M.D., *The Absurd Healer* (New York; Science House, 1968), p. 91.
[35] Arthur Gelb and Barbara Gelb, *O'Neill* (New York: Harper and Brothers, 1960), p. 873.
[36] Hannerz, *op. cit.,* p. 54.
[37] Spradley, *op. cit.,* p. 23.
[38] See: "Alternatives to Arrest," prepared by Philadelphia Diagnostic and Relocation Service Corporation, 1967; Walter C. Hart, "Potential Rehabilitation of Skid Row Alcoholic Men," Volunteers of America, Los Angeles, 1961; and *Perception,* newsletter published by Greater Boston Council on Alcoholism, Vol. 8, No. 2 (October, 1966).

VIGNETTE #1

N. D. is a 38-year-old black, born and raised in the deep south. He is unfailingly pleasant although his appearance is sloppy. His clothes are torn and dirty and he is usually unshaved. He was a participant in a program for hard-core unemployed while simultaneously employed as custodian of the building.

The trouble with N. D. was that he had been on the job for nine months but had not reduced his drinking, which consisted of at least a half-gallon of wine every day. Despite that, his work was satisfactory and he seldom got drunk. He was on the job every day and drank all through the day primarily to maintain a "no feeling" condition.

But there were other clues. He was hospitalized twice and suffered agonizing withdrawal, was dismissed from school when he started drinking too much at the age of sixteen, had been arrested six times for intoxication, and was deferred from military service because of alcoholism.

N. D. attended group therapy sessions at the clinic because he was threatened with the loss of his job and expulsion from the training program. He was articulate and always participated but he never decreased his drinking. All evidence to the contrary, N. D. stubbornly refused to admit he was an alcoholic.

He did have a brother who was an alcoholic and who was the only person with whom he had a close relationship. He found his brother dead one morning from alcoholism. Both had been jailed the night before. This was the crisis for N. D.

The therapists decided they had to do something and the only something available was a voluntary program at the house of correction. Not ideal, but something. N. D. agreed. It provided a period of "drying out" and one of the co-therapists visited twice a week for counseling sessions. At least, N. D. would know someone cared.

When he returned to the group at the clinic, he had resolved to make something of his life. "A man can, you know, if he wants to." Two months later he was working and had pride in his well-groomed appearance. He did not give up drinking completely but he no longer had to drink on the job and he "felt like a man."

VIGNETTE #2

C. T., a 36-year-old man, began drinking in his teens and later became a chronic alcoholic. For several years he and his wife, also an alcoholic, earned a meager living by manufacturing and selling moonshine liquor. One of their children died because of lack of medical attention which was related to the neglect caused by the parent's alcoholism.

This man is almost illiterate, and, for two years after separating from his family, he drank a gallon of wine daily. His job-training counselors saw little hope but they did bring him to the Center. During the first two group sessions, he was in an alcoholic stupor. He could see no reason to stop drinking; this life didn't have anything for people like him. However, he was constantly encouraged to give sobriety a try. What could he lose, because he could always go back to drinking? Now, he apparently likes sobriety. He feels good about himself, can sleep through the night for the first time in years, and has been able to save money to buy needed clothes. Arrangements have been made for an operation on his varicose veins and this could not be done while he was drinking. He is enthusiastic about learning to read as well as the possibility of a job.

VIGNETTE #3

G. D. is a man who gives his age as 42 although he looks much older; in fact, he was not sure himself whether he was 22 or 42. He is a derelict who has spent most of his life in jail. He has never committed a major crime but has been sentenced for innumerable petty offenses. He is extremely disoriented with regard to time and it is impossible for him to give any sort of chronological history. With the exception of the first day, when he had come directly from jail, he wore a tie, a heavy overcoat patched with string, and two jackets. His shirt was extremely dirty and when he took off his jackets it was stained all over with dried perspiration. He frequently came late for his appointments, but as he cannot tell the time this was not surprising. He showed very little emotion and never smiled throughout the interviews, always keeping blank expressionless looks on his face.

G. D. was the middle of three illegitimate children, each of whom had a different father. He had one sister about ten years older than himself and one two years younger. He grew up in a two-room rented house with his mother and grandmother. His mother worked at a laundry from seven in the morning until six at night six days a week. As a result, he was alone much of the time and was reared mainly by his grandmother and older sister. By the time his sister was fifteen she started to work with her mother in the laundry, and his grandmother did domestic work sporadically throughout his early years. Because of this he and his younger sister would sometimes be left alone all day, with their mother leaving them some food when she left for work in the morning. G. D. recalls this happening when he was as young as four years of age.

As soon as he was old enough he began to associate with a gang of boys in the area where he lived, most of whom came from a similar background and were equally anxious to escape from their homes. Their average age was about eleven and their primary occupation was indulging in petty larceny. When he was twelve, he was caught stealing a suitcase from a house together with two other members of his gang. They were sent to the reformatory where G. D. spent around thirteen months. His mother, he says, was glad that he was sent there, because she thought it would "straighten him out." When asked what the reformatory was like, G. D. replied that it was all right and added, "they whip you all the time just like your folks do." His period of confinement seemed to do little more than fully initiate him into a life outside the law.

When he was released, he went to school for almost one month, but he probably has the time period wrong if he ever did in fact go to school.

Also, he claims that at the age of thirteen he was married for a few months. At another interview, however, he said he was 25 when he was married. Such a tremendous confusion in basic facts represents an extreme state of mental disorientation rather than a conscious attempt to supply false information. After leaving the Reformatory, he returned to living with his mother, and, during the short period that he was married, his wife lived there with him. However, he continued to associate with the same group of boys for a while, most of whom had by then spent some time in a penal institution. His mother continually upbraided him about these associations telling him that they would only lead him into trouble. However, as in all her other reproaches, he saw no reason or advantage in obeying her. He was also drinking frequently and heavily, and his mother, he says, would whip him for being drunk. It was not until the police shot several members of his gang for beating people and stealing their money that he decided to disassociate himself from them.

After his gang broke up, he obtained a job as a janitor in a theater. He says he does not recall how long he worked there, but it was until the establishment closed down which means he may have held the job for ten years. When he lost his job, now nearly fifteen years ago, he made little attempt to get another. He claims that the main reason was that he could not get a social security card, but he is unable to explain why. He found that he could survive merely on his many illegal activities without ever obtaining a legitimate job. The price he had to pay was to spend the majority of his time in one jail or another throughout the state. In the last fifteen years he claims to have been in every chain gang in the state and readily listed five of them. All offenses were for stealing or for selling whiskey, and he regards these periods of incarceration as being accepted consequences of his way of life. In fact, he says quite proudly that he has spent nearly all his life in jail. Most of the rest of the time he lived with his mother and spent his time either drunk or in petty larceny. He would only steal small objects from cars or houses and would sell them immediately, using the money he obtained to buy food or alcohol. He never accumulated any money and in retrospect this is one of his greatest regrets. He says that he would like to have some decent clothing and attend church regularly. On one or two occasions, he did find employment as a dishwasher, but he says that he has not done this for the last year.

In 1962 he was given six months in jail for distribution of illegal whiskey and he was sent to the chain gang. While he was there, his mother died, but the prison authorities would not allow him to attend the funeral as it was too far. He was very resentful about this, but it was essentially the only incident in his life about which he showed any significant emotion.

Since he was released in June he has lived wherever he could and has eaten whatever he was able to find. Much of the time has been spent at the stockade, as he is arrested continually for being drunk and never has any money to pay out. At the present time he has a room in a house which belongs to a woman whom he knows only as Annie. She lets him live there for free, in return for which he chops wood and does other small chores.

G. D.'s drinking began at a very early age and has been a constant part of all his activities throughout his life. He claims that since he was 15 he has become drunk every day, except when financial shortage made this impossible and when he was in jail. He can explain his drinking only by saying that it makes him feel good. He drinks with others or by himself, depending on where he can obtain his alcohol. The only time he has drunk legal liquor was when somebody gave it to him, He generally would drink bootleg, but if this was not available he would drink anything containing alcohol that he could obtain. The world in which he lived was one in which the most successful person was the one who stole most, fought the best, and escaped the police most often. Even when he had a job he found that this did not fulfill his needs as well as his less legitimate activities. And when he lost his job he returned to the borderline existence from which he had come. There he has remained more because of its familiarity than because of his lack of ability to change.

G. D. has had to learn to live a life devoid of anything but the most simple emotional responses. He has learned never to plan ahead as the future inevitably holds so many uncertainties that planning is futile. Superimposed on this, he has the effects of many years of drinking poorly refined alcohol so that the organic brain damage he has suffered has left him in a stage of considerable disorientation.

Reprinted with the permission of Dr. Peter Bourne, Atlanta Southside Comprehensive Health Center, Atlanta, Georgia.

VIGNETTE #4

Perhaps the bitterest, most obvious, and pitiful poverty thrives four blocks south and two blocks east of City Hall–Skid Row, where the alcoholics, the misfits from all strata of society, finally make their way.

For two years this has been the home of Talmadge Green, a big, soft-spoken Negro of quixotic moods. He spends his days and his often drunken nights in the missions, the garishly lighted liquor stores and his favorite hotel on 5th St.

Like the others, he drinks "mickeys" of rotgut wine (18 cents for four-fifths of a pint), and often wears the semi-human, glaze-eyed look men get at the end of a long, terrible drunk.

Talmadge, who at 41 says, "I've done nearly every kind of job and I didn't like any of it" has mastered the hard economic facts of the place. He collects $21 worth of chits from the county's Skid Row office every week, to pay for his room and his meals at a cafe called Tillie's kitchen.

To buy wine he steals and sells his food.

"I have to steal," he explains. "I steal whatever I see the best chance to steal. If I'm walking down 5th and I see a guy drunk on the sidewalk, I'll take money out of his pockets. Sure I know anybody around here would do the same thing to me."

While drunk, Talmadge has been brutally beaten by men he considers his friends and has come to not knowing how he was hurt. Yet, bearing the scars of these battles, he'll share his good wine if he pawns something he has pilfered from one of the little shops.

Skid Row offers a rough and ready camaraderie and Talmadge talks dreamily of the good times he has had there.

"Sometimes, a couple of us will put our money together, buy chicken necks, potatoes, and a little carrot and cook in our rooms. That's real nice."

When he is dried out, Talmadge can rationalize his behavior and explain it in the terms a college psychology major, newly acquainted with Freud, might use.

"My trouble all started when I was 2 years old, when my father killed my mother. I was too young to remember but my sister told me about it. She used to say, 'When we get big, we'll kill him, too.'

"I was in trouble with the police at 11 or 12, and finally I was sent to reform school. It was bad. In those days they treated kids like they did adults. After being in that environment, there was never any hope of my changing."

Since his first arrest, Talmadge has spent about half his life in prison, with uncounted additional days in jail. He has worked—"When I was forced to," he admits—as a locker room attendant, a fruit picker and a day laborer.

Just a few weeks ago, he enrolled in a job-training program, more to please his social worker than because it was something he wanted.

"I don't know if I'll stay with it. But they told me if I don't get a job, they're going to put me off welfare."

To Talmadge, that would spell the end of his life as he knows it. And it is a life he likes, despite its misery; it is familiar and he admits he is afraid of the unknown.

"If I could do anything or be anything I want," he says, looking out the window of his unspeakably filthy hotel room, "I wouldn't change. I'd just like to be down there on 5th St. drinking wine."

From "What is it Really Like to be Poor? It's Like This . . .," by Linda Mathews, *Los Angeles Times,* September 9, 1968.

CHAPTER VII

Social Work Treatment of the Alcoholic

THE PURPOSE OF treatment, especially the psycho-social kind, is to help a client grow toward his full potential and enable him to live with reasonable effectiveness within his primary group and to function on the job and in community relationships. In the case of the alcoholic, the immediate obstacle (although not necessarily the only one) to this goal is the destructive effect of his drinking. If he continues to use alcohol to escape from his problems or to try to solve them through drinking, he is unable to mobilize his resources for effective action.

The conviction that this goal can be achieved only through total and permanent abstinence is still widely held and deeply entrenched. It derives from the philosophy of Alcoholics Anonymous, which declares the alcoholic powerless to have control over alcohol for the rest of his life. In their view he will always be an alcoholic; an arrested alcoholic, perhaps, but no less an alcoholic. They see him as the victim of a chronic and progressive "disease" and for all his days only a single drink from disaster. Such slogans as "One drink is too many and a hundred are not enough" have exerted powerful influence and for decades have been accepted by many as eternal gospel of universal application.

As professionals have become involved in treatment of those for whom AA does not work, those it does not reach, or those who never try it, there has been a re-examination of principles and goals. Most professionals still agree that the best goal is permanent abstinence and encourage the client to achieve it, but it may not be practical for some. There is increasing acceptance of the fact that clients and therapists occasionally have to settle for less.

It might be too much for example, to expect a person whose alcoholism has persisted for many years and who lacks either inner resources or support and protection in the environment to stop drinking completely. Economically and culturally deprived people may, *in general,* have more difficulty because of the absence of resources. This was discussed in Chapter Six "Alcoholism and Poverty." Such difficulties are, however, not exclusive to that population.

Pattison has suggested that "there is a need to define the prescription of abstinence. For some patients, immediate and life-long abstinence appears imperative; but that does not apply to all of the alcoholism syndromes. Other patients cannot and do not achieve abstinence and therapeutic opportunity may be obstructed by demanding that they do so. . . ."[1]

Polemicists will debate the merit of various approaches but there is need for flexibility. Many professionals feel that all hope is lost if the alcoholic takes one drink after he has accepted the need for help. There is nothing like a slip to arouse the anxiety of a worker who may see it as personal failure or as a betrayal of the therapist by the client. With some clients there will be many slips and the therapist cannot afford to be angry, bored, or defeated. The only test is whether the alcoholic is making a genuine effort. Peltenberg pointed out that overanxiety on the part of the therapist about uninterrupted abstinence may inspire the patient to use drinking as a weapon of retaliation whenever negative feelings emerge.[2]

Long before the social worker has to worry about relapses, however, he must be concerned about enaging the alcoholic in treatment even after the latter has appeared for his first appointment.

As indicated in Chapter Four, *Enabling the Alcoholic to Accept Treat-*

---

[1] E. Mansell Pattison, M.D., "A Critique of Alcoholism Treatment Concepts," *Quarterly Journal of Studies in Alcohol,* Vol. 27, No. 1 (March, 1966), p. 63.

[2] Catherine Peltenberg, "Casework with the Alcoholic Patient," *Social Casework,* Vol. 37, No. 2 (February, 1956), pp. 81-85.

ment, the alcoholic has frequently struggled to reach this point and he has not resolved all his conflicts about drinking. These conflicts contribute to the difficulties that threaten the worker. For one thing, he is often there under some duress and may identify the worker as another person in authority who will ask him to give up his major support. (Vignette #1)

If the alcoholic displays hostility, there is little point in looking for the hidden wellsprings. It is better to face it and go on from there. After all, he is hostile and may be doing his damndest to arouse negative responses from the therapist. If the therapist is anxious and insecure and needs to be loved by everyone, he is likely to go overboard in his efforts to be loving and accepting, and this can be a disaster for a client already on the brink of loss of control. However, it is important to be aware that he may be using this hostility and resentment to test the worker by provoking rejection. If he can show that the worker, like everyone else, doesn't want any part of him, he can, with clear conscience, turn his back on treatment and continue drinking.

He may present himself as worthless and sometimes overdoes it by insisting that "I'm the worst you've ever seen" or "You may have helped others but I doubt if you can do anything with me." This may be a variation on the effort to provoke rejection by trying to force the worker to make a moral judgment. The alcoholic is supersensitive to the slightest hint of moral indignation. It is essential to recognize that this and similar behavior is threatening. The alcoholic may feel demoralized and hopeless but he cannot be permitted to cause the therapist to identify with these feelings to the extent that the latter becomes defensive and critical.

Adelstein summarized the qualities any helping person working with alcoholics must be concerned with:

1. one's own need for success as it is obvious that recovery from alcoholism is marked by many frustrations, relapses and failures;
2. one's ability to meet the demands of extremely dependent persons and not become either overwhelmed or rejecting;
3. one's own ability to set realistic levels of aspiration in treatment goals for one's patient or client;
4. one's ability to accept hostility and rejection and still maintain a supportive relationship.[3]

RELATIONSHIP

The most powerful weapon in the arsenal of the worker who must over-

[3] Joseph Adelstein, M.D., "Clinical and Social-Psychiatric Aspects of Alcoholism," Lecture at 1963 Rutgers University Summer School of Alcohol Studies. Reprinted by National Council on Alcoholism, Inc., New York, N.Y. (mimeo).

come the initial difficulties and provide thorough treatment is *relationship*. Despite his show of hostility and denial, the alcoholic desperately needs acceptance as a worthwhile human being rather than as a drunk. His self-esteem requires bolstering and he must see hope for it in sobriety.

Incidentally, what the client calls himself is unimportant. Some therapists regard it as a matter of honor to compel the client to call himself an alcoholic even though the label is an anathema. Such inflexibility can only reinforce denial. It is enough if he concedes he has a problem with drinking whatever he calls himself. A client of this writer was repelled by the label *alcoholic* but was so convinced he had a problem that he and his wife drove 120 miles round trip to attend group therapy meetings for eighteen months, regardless of weather hazards. He achieved sobriety without ever believing that he was an alcoholic, although he was certainly alone in his disbelief.

There is a feeling that there is something special, and therefore frightening, about the worker-client relationship with the alcoholic. Actually, it is not too different from any other casework relationship except possibly for greater demands on the therapist for acceptance and support and on the client to give up the one thing that may have held him together. Also, it is essential, given the alcoholic's distrust and wariness, to impart to the client the feeling that the worker is a real person in this encounter. There is, as Truax has suggested, "the temptation to present a facade, a mask of professionalism, or some type of confessional-professional screen; the temptation to be incongruent with the self or ingenuine as a person." [4] A more earthy way to say it is "never be phoney" because alcoholics, more than most people, can spot it instantly and will either reject the worker or use this weakness in his game playing.

The first contact can be crucial because the alcoholic does feel anxious, threatened, and scorned by society. Chafetz and his colleagues suggested that in handling the initial contact, "respect for the alcoholic's tenuous feelings of self-esteem and constructive utilization of his dependency needs does not imply indiscriminate giving but gratification within limts that do not harm the patient or the caretaker and gratification that serves to establish further the patient's trust and confidence in the caretaker." [5]

This may mean, for example, helping the alcoholic's spouse to understand some of the difficulties he is facing in trying to give up alcohol; it does not mean trying to persuade his wife he can control his drinking if he drinks at home instead of at the bar.

It does not mean acceding to the client's demand that the worker's influ-

[4] Charles Truax, M.D., "Effective Ingredients in Psychotherapy: An Approach to Unraveling the Patient-Therapist Interaction," *Journal of Counselling Psychology*, Vol. 10, No. 3 (1963).

[5] Morris E. Chafetz, M.D., *et al.*, "Establishing Treatment Relations with Alcoholics," *The Journal of Mental and Nervous Disease*, Vol. 134, No. 5 (May, 1962), p. 396.

ence be used immediately to have his driver's license reinstated. It means that help will be given when the client earns this reward through sobriety.

Most therapists who are successful with alcoholics regard acceptance as far more important than insight because it can frequently relieve pressures and reduce the need to drink. The knowledge that someone cares is the most urgent need of many alcoholics. A man who had been in and out of nursing homes sixteen times in one year said gratefully that the social worker was the first person who seemed to understand the tortures in the struggle for abstinence. "It's been hell for me this past week," he reported, "but it meant so much to know someone knew and cared. Maybe that's why I was able to stay dry without falling apart and maybe, with that kind of support, I can make it next week too."[6]

A psychoanalyst told this writer that she used LSD as a therapeutic aid when that treatment was enjoying its brief and now largely discredited popularity among physicians. Because she recognized the dangers, she stayed with the patient almost constantly for ten hours. It finally occurred to her that some alcoholics were responding more to the fact that she cared enough to give them that much attention than they were to the drug. A few tests confirmed her hunch, and she seldom used LSD after that.

Although it may seem paradoxical, acceptance of the alcoholic can sometimes be enhanced by focusing on his drinking. Up to this point most people have probably denounced his drinking and have been too hostile to listen to or care about the details. Now, for the first time, in the therapist-client relationship, someone is interested in knowing what drinking *means* to the alcoholic.

Acceptance is likely to be achieved with alcoholics only if the worker is able to move quickly. Alcoholics are unwilling or unable to tolerate delays inherent in extensive investigations, at least at the outset, into their difficulties. They are equally impatient wih probing for suble meanings. One woman, when asked why she drank, said it was boredom resulting from "a dull and stale marriage." And, in truth, it was a dull marriage.

Another woman first said she didn't know why she drank, but then she added: "I guess it's because of my husband." When asked what he did to make her drink, she replied: "He doesn't do anything, he's just too damned dull to endure sober."

Both were oversimplifications and did not tell the whole story, but they had reality for clients. They bring to mind a bit of dialogue in the play *The Pleasure of His Company* by Samuel Taylor and Cornelia Otis Skinner. A young woman says to her father: "You were never very happy with mother, were you?" He replied: "Your mother was a saint who made our

---

[6] Elaine Kepner, "Application of Learning Theory to the Etiology and Treatment of Alcoholism," *Quarterly Journal of Studies on Alcohol*, Vol. 25, No. 2 (June, 1964), p. 283.

home an outpost of heaven. It's why I spent so much time in saloons."

Acceptance does not mean that the worker relinquishes authority that is an integral part of the therapeutic relationship. The potential danger of this is greater with alcoholics than with most clients because so many of the former parrot the discredited formula that it is not possible to understand an alcoholic completely unless you have been one. As Perlman points out, however, "the therapist is most constructive when he persuades the client that he is feeling, not like him, but with him."[7]

Dr. Jackson Smith once told an annual meeting of the Cleveland Center on Alcoholism:

> A professional relationship differs from a non-professional one in the following ways: there is an implication that one of the two people is more expert, better informed and less involved in the problem than the other. Too, the relationship is not carried on for the satisfaction, pleasure or comfort of the professional individual, his only function is to render a service for which he is particularly qualified.
>
> The professional person's problems, drinking habits, children and, in fact, his entire existence is of no interest to the alcoholic. Most alcoholics when sober are polite people and they may listen too courteously to the interviewer's experiences–which may benefit the interviewer but will offer little help to the patient.
>
> A friend in the clergy told me that after visiting a prominent but severely alcoholic parishioner a number of times without any visible results he remarked 'There's always hope; in fact, I've worn out a pair of pants praying for help', to which the alcoholic immediately replied, 'Bishop, I had no idea you had a problem!'
>
> The need to avoid discussing your own experiences, opinions and conclusions, regardless of how interesting they may be, with an alcoholic cannot be overemphasized. . . ."

The relationship is, in the terminology of some, part of the system of treatment. Steiner sees alcoholism as a game played by those who "willfully engage in repetitive, interpersonal behavior sequences involving alcohol, with the production of an interpersonal payoff as the covert motive."[8] He sees the therapist as a possible victim of the kind of manipulation employed in the "Drunk and Proud of It" game described in Chapter Five, *Alcoholism and the Family*.

---

[7] Helen Harris Perlman, *Social Casework* (Chicago: University of Chicago Press, 1957), p. 71.

[8] Claude Steiner, M.D., "The Alcoholic Game," *Quarterly Journal on Alcohol Studies,* Vol. 30, No. 4 (December, 1969), p. 92.

Steiner says the expectation of the therapist can have a powerful impact on the client and warns that alcoholics treated by therapists devoid of confidence in themselves and their clients are "likely to become alcoholics, even if they were not when they began treatment."

COMMITMENT BY THE CLIENT

A relationship cannot be a one-way process and the client must commit himself to active participation in treatment. Most will try to avoid this because ultimately the commitment means giving up drinking. It is a continuing test of motivation and the degrees of commitment required by the therapist are variable.

Dr. Max Hayman reported an experiment in which sixteen patients were hospitalized, given physical and mental tests, and placed on Antabuse, a drug which is innocuous if the patient abstains from alcohol. A single drink, however, will induce two to four hours of severe illness that may include terrifying accelerated heartbeat, intolerable itching, wracking nausea, and other equally unpleasant consequences. The patient who knows this will not take a drink unless he is determined to test every experience for himself. In any event, it can be useful as an inner policeman for some alcoholics who cannot stop drinking on their own.

Dr. Hayman's patients contracted for a year of treatment and the money was not refundable, although the patients were permitted to resume treatment after slips without loss of face. Twelve of the patients were counted as successful and Dr. Hayman felt that commitment was a major factor because it involved both patient and therapist for a full year. The patient knew he would not be abandoned but also knew he had no more right to break the commitment than did the therapist. The payment in advance certainly provided some incentive. One patient said: "I should never have started this. Now I can't quit. It would cost too much."[9]

That is an extreme illustration and not feasible in many places but the components are valid in a variety of settings.

Essential to the effectiveness of the acceptance-commitment relationship is an understanding on the part of the client as to what he can expect. He should understand what will be done for him and why. He should know why the immediate goal is some degree of sobriety but it is a means rather than an end. He should understand that the long-term goal is a re-synthesis of his life without dependence on alcohol and may require a slow, painful, undramatic search for constructive substitutes.

The alcoholic is easily scared off by the threat of depth therapy and many practitioners feel that the major thrust of treatment should not be

---

[9] Max Hayman, M.D., "Disulfram Oriented Treatment Technique," *Quarterly Journal on Alcohol Studies*, Vol. 26, No. 3 (September, 1965), pp. 460-467.

toward an intrapsychic reorganization or fundamental change in personality but toward a modest and reasonable change in social functioning to enable him to lead a constructive and personally satisfying life. Because recovery is on the ego-adaptive level, it is seldom necessary to resolve deep unconscious conflicts. Instead, "The alcoholic must be helped to find a means of interrupting the self-perpetuating mechanism of addictive drinking, so that his 'ego-apparatusses' can become available to him for coping constructively with his life situation."[10]

The relationship is the basis of the first step in helping the alcoholic which is to attack his alcoholism directly. Without a relationship on which to lean, he cannot tolerate this threat to his defenses. With the alcoholic, says Menninger, the classic psychiatric approach of trying to find and remove causes is like looking for the cause of a fire before starting to put it out."[11]

The story is told of one alcoholic who went to see a psychiatrist when he couldn't stop drinking. "I was shaking and in a hell of a shape. He started asking me questions about my childhood; I thought to myself, 'The damn fool!' I didn't go back."

For the most part, uncovering therapies have been unsuccessful in treating alcoholics because they fail to deal directly with the symptom. Sometimes, they unintentionally permit the alcoholic to continue drinking. Terrified by the thought of giving up alcohol, the client may be delighted by the reprieve granted while the therapist explores the crypts of his psyche for buried clues. With the therapist thus engaged, he can continue to drink, rationalizing that the "basic cause" has not been purged. No matter how hard the therapist tries, the alcoholic is likely to frustrate his efforts. When a suspected cause is found, the alcoholic will protest it isn't the basic one and he will suggest that the therapist continue to search while the alcoholic continues to drink.

One recovered alcoholic wrote:

> How could I remember whether or not I had had trouble with my mother when I was three—when I couldn't even remember what I had done today, much less yesterday? I could no longer distinguish what I'd lied about from what I'd dreamed about. Reality itself was distorted by my endless rationalizations.
>
> But psychiatry can be a great sop to our loved ones, who never stop yakking about 'doing something' about our 'drinking problem.' When we go to a psychiatrist who does not insist that we stop drinking while we undergo treatment we may

[10] Howard Clinebell, *Understanding and Counselling the Alcoholic* (New York: Abingdon Press, revised ed., 1968), pp. 19-20.
[11] Karl Menninger, M.D., *Man Against Himself* (New York: Harcourt Brace and World, Inc., Harvest Books, 1938), p. 160.

appear to be very cooperative patients, indeed—we secretly hope that he'll get so lost in our past that he'll leave our present drinking behavior alone. We speak frankly and at length about every area of our life, past and present—our sex life, our family life, our business life and our social life. It's only when we are questioned about any of these in relation to drinking that we find it impossible to be honest.

The only real interest we have in finding out why we drink excessively is to find out how we can go back to drinking as we used to. But in the meantime, while the psychiatrist is poking around in our past, we'll continue to drink, cagily ducking questions whenever he touches upon our current or past drinking behavior, lying to protect the last defense we have.

As the psychiatric treatment continues, our tensions often increase beyond our threshhold of pain; we drink even more excessively—thereby preventing any psychiatric penetration of our past or present—or we stop going to the psychiatrist because 'the doctor just isn't helping me.'"[12]

Psychiatrists happen to be the "whipping boys' 'in the above illustrations but therapists and counselors of all professions invite failure if they do not attack drinking as the primary problem. Indeed, it was a psychiatrist, Dr. Harry M. Tiebout, who was one of the first professionals to urge this approach.

"The mistake we made," he said, "was our failure to recognize that the task was twofold. In rather doctrinaire fashion, we persisted in treating the alcoholism as a symptom which would be cured or arrested if its causes could be favorably altered. The drinking was something to be put up with as best one could while more fundamental matters were being studied. The result of this procedure was that very few alcoholics were helped. The drinking continued and the symptoms remained untouched."[13]

To help the alcoholic give up or modify his drinking the social worker must:

1. **Help the Alcoholic Feel Like a Worthwhile Human Being.**

This theme has been repeated many times in these pages. We can only plead that it is a requisite of treatment. Unless the alcoholic can feel like a worthwhile human being, he cannot mobilize his ego strengths constructively. The worker must help him conquer feelings of inadequacy, uselessness, and weakness.

---

[12] Anonymous, *The Drinking Game and How to Beat It* (New York: Simon and Schuster, 1968), pp. 54-55.
[13] Harry Tiebout, M.D., "Direct Treatment of a Symptom," in *Problems of Addiction and Habituation* (New York: Grune and Stratton, Inc., 1958).

It isn't easy because alcohol has frequently worked so well. Now he will argue sobriety won't mean anything unless he can achieve it on his own. Or he still cannot accept the fact that he has been defeated by alcohol so, to him, giving up drinking is in itself evidence of weakness. Brendan Behan, a burned-out tippler, died in a Dublin hospital but on his death bed was declaring angrily that he was tougher than the booze. Obituaries quoted him as saying "I'll beat the gargle yet."

Naturalist-author William Seabrook managed a lengthy period of sobriety, but one day, recounts his biographer, Marjorie Worthington, he "came home with a brown paper bag. Out of it he drew several bottles of whiskey. He set them down on a table in the cottage and said: 'I'm sick of being a cripple. *From now on I'm going to prove that I can take a drink or leave it alone, like any other man.'* [Italics mine] He poured himself a drink and swallowed it. It was the first time he had taken one since he left the hospital in White Plains. It was not to be the last."[14]

This feeling is strong with many alcoholics and sometimes it resists all the efforts of the most skillful workers on the first attempt. It can be pointed out that the client frequently has told many others that he could stop drinking without help. Sometimes the only strategy is to say: "All right, try it once more, but the next time you slip, you might agree to call for an appointment or let your wife or employer call." This has risks, but, as a last resort, it may work if the wife or employer is involved and is prepared to impose the consequences of not seeking help.

There are also other interesting strategies to use with the person who is ambivalent about his drinking. Workers in a special alcoholism project of the Family Service Association in Cincinnati use a test in which the client must take three drinks a day for 30 days. If drinking is a problem, he will lose control during that month. (Vignette #2)

The sense of worth, the achievement of independent masculine status among male alcoholics, may come slowly and painfully. They are, as we have seen, largely dependent people who have used alcohol to cope with anxieties and tensions on the job, in marriage, in the raising of children, and in countless other life situations. And, no matter how much they protest their determination to be strong and independent, dependent wishes persist.

The worker may have to accept this dependency for a considerable period until, over the months, it is replaced by the inner feeling of self-sufficiency that makes life without alcohol possible. Blane suggests some implications for treatment, especially in the vocational area:

> Positions offered the alcoholic must contain built-in satisfac-

[14] Marjorie Worthington, *The Strange World of Willie Seabrook* (New York: Harcourt Brace and World, Inc., 1966), p. 197.

tions of dependent needs; conversely, they must not make intensive demands for work or activity rewarded only for its own sake. Prior to offering jobs to an alcoholic client, the counselor must establish a warm and trusting relation with him; at first he must be available to the alcoholic on demand. This gratifies the alcoholic's needs, placing him in a more highly motivated state. The counselor must also work within the limits of his client's skills. Starting the dependent alcoholic on a new line of occupational endeavor is usually more than he can bear. Jobs approximating the service situation, regardless of the level of skill involved, are highly appropriate, for example, jobs with living-in arrangements, or where meals are provided, or with clear-cut relations to a firm, but benevolent, authority.[15]

The development of the client depends to a great extent on the genuine confidence shown by the worker that the client can eventually learn to deal with anxiety and create defenses without alcohol. It is, said one client, "learning to face and cope rather than to escape and avoid." Dependence in the relationship can be quite positive during the metamorphosis. One man who refrained from drinking for five days after his first appointment said "the therapist's expression of pleasure when he related this was 'just like getting a good report card,' and he wanted to 'stay dry' to get another 'E' for excellence."[16]

In existentialist terms it involves a reassertion of human choosing, feeling, and acting to combat anxiety and feel more significant in the face of anomie and passivity. One woman decided to return to school although the odds against success were formidable. A man worked hard at repairing his marriage but finally had to make the decision that it had reached a point of no return. He decided to accept his wife's divorce suit (although he did not want a divorce); and he was able to do it in a mature way, without resorting to the bottle for support, and with the prospect of constructive alternatives.

2. Help the Alcoholic to Abandon Denial and Face Reality.

The difficult task of conversion from dependency to independence requires the alcoholic to face the reality of his condition and to use his potential at a realistic level. Some alcoholics express themselves as unable to accomplish anything. As Blane suggested above, they can achieve a sense of confidence gradually by doing things at which they can succeed. Others express their inadequacy in delusions of grandeur and seek unrealistic goals. The counselor must keep ambition attuned to realistic goals.

---

[15] Howard Blane, *The Personality of the Alcoholic* (New York: Harper and Row, 1968), pp. 24-25.
[16] Kepner, *op. cit.*, p. 283.

Some of the factors that impaired motivation, especially denial and rationalization, continue in treatment. Confrontation is a technique that is indispensable to alter these defenses. It is no service to the alcoholic for the worker to pretend to believe him when he is lying. (Vignette #3) A client may come to the office with breath that reeks of the pungent residue of a binge with every exhalation, yet he denies having had a drink during the past week. He may still deny it after the confrontation but he now knows the worker is aware and that is healthy for any would-be deceiver.

Confrontation has many uses. It can be used to break through when the client projects all responsibility on someone else. A woman alcoholic told the caseworker many times about her husband's shortcomings. He walked out on her when the children were born and withheld drinks from her when they entertained. For years, she was unable to go to the grocery store without asking permission. She endured all sorts of humiliation. But she continued to drink and finally the worker, admitting the difficulties of the situation, inquired sharply: "All that may be true but you have only talked about your husband. What have you done to change in the last twenty-four years?"

Much of the confrontation has to be done by "significant others" in the alcoholic's life and the worker's job is to help them confront wisely and to recognize its pitfalls. Blane, for example, describes what can happen in a family and says that an alcoholic may respond to attacks on denial in one of three ways:

> . . . He counterattacks and gets angry; when successful, the alcoholic so thoroughly cows his wife that she fears to raise the question of drinking with him except at times of extreme crisis, such as job loss, arrest, or an accident. Or he attempts to conceal drinking practices more cleverly than before: He exercises greater ingenuity in hiding the source of supply, drinks alone or in secret more often, or increases drinking away from home. Reliance on either of these techniques further endangers the marriage, isolating husband from wife and eroding mutual trust. The alcoholic increasingly seeks out groups where heavy drinking is sanctioned or at least condoned. Even this becomes awkward or impossible to do if he drinks more than others, or if episodes of vomiting, blackouts, inexplicable anger, or other unacceptable behavior occur and reoccur. Thirdly, his wife's confrontations may be taken seriously, and the husband may examine his behavior in a new light. I know of instances where drinking problems of serious proportions were stopped when the individual came to realize and accept what he was doing. Caretakers don't see examples of this in the way of business. It

may be an underestimated occurrence.[17]

Confrontation is not synonymous with entrapment. The worker is not lying in wait to catch the alcoholic client in falsehood or distortion. His purpose is to recognize evasions and denials and expose them because the alcoholic has to see and admit what he is doing before he can change. A man referred by the court for child neglect may come loaded with resentment, hostility, self-righteousness, and denial. The worker helps him see the effect of his behavior on his children or on his wife, or, even more important, on himself. He does not do this through accusation but by hearing out the client and "feeding back" the story pointing out the positive behavior when sober as opposed to destructive behavior when drunk.

3. **Help the Alcoholic to Learn Sobriety.**

There is growing conviction among those who work with alcoholics that the basic component of treatment is learning. In the chapter on causation, the process of becoming an alcoholic was described in terms of learning to use alcohol as a means of coping with environment. A person learns that alcohol provides a mechanism for achieving release from tension or escape from crisis, and as that learning is reinforced it becomes a way of life. It is a way that is self-defeating because it develops at the expense of learning more socially approved means.

If this premise is valid, treatment of the alcoholic means that the process must be reversed. He must unlearn one way of coping with the problems of living and find a new way. This means he will ask what substitutes are as good and he will look for rewards in sobriety. "Establishing the response of sobriety," says Kepner, "is not easy since sobriety, like drinking, is not a simple response. It is a pattern or chain of responses established through repetition over a period of time. To help the alcoholic acquire the responses which will build a pattern of sobriety, the process is broken into a series of graded tasks. If successive and closer approximations to the final goal are consistently rewarded, the new pattern of sobriety may be firmly established. . . ."[18]

The immediate rewards do not have to be spectacular. One of the most effective is recognition by the therapist. This does not mean going overboard by suggesting that a week of sobriety confers the right to wear a halo. It does mean that the therapist recognizes the accomplishment realistically and can show whatever confidence is merited in the client's ability to work out his problems without alcohol.

Substitutions are essential. An individual may refrain from engaging in behavior which leads to punishment by energetically engaging in some-

[17] Blane, *op. cit.*, p. 54.
[18] Kepner, *op. cit.*, p. 282.

thing else. One counselor reported the case of a man who visited prisons every week, rain or shine, sick or well, and became an outstanding amateur penologist. Another man decided to provide transportation for the town's mentally retarded children to and from school to picnics and ball games which he helped to organize.[19]

A client wanted to paint landscapes and portraits and he had considerable talent but no money to purchase supplies. The immediate goal set with the help of the worker was to save enough money through abstinence from liquor to purchase a minimum of art supplies and to start painting.

Alternative ways of coping should be socially acceptable or the alcoholic may exchange one set of troubles for another. One man decided to substitute sex for drinking and his goal was to seduce every woman in the place where he worked. If successful, this guaranteed long-term sobriety because there were several hundred women employed and the numerical potential was increased by routine personnel turnover. Unfortunately, he was almost as indiscreet in his sexual exploits as he was in his drinking behavior and the management cut short the project by firing him. The social worker, intrigued by the client's choice of an alternative, which, needless to say, was arrived at independently, did point out the risks as well as the absurdity. After an alcoholic relapse, the client was encouraged to return to school and earn a degree. At this writing, he is married, well along in a career, and has not had a drink for several years.

There must be long-range as well as immediate rewards and for most alcoholics this involves finding new satisfactions or relearning the pleasures of being a husband and father or wife and mother. The rewards may require the participation of others who react to his changed behavior by responding more positively. "The wife who has been sexually rejecting her alcoholic spouse becomes accepting because the patient is again a husband rather than a 'drunk.' The children can respond without fear, and the employer can once again trust him to do a responsible job."[20]

As Kepner points out, the treatment of alcoholism based on learning principles "is not a simple reconditioning process to remove the symptom. The drinking has been used by the patient as a means of avoiding emotional and personal problems, and these must also be treated before, during and sometimes long after a stable period of sobriety has been achieved."[21] The alcoholic must acquire the self-knowledge that permits him to become aware of the thoughts, feelings, values, and goals which activate his behavior.

Some might view this as insight therapy, but insight, said Hobbs,

[19] William D. McKenna, "Counsellors on Alcoholism: An Observation" (St. Paul, Minnesota: Commission on Alcoholism Problems, 1970), p. 3.
[20] Kepner, *op. cit.*, p. 284.
[21] *Ibid.*, p. 287.

"merely means that one client is catching on to the therapist's personal system of interpreting the world of behavior." He also suggested that insight "is not a cause of change but a possible result of change."[22]

Learning is necessary in many ways and one thing the alcoholic must learn is self control. Most have an underdeveloped superego and have never acquired the techniques of restraint.

> An example of this type of learning deficit was the young divorcee with five children who knew almost nothing about how to care for, feed or clothe a family. She never had a maternal model from whom she could learn, and the task of the therapist was to supplement the previous learning experiences of the patient. For a time the therapist was an educator who helped the patient learn about the management of time, money and energy in the simple routine tasks of daily living. The most important deficit, however, was in the area of impulse control. This patient lived only in the present. She never put off for tomorrow what could be satisfying at the moment, whether it was alcohol, narcotics or sexual relations. Consequently, she was either in difficulty with the police, her relief worker or one of her many boyfriends. The patient's dissatisfaction with her confused and depressing life situation provided the motivation to change. The therapist gave her support, encouragement and a new way of appraising the possibilities still open to her. Gradually, this patient learned to give up certain immediate gratifications, including alcohol, in favor of long-range goals.[23]

The learning must always provide rewards—some large, some small—that will ultimately provide a satisfactory *modus vivendi* without alcohol or with a comparatively safe intake of alcohol.

This unlearning-relearning process can be lengthy and the time required varies with individual needs. Setting minimum or maximum limits is sheer speculation although Dr. R. Gordon Bell says the "inactivation" of habitual chemical dependence, which includes alcoholism, requires "continuous, conscious attention and effort for at least a year. During that year the possibility of periodic wide fluctuations in mood, either toward the tension and anxiety that recall the withdrawal reactions or toward episodes of deep depression, must be appreciated. The power of habituation—the 'force of habit'—will make itself manifest over and over again as 'awareness of something missing' occurs in so many of the daily adjustments. The drinker recovering from a dependence on alcohol, the drug addict recovering from a dependence on drugs, the smoker recovering from a dependence on to-

[22] Edward M. Scott, *Struggles in an Alcoholic Family* (Springfield, Illinois: Charles C. Thomas, 1970), p. 54 (quoted).
[23] Kepner, *op. cit.*, p. 289.

bacco—all experience it, and all need to have faith in the fact that habitual desire will become inactive within the first year or soon thereafter. . . ."[24]

The danger of relapse, says Bell, comes when a person who has inactivated an uncontrolled desire for alcohol suddenly decides to have "just one beer" a year or more later. This decision "does not reactivate a physical craving" nor is there "disturbance from intoxication or malnutrition and [there is] no drunkenness. He simply reawakens his old need to think about alcohol. Whether he wants to or not, he will be plagued by thoughts of drinking, and he stands a good chance of having such thoughts again assume dominance over his thinking and behavior. It is for this reason that I so strongly oppose the arguments of those who believe that something less than total abstinence can succeed in treating harmful dependence."[25]

THE ENVIRONMENT OF TREATMENT

Some of the techniques that are useful in treating alcoholics have been discussed, but the alcoholic does not live in a vacuum. He must be treated in relation to his environment. "If becoming a problem drinker," said Mulford, "is a product of social interaction, then becoming a recovered problem drinker is likewise a product of social interaction. To affect recovery is a reintegration process involving other persons, usually those involved in the process when he became a problem drinker. It involves something more than a therapist doing something *to* a patient, whether it be adjusting his liver or adjusting his psyche."[26]

This was suggested in the chapter on the family, and, for those alcoholics living in family constellations, the prognosis for successful treatment is limited unless the family is included—thus the growing recognition of family therapy. This may include only the alcoholic and his spouse, or it may include children, parents, or anyone in the "natural group."

Man and wife in an alcoholic marirage have, as we have seen, a complementary pathology whether it was brought to the marriage or developed later. As the alcoholic must learn to stop drinking, so must a spouse learn to avoid provoking drinking situations. One husband insisted on his right to drink moderately despite his wife's alcoholism. The worker supported this right but observed how provocative the man was when he left a half-filled bottle of bourbon on the table as a temptation to his wife who was in a vulnerable emotional condition. Some manifestations of this distress were upsetting to the husband and it was just possible he wanted to retaliate.

---

[24] R. Gordon Bell, M.D., *Escape from Addiction* (New York: McGraw Hill Book Co., 1970), pp. 138-139.
[25] *Ibid.*, p. 140.
[26] Harold Mulford, "Meeting the Problems of Alcohol Abuse: A Testable Action Plan for Iowa," (Cedar Rapids, Iowa: Iowa Alcoholism Foundation, 1970), p. 8.

The emotional growth of a spouse can be most effective. A worker reported the case of an alcoholic woman who had not responded to individual treatment but stopped drinking a few months after her husband was engaged in counseling. The worker attributed a year of sobriety at least in part to the fact that the husband grew in his own self-understanding and confidence. He was then able to offer his wife sympathetic support and firmer controls as protection against her own volcanic impulses. His need to make her the strong and guiding partner (as his mother had been) diminished. When he gained security in his own masculine role, problems around money, management, social activity, child rearing, etc., began to get more appropriate attention. He was also able to accept the fact that his wife's drinking was her problem for which she was primarily responsible.

Families must be helped to avoid contributing to the drinking by protecting the alcoholic or by participating in stratagems that are only excuses to continue drinking. They must be helped to help the alcoholic accept responsibility.

The involvement of families is accomplished in various ways. Sometimes alcoholics and family members are seen separately; sometimes together. One of the advantages of the joint interview is the opportunity provided the worker to observe nuances in the relationship that might otherwise elude him. (Vignette #4) He can also point out "on the spot" the consequences of acting out unreasonable expectations and mutual provocations.

In a joint interview a wife may, for example, say many things to belittle her husband and it becomes clear that she does the same thing at home and in other situations. It is equally clear that she doesn't realize what she is doing. For his part, he listens without uttering a word in his own behalf. It is possible for the therapist to encourage him to speak up and to help both learn to talk with each other. The situation in which the wife has become dominant (perhaps domineering) and the husband has lapsed into passivity is encountered frequently. (Vignette #5)

When both partners drink the problems can be compounded, especially for the children. Family therapy can be advantageous and Meeks and Kelly have indicated the advantages of including children in the therapy. However, they caution that parents are sometimes threatened. When it can be done, however, "family rules against open expression of feelings, discussing weaknesses in one partner or allowing children to comment openly on family problems may shift as the parents become more comfortable in the family therapy setting."[27]

Meeks and Kelly studied five families and reported that the two men

[27] Donald E. Meeks and Colleen Kelly, "Family Therapy with the Families of Recovering Alcoholics," *Quarterly Journal of Studies on Alcohol,* Vol. 31, No. 2 (June, 1970), pp. 407-408.

who were still drinking when family therapy began withdrew their families early in treatment because they insisted they could control their drinking without help. However, when drinking again became a problem, they brought the families back.

They reported also that in the initial phases fear of relapse "hovered over therapy until the fear was brought into the live processes of family interaction." Focus on interaction was always the goal "for so long as the alcoholic was identified as the sick member, our families, at home and in treatment, continued to be preoccupied with the alcoholism as the sole source of their problems; healthy communication was stifled. When family members were able to accept their shared responsibility for family problems, the identified-patient effects became less influential."[28]

The importance of family therapy is underlined by the fact that changes in one member of the family are not always accompanied by corresponding changes in the family as a whole. This is strikingly apparent when the alcoholic stops drinking and the expectations of the family are unrealistic. After the pain of active alcoholism, families are inclined to assume that sobriety is *the* answer to all their problems. It isn't. It is only a step that makes it possible to work out problems that may have existed prior to the alcoholism, were aggravated by the drinking, and remain unresolved.

Every marriage and every family has internal problems. When the alcoholism was active, this problem dominated the scene. All difficulties in the family could be attributed to it so no adjustment was made to other problems. Now there is a realization that the former alcoholic was not an "ideal" person even aside from the alcoholism. And the alcoholic, after experiencing the so-called "pink cloud" elation, suddenly discovers that sobriety is not a panacea.

A wife's understanding of what her husband gave up when he stopped drinking is vital. For one thing, he may have surrendered his technique for being the center of attention without learning new and more constructive techniques.

Disillusionment can be related to sex. After years of sexual conflict and frustration comes the hope that sobriety will inspire a kind of fairy tale romance. But misunderstandings stubbornly survive. (Vignette #6)

Sometimes much can be accomplished by helping the non-alcoholic with anxiety around relapses. It has been charged, in support of the thesis that women marry alcoholics to satisfy unconscious needs, that wives cannot abandon control because they require the dependency imposed by drinking. Most clinical observation and the reports of Bailey and Jackson have not confirmed this, but workers are afraid that if financial control is returned to the alcoholic he will be tempted to squander the money on

[28] *Ibid.*, p. 409.

another binge. The risk has to be taken if he is to recover his self-esteem.

Another display of anxiety is interpreted by the alcoholic as suspicion. If every marital kiss is seen as a sobriety test, the alcoholic may decide that if he is going to be accused of drinking he might as well do it.

Mention should be made of the ubiquitous school of thought that says that many wives do not—at least unconsciously—want their husbands to stop drinking. The wife in this category requires her mate to continue drinking for her own personality equilibrium because her basic need is to have him remain inadequate. Chafetz has recently restated this syndrome "in which an individual is more tolerable to his social unit intoxicated than sober. This syndrome is most clearly seen in configurations whereby nonalcoholic, extremely dominating mates or parents exist. On the one hand, the nonalcoholic mate or parent appears on the surface to suffer greatly as a consequence of the alcoholic state of another. If treatment or extraneous events result in sobriety, however, opposition to this state in so-called healthy members rises. They become proportionately more disturbed as the alcoholic member becomes less alcoholic. What becomes clear is that acceptable and readily obvious to society, was a cover-up for disturbances the pathological drinking behavior of the alcoholic person, socially un-in another. Improvement in one exposes the problems in another and the unhealthy drinking in such cases satisfies, in part, emotional needs of another. Furthermore, we see some mates, who cannot tolerate the dependency and demands put upon them when the alcoholic person is sober but can readily provide emotional sustenance instead of rejection when he is drunk."[29]

That system does operate but it may not be as universal as some writers suggest. It means, in a marriage, that, if the husband achieves sobriety and resumes the traditional role of husband and father, the wife might be expected to go promptly to pieces because she is no longer in control. Studies by Bailey and Jackson indicate that most wives accept the sobriety of their husbands without marked decompensation. When the drinking problems have been conquered *and adjustments to sober husbands have been made,* these women are remarkably like the general population of wives. The most important point to emphasize is that sobriety alone does not always produce miracles.

GROUP THERAPY

Alcoholics, like everyone else, function in a much larger social constellation than the family. Many find effective help in learning social interaction through group therapy which, in some respects, can be seen

[29] Morris E. Chafetz, M.D., *et al., Frontiers of Alcoholism* (New York: Science House, 1970), p. 316.

as an extension of family therapy. A couples' group is essentially a number of family groups.

The most enthusiastic advocates of group therapy are convinced this should be the most widely used treatment for alcoholics. Dr. Ruth Fox has declared group therapy so helpful to the alcoholic "that it should be instituted as soon as possible, often on the very day of the first contact when resistance to this kind of help may be surprisingly low. . . ."[30]

Not all would go that far but there is little doubt that group therapy creates a climate conducive to helping many alcoholics. Strayer sees the interaction of the members of the group allowing "an alleviation and dispelling of anxieties so that a patient can realize that his problem is not unique to himself. In alcoholics, this results in diminution of the guilt connected with drinking and the related behaviors. Tensions and pressures associated with the guilt can be utilized constructively by the patient who learns to verbalize his positive feelings concerning the problem."[31]

At the Cleveland Center on Alcoholism we found that a small therapeutic group provides a *safe* setting in which alcoholics can test their relationships with others, including their spouses. Because they may be alienated and lonely people, this is a kind of testing that frightens them in daily living. For example, many alcoholics can express anger toward other members of the family only when fortified with alcohol and at those moments they frequently erupt violently. At the other end of the emotional spectrum, they are afraid to express tenderness. In the sanctuary of a small group they can learn to express hostility without destroying relationships just as they can test honest affection and accept rejection for what it is. Anger and affection are inescapable components of the best relationships, including marriage.

This is the basic concept familiar to all helping professionals. However, it is not so simple for the alcoholic, who is so often a perfectionist, and if things cannot be perfect he is likely to drink to eradicate consciousness of them or to give himself the illusion of perfection. In a group, he can frequently accept realistic goals. He learns that intimate human relationships involve accommodation as well as comfort. For the egocentric, impulsive, albeit essentially self-denigrating alcoholic, this requires considerable learning.

One woman, when asked what she thought was most important about a group, replied: "It is an overused word these days but I am sure it has something to do with learning to communicate. Sometimes in a group a wife hears for the first time what her husband has been trying to com-

---

[30] Ruth Fox, M.D., "Group Psychotherapy with Alcoholics," *International Journal of Group Psychotherapy* (January, 1962), p. 57.
[31] Robert Strayer, "Social Integration of Alcoholics through Prolonged Group Therapy," *Quarterly Journal of Studies on Alcohol*, Vol. 22, No. 3 (September, 1961), pp. 471-480.

municate for years. Maybe it is because she observes the attention others are giving him and she thinks she better begin to listen. You find you can talk about things you found impossible to talk about at home; sex problems, for example, because you find out other couples have similar hang-ups. You can experiment a little at a time with new ways of handling dreaded situations that no longer seem so dreadful."

The goal of group therapy is improved function and this may include better performance on the job, improved ability in social situations, and more effective handling of stresses. As with most treatment of alcoholics, the focus is on "here and now." After months of pretending mutual affection, one couple had it out when the wife shouted at the husband; "Let's forget this nonsense and trying to put on a show. I don't love you. I don't even like you at this point and you know it." It was a shattering moment for her husband, who weakly protested he had not even suspected a rift. At long last, however, the truth was revealed, and with help and encouragement, it could be examined. This actually was the beginning of the road back to a fairly stable marriage, although it never achieved the romantic ideal. As weeks passed, he learned not to press too hard for affection that required time for rebirth and she learned to respond when relieved of pressure.

Many who work with married alcoholics find that couples' groups engaging the alcoholic and the non-alcoholic spouse are effective. At the Cleveland Center on Alcoholism, where the alcoholism was about equally divided as to sex, it was the kind of group that had the highest rate of success. Burton reported that a couples' group in Philadelphia, in which only the husbands were alcoholic, also was rewarding. In the beginning, as she said, "there tends to be a concentration on one's own problems but, as the sessions continue, there is identification with others, an awareness of distortion, and the interaction that is so vital." She also confirmed the observation of the Cleveland therapists that drinking is the major topic for discussion in early meetings but later there is a shift to a variety of other marital and family problems. As she described the process:

> The early emphasis on the drinking gave the wives an opportunity to display their particular patterns of rightness. In the beginning they leaned over backward in their willingness to accept their share of the problem. This was in keeping with their self-concepts as "good" wives. However, their awareness and acceptance of their contributions to their husbands' behavior were usually on an intellectual level. An emotional acceptance of their own roles in their marital problems was hard won, if achieved at all. In later sessions they tended to excuse their own behavior on the basis of their husbands' drinking or

> other undesirable traits. It was at these points that some of the wives would begin to gain a glimmer of insight through listening and responding to comments of other wives. For example, wife A described her extreme angry outbursts when her husband failed to come home from work on time. Her anger was the result of her anxiety that he would come home drunk again. Wife B then pointed out to wife A how her unjustified anger may play a part in contributing to her husband's need to drink. In later sessions positions of wives A and B might be reversed and when wife B is angry, wife A will remind her of the stand she had taken previously.[32]

One point illustrated by Burton is that a couples group can be helpful to some even when the result is not the fairy tale ending of living happily ever after. She described the advantages of ultimate separation of one couple in a marriage so toxic it would have been disastrous for the man and wife to stay together. (Vignette #7) This again emphasizes the need for workers to sometimes accept less than total success.

The egocentricity of the alcoholic makes it difficult for him to see beyond himself and he seldom knows what image others see. In groups, people learn to see themselves as others see them. In one case, job interviews were re-enacted in the group so the applicant became aware of the negative impression he must have made on the interviewer. This effectively modified his previous conviction that he had been articulate, charming, and generally impressive, and revised his misbegotten notion that he had been rejected because the personnel man was mentally defective in addition to being biased. "My god!" hooted one member of the group, "you sound as if you were sure you couldn't do the job."

The group gives freedom but it also imposes the limits an alcoholic needs. Therapists do not have to worry about alcoholic lapses because the group takes care of offenders, usually in a constructive way. A woman who had a slip reported that the group helped "where all the pleading and nagging of my husband wouldn't have. I had the feeling they understood but certainly did not condone or pity me. You may remember that was the time I first agreed to take Antabuse because the group convinced me I needed it."

Members of a group are not easily conned. They are quick to detect and attack rationalizations. A lawyer in one group had a job unrelated to law. He detested the work and his employer and wanted to re-establish himself as an attorney but complained that the forces of evil were arrayed

---

[32] Genevieve Burton, "Group Counselling with Alcoholic Husbands and their Nonalcoholic Wives," *Marriage and Family Living*, Vol. 24, No. 1 (February, 1962), p. 59.

against him. The power structure in the bar association, he whined, would never permit "little fellows" like him to get ahead. Moreover, he could not endure the transition period because his wife would complain about lack of money. He did rent office space a few evenings a week, but there were no lines of waiting clients and he blamed this on his wife (although her role was ambiguous) and the bar association.

A physician, also a member of the group, listened to these complaints for several weeks. He then pointed out that he might refer clients but the lawyer had not even bothered to have cards printed with his address and telephone number. He added that this indicated all complaint and no action. The doctor's words carried weight because he had returned from the imminent danger of losing his license to a successful medical practice. The group rallied to the challenge and assigned the attorney the task of having cards printed before the next meeting. He responded to the pressure and, while that simple act did not make him an instant Clarence Darrow, it provided the satisfaction of doing something–however minimal –about his problem and at least a glimmer of awareness that small steps in the right direction might lead to a more promising future.

Some workers have hesitated to use group therapy in poverty groups. In a group the network of community is usually more complex than in one-to-one relationships and it has been argued that the poor are not as articulate as other people. That is, to say the least, condescending and erroneous. Where members of the group have failed to participate, they may be deterred by a professional therapist who monopolizes the gathering with a non-stop lecture. Some of the language richest in simile and analogy has been introduced from the ghetto.

Contrary to the myth of the inarticulate poor, "the skill of talking well and easily is widely appreciated among ghetto men. . . . 'Rapping', persuasive speech, can be used to manipulate others to one's own advantage. . . ."[33] It is the latter that can be a trap in a therapy session. Intrepid staff members at Eaglesville Hospital near Philadelphia successfully used marathon group therapy with men from Skid Row and found that "the marathon experience seems to break through the defensive facade to provoke remarkable confrontation." Feelings of isolation, a false self-image and inability to accept love gradually diminish or even dissolve. Of the 83 men in the first 10 marathons, 29 percent were classified successful and 28 percent partially successful. Thus, a total of 57 percent were considered improved. A letter from one graduate of the marathon therapy read: "I want to express my love and thanks to everyone for

---

[33] Ulf Hannerz, *Soulside* (New York: Columbia University Press, 1969) p. 84.

their anger, patience, disgust, frustration and most of all for their care and love."[34]

The ingredients are the same in all groups of alcoholics. They are support from the group, confrontation of self, assault on and restructuring of defenses, and group pressure toward commitment to change.

There are a variety of groups, including couples (alcoholic and non-alcoholic mates), those formed without regard to marital status, and groups of wives of alcoholics. The latter, incidentally, can be most helpful to families, but drinking husbands who do not want their spouses to "gossip" about them can provide formidable opposition to their wives' attendance. A student who didn't make it in trying to form one group of wives, reflected ruefully in a class paper that he might have interviewed each husband and tried to "sell" him on the idea of supporting his wife's participation so she could learn to react with less anger to his drinking. Also she might learn to make the home more pleasant. "Nothing could have been lost by such an attempt" he wrote, "and much could have been gained." Frankly, the worker did not attempt this because he was afraid the resisting husbands would not trust what he said and would only imagine that the worker's *real* intent was getting the wife to separate, or advise her how to con him into giving up his drinking, which, in light of past performances by relatives, other professionals, and the wives themselves, would not have been a completely unrealistic or paranoid expectation.[35]

BARRIERS TO EFFECTIVE SOCIAL WORK TREATMENT

The foregoing text and illustrations make it clear that most of the services required to help alcoholics are well within the competence of social workers. Relationship, support, perhaps some insight, assistance in mobilizing resources to make choices, relief from alienation, reality testing, are therapeutic contributions made by social wokers to all kinds of clients every day. Why, then, are social workers so insecure and uncertain in the presence of alcoholics? Actually, to quote a former president of the United States, the only thing to fear is fear itself.

One source of fear may lie in the years of emphasis on alcoholism as primarily a medical problem suggesting that all or most alcoholics require the ministrations of a physician. Certainly, there are medical complications involved and when a medication like Antabuse is indicated, medical participation is essential. This means that a social worker should

[34] S. S. Jordy, "Marathon—A New Technique for Treating Alcoholics" *Connecticut Review on Alcoholism,* Vol. 22, No. 3 (February, 1971), p. 9. (Complete paper on marathon therapy at Eaglesville is in the *Quarterly Journal of Studies on Alcohol,* Vol. 32, No. 2 (March, 1971).

[35] William Priestly, "A Lack of Structure: A Learning Experience in Group Treatment," Unpublished student paper, University of Michigan School of Social Work, pp. 4-5.

know when to enlist the assistance of other disciplines; it does not mean "copping out" by abandonment of the client.

Even more intimidating is the implication in the medical model of alcoholism that treatment requires hospitalization for most alcoholics to provide a "drying out" period. Some think withdrawal is best accomplished by the use of drugs and that restoration to physical health is a major concern. Physical damage is found most often in chronic alcoholics and treatment is needed, but the large majority of alcoholics have not reached that stage. Despite the loud and incessant demand for inpatient facilities there are those who feel that they should be used only for a minority and only for *bona fide* medical emergencies. Dr. Griffith Edwards told the twenty-eighth International Congress of Alcohol and Alcoholism:

> . . . . If we are right in supposing that when our patients so often tell us that "drink isn't the real problem" they are in a certain sense speaking the truth and that the real problem is their inability to meet the demands which their wife, job, world make upon them – that drink is only a symptom choice, one of a possible range of defenses, retreats, nonanswers – then we might expect that treatment which was carried out in the totally artificial setting of an in-patient hospital unit, for such-and-such arbitrary number of weeks, might not be the best way of equipping this man to face the realities of his real and demanding world. Although the beneficial experience of group therapy, finger painting, basket weaving or chats with the padre might by some be expected to generalize to a better ability to meet the demands of emotional exchange with one's wife, and equip one with a more viable self-image with which to arm oneself as one sits behind one's desk at work, the postulate of generalization is nonetheless a very considerable assumption. The question here is whether taking the alcoholic into the hospital has in the long term any effect on outcome, or whether he might as well be treated as an out-patient, without removing him from the stresses and realities of his environment. This is a matter which has obvious bearing on the planning of treatment services.[36]

Medical services are necessary in some cases – although they are seldom readily accessible – but that does not make alcoholism primarily a medical problem.

---

[36] Griffith Edwards, M.D., "The Role of Therapy in Meeting Complex Social Problems," Proceeding of the Twenty-Eighth International Congress on Alcohol and Alcoholism (Highland Park, N.Y.: Hillhouse Press, 1969), Vol. 2, p. 219.

There is, however, an even more pernicious myth that has long scared off social workers and others. For some reason it has been assumed that alcoholics can be helped *only* with a team approach and if this is not available in one's agency, clients are sent to a specialized clinic. It is usually not available there either but most people like to think it is.

In professional circles there is something hallowed about the phrase *team approach,* as if it were one of the loftier creations of the mind of man. Be that as it may, it is not even practical with the shortage of manpower in our society. If, as someone has calculated, all the nation's psychiatrists were assigned to participate in the treatment of the alcoholic in a single state, California, they could arrange only one interview a month. The other 49 states might have to bumble through without a complete team.

Things are not as bad as they seem, however. The assumption that multiple treatment is synergistic has never been adequately investigated and, through the years, the evaluation of treatment has dealt with so many variables that it has been difficult to decide which therapeutic processes were being evaluated.

The Cleveland Center on Alcoholism was established in 1956 with a classical team – social worker, psychologist, internist, and psychiatrist. Every client was required to have an appointment with each member of the team. The latter then convened in a staff conference to pool their wisdom and design a treatment plan with one person assigned as primary therapist. It was not a notable success. The clients did not always agree with the decision of the team and manipulated appointments to see the therapist of their choice. (This was possible because the medical personnel were part-time and backlogs accumulated.) Their choice was not made by the profession of the therapist but by their relationship to an individual, and after a few months, many clients seemed largely unaware of the discipline of the therapist with the possible exception of the internist who was identified because he dispensed pills and wrote prescriptions. The multiple approach as a routine procedure was abandoned. A study two years later revealed no significant difference in the success of those treated by two or more disciplines and those engaged with only one.

Others have challenged the sanctity of the team. When the organization is too formal, says Neilson, it "may be so rigidly structured that it really does not operate as a team. In some instances the team leader pays lip-service to shared responsibility, but gives it no real support. This kind of team often has the most defined roles, the most explicit procedures and the most regimented staff conferences. It is doubtful how much effective service it provides, since it is not designed for service but for the comfort of the team leader. . . ."[37]

Mulford and others have questioned the significance of the modality of treatment and said that it has little or no relationship to success. Recovery, they say, will be 25 to 30 percent regardless of the type of treatment.[38] There might be some argument over that, but it is certain that the treatment of alcoholics is not the exclusive franchise of any group.

Another bugaboo for many is the prospect of long-term treatment. It is true that many clients need months of treatment, but not all do.[39] Also, when the length of time is extended there is no indication that treatment must continue to be intensive. Wedel's study revealed no significant relationship between improvement and frequency of contact with the therapist and it cast doubt on "the assumption of some clinicians that the extent of therapeutic success varies directly with the length of time spent in treatment."[40]

Gibbins and Armstrong were even more dogmatic after reviewing the effect of clinical treatment. They declared unequivocally that the length of treatment was not significant. "It may be," they reported, "that when alcoholics are sufficiently motivated to seek treatment within certain gross limits the specific nature and duration of the treatment they are exposed to is of less importance so far as response is concerned than the personal and social characteristics they bring with them."[41]

In the final analysis, however, the greatest frustration for most helping persons who work with alcoholics stems from an inability to compromise on goals, but there are degrees of success. This was alluded to earlier but bears repetition because there are increasing doubts about the assumption that total abstinence is necessary during treatment or that it should be the measure of success in all cases.

A caseworker employed in the stockyards area of St. Paul, Minnesota, was assigned to examine police reports each morning and select men who had been arrested for alcohol-involved offenses. With some help, they all promised never to take another drink but none kept the promise. After several months of effort, the caseworker morosely reported that not a single person had been rehabilitated. Closer examination of results, however, revealed that for most there had been a significant reduction in number of days hospitalized, number of days in

[37] John A. Neilson, "Developing Existing Services," *Addictions,* Vol. 13, No. 3 (Fall, 1966), pp. 7-8.

[38] Mulford, *op. cit.*, p. 6.

[39] Herman E. Krimmel and D. Bruce Falkey, "Short Term Treatment of Alcoholics," *Social Work,* Vol. 7, No. 3 (July, 1962), pp. 102-107.

[40] Harold L. Wedel, "Involving Alcoholics in Treatment" *Quarterly Journal of Studies on Alcohol,* Vol. 26, No. 3 (September, 1965), p. 477.

[41] Robert J. Gibbins and John D. Armstrong, "Effect of Clinical Treatment on Behavior of Alcoholic Patients," *Quarterly Journal of Studies on Alcohol,* Vol. 18, No. 3 (September, 1957), p. 448.

jail, and an improvement in health.[42] There was some success with one of the least hopeful of alcoholic populations and with most alcoholics the prognosis is much more favorable. As Dr. Pattison has said, a "willingness to accept a partial improvement in some areas of total life adaptation seems to be not unreasonable and perhaps is realistically the most feasible for many alcoholics. . . ."[43]

It may be appropriate to comment on those alcoholics who return to social drinking because this phenomenon commands increasing attention. In 1962, Dr. Davies of The Maudsley Hospital in London outraged the faithful when he published the results of research showing that seven patients who had been hospitalized for excessive drinking did resume drinking following a brief period of complete abstinence after discharge. They were followed up seven to eleven years later and their use of alcohol had "never gone beyond the limits regarded as permissible in their cultural groups." None had been drunk. One, a business executive, did take Antabuse before business trips, but he was the only one to use medication.[44]

The reaction was predictable and outraged.[45] Dr. Davies, however, was not the first to challenge the holy orders; he just attracted more attention. Several years earlier, Dr. Marvin Selzer reported that thirteen confirmed alcoholics committed to a state hospital later became social drinkers but the agency that had provided funds for the study virtually ordered him to omit those "embarrassing" findings from his paper. Psychiatric colleagues scoffed that the patients probably were not alcoholics anyway.

In recent years, the evidence has continued to accumulate and it is no longer possible to ignore it. Some principles arbitrarily enunciated more than three decades ago are subject to modification. Dr. Pattison has summarized the views of those who do accept this phenomenon:

> If we may conclude that addictive drinking behavior represents a particular gestalt–a particular combination of cultural norms, character structure and social-familial context–then a person may behave in a pattern of addictive drinking only so long as that particular combination obtains. It may be that if any one of those factors is changed, or the relationships between the factors are changed, i.e., the psychosocial gestalt for addictive drinking is changed to a psychosocial gestalt for abstinence or

[42] Gordon Gilbertson, "County Alcoholism Program," *Conference Proceedings,* Social Welfare and Alcoholism (Washington, D.C.: U.S. Dept. of Health, Education and Welfare, 1967), p. 51.
[43] Pattison, *op. cit.,* p. 61.
[44] D. L. Davies, "Normal Drinking in Recovered Alcohol Addicts," *Quarterly Journal of Studies on Alcohol,* Vol. 23, No. 2 (March, 1962), pp. 94-104.
[45] Marvin Block, M.D., "Comment on Article by D. L. Davies," *Quarterly Journal of Studies on Alcohol,* Vol. 24, No. 2 (March, 1963), pp. 109-121.

> normal drinking, then the alcoholic living and behaving in the altered gestalt (Kurt Lewin's "field") can change from his addictive drinking to a different pattern of drinking.
>
> This hypothesis is illustrated when alcoholism develops from family disequilibrium in response to crisis, which Pattison has outlined in detail elsewhere. Briefly, if a family is subjected to stress, it may no longer be able to use its old adaptive maneuvers and must seek new patterns to achieve equilibrium. If the new patterns are unsuccessful, the family members may exhibit social dysfunction, such as alcoholism in one of its members. Restoration or reformation of a stable family equilibrium, however, may replace the dysfunctional adaptive maneuvers which supported the alcoholism. What has been changed then is not the basic personality structure but rather the psychosocial equilibrium involving and including the personality of the alcoholic. This may explain why seemingly minor intervention may effect a dramatic change in member behavior: the dysfunctional equilibrium is broken up and the family and person are afforded an opportunity to weld a more stable adaptive equilibrium in which alcohol is no longer a necessary functional component.[46]

The implications for social work treatment of the alcoholic are not momentous. An approach to treatment that encourages a return to normal drinking is probably unfair to the client. The odds against success are prohibitive for reasons mentioned earlier in this chapter. In Dr. Bell's words, the danger of reactivating an inactive habit is considerable, or, stated in slightly different words, an overlearned response is difficult to eradicate completely. In any case, sobriety seems to remain the best possible goal for the man or woman who has endured the devastation of alcoholism.

The implications for peace of mind are somewhat clearer. There are various measures of success and permanent abstinence is only one of them. An alcoholic client may return to social drinking under radically altered conditions of life and the fact that he drinks again does not necessarily imply failure on the part of the social worker.

[46] E. Mansell Pattison, *et al.*, "Abstinence and Normal Drinking" *Quarterly Journal of Studies on Alcohol,* Vol. 29, No. 3 (September, 1968), p. 627.

VIGNETTE #1

THE CASE OF MR. G.

The case of Mr. G. demonstrates the types of resistance with which the worker must deal. Mr. G., single, thirty-three years old, came to the clinic as a court referral, having been arrested for breach of the peace. A self-employed and fairly prosperous upholsterer when his drinking began to affect his capacity to work, he left the management of his business to his foreman. When he came into the clinic, his bloodshot eyes, flushed face, and tremulous hands testified to his recent drinking. He initiated the interview by berating the police who had arrested him and the judge who had lectured him. "Why was I sent here?" he inquired. "I'm not a Skid Row drunk." The worker allowed the patient to ventilate his feelings, interrupting him only to ask an occasional question or to clarify a point of information. Mr. G. had at one time been employed by his father, also a self-employed upholsterer. This father, also guilty of reprimanding and scolding him, had once told his son that he would never amount to anything, that he was a "no-good drunk." Mr. G finally left his father's employ, first because he could not tolerate his nagging and second because he wanted to prove he could make it on his own.

All these facts gushed forth in a spontaneous expression of feeling. Once having finished with them, however, Mr. G. glared in challenge and expectation at the worker, whereupon the worker then asked Mr. G. whether he expected to receive still another lecture at the clinic. At first Mr. G. hesitated. Then he smiled and remarked, "I hope not. At first I thought you were going to behave like all the others."

Having thus identified the basis of Mr. G.'s hostility and having set up a beginning rapport, the worker went on to explore with Mr. G. the reasons for his referral to the clinic. Mr. G. admitted to excessive drinking but identified the term "alcoholic" with the Skid Row type of drinker. Here the worker, using a strictly informative approach, indicated to him the distinction between the actual meaning of the word and some of its more pejorative connotations. Mr. G's response to this was equivocal. He doubted whether he drank enough to require treatment. True, he put away a pint of whiskey a day, but there were others who did the same thing and they were not alcoholics. Anyway, he drank only because he was nervous and had a lot on his mind and a lot of responsibilities. At this point, upon encouragement from the worker, he went on to discuss his need to prove himself to his father. He described the pressure under which he functioned in business in meeting deadlines, making decisions. When the worker inquired, "Do you think drinking is a good way of handling pressures?" Mr. G. smilingly stated that he realized it wasn't but what could he do about his nervousness? "Look at me now," he said, raising his tremulous hands for the worker to see. "I'm a nervous wreck. The booze is doing this to me. I don't eat, I can't sleep, I feel all wound up." The worker then asked Mr. G. whether he wanted some help in working through some of his pressures. Mr. G. agreed that he did but couldn't see how he might be helped. Referral to the physician for medication was suggested to him as a means of securing immediate relief from his symptoms. In addition, the worker offered to discuss Mr. G.'s problems more fully at a future date. He emphasized that any decision Mr. G. might make to do something about his problem was entirely his own—not the court's or his father's—and added that the clinic would be glad to help him if this was what he wanted. To this Mr. G. consented.

An analysis of the dynamics of this case makes it quite clear that the patient was confused not only about his drinking problem (in which he failed to accept himself as an alcoholic) but also about the identity of the social worker, whose image he unconsciously replaced with that of his punitive and domineering father. This misconception, or "transference," as it is called, could be cleared up only through the worker's nonpunitive, permissive attitude. Also, the worker did not make an issue over whether Mr. G. was or was not an alcoholic but merely accepted him on the patient's own terms, offering service in proportion to the need as Mr. G. saw it. No matter what technique is used, however, the worker must always be flexible and responsive to his patient's individual needs.

Reprinted from Robert Strayer, "The Social Worker's Role in Handling the Resistances of the Alcoholic," *Crime and Delinquency,* January, 1963, pp. 39-45. Reprinted with permission.

VIGNETTE #2

ONE EXAMPLE OF THE "FOUR WEEK TEST" TECHNIQUE

We inform the person who is ambivalent about their drinking problem that there is a test they can take to diagnose themselves. The test involves taking three drinks (three beers, three shots or whatever form he likes) each day for 30 days without fail; he must drink every day for the test to be valid. Theory is that if control of drinking is a problem he will lose control during that month and thus have more than three drinks–the quota he set for himself. Obviously there must be some conscious ambivalence for the client to even try this test. In a way he is in a paradoxical position; i.e. if he does not try the test he cannot be certain of his denial of a drinking problem; yet if he takes the test he may fail; it is likely that either way he may do himself in.

Mr. C. on impulse turned to his wife in a joint interview to say if it was only drinking that was his problem, he would certainly quit and did so for approximately ten days. He is a very determined man who always does what he sets out to do. His wife reported he was like a "caged animal" during those ten days and he was so angry that he had boxed himself in that he would hardly speak to her. It was as if she had trapped him.

Two weeks later he decided to take "the test." His behavior and response during the four weeks of the test could be considered a "bird's eye view" of the alcoholic's struggle in accepting the responsibility for his drinking problem.

Week I–He announces in an individual interview with me that he is beginning the test that day (it had been described to him two weeks before in a joint interview). He announces this with pride, seeks encouragement, checks out the rules of the test, etc. He says it is going to be a "breeze" for him; keeps reassuring me it is going to be no problem (has to keep up his denial to handle the anxiety and I don't challenge this at all).

Week II–He reports the test is fairly easy (tempering his bravado). He is drinking cokes, coffee and carrying hard candy (gave me a piece at the end).

He is seeing some things clearer at home; not sure he likes what he sees though. He brings up how he feels his wife attacks his adequacy and when he feels inadequate, he just withdraws. As the test goes on he is feeling less adequate in the sense he is becoming more fearful of losing control. This interview was prior to Thanksgiving and he cautions me to "watch that cranberry juice." He is more fearful–this week he begins to talk more about the history of his drinking which seems to date back to a business failure. Also, much discussion of how supportive his wife was prior to his drinking problem–she has changed so, maybe he has changed also. Then talked about all the recent changes his wife has had to make with which he sympathizes and agrees are hard for her (last child of ten going off to school; daughter got married). Easier for him to talk of wife's adjustment to these changes than his own.

Week III–He jokes with me that this is his last week of the test (the drinker's con game), knowing that he has another to go, but he is more serious, obviously more anxious. Less denial about the effects of his drinking problem; he is taking more action in the handling of the children now. He recalls a memory of a few years ago, going into a bar for a quick beer and seeing a boy in the bar trying to get the drunk father's pay check for the family and how touched he was by that scene, and then joked that "man didn't know about Family Service." No breeze now. He has been able to talk to his wife, though–she is looking greater to him and had been real nice; what have I said to her?

Week IV–This past week he went into a bar for a drink–never has frequented bars. He took a good look at the people there–did not like what he was. He knew his wife had seen me earlier that day–what did she say, what did we discuss (unusual interest for him). He wanted to get me to report her version of his failure on the test. He had told her he had "sinned so he might as well sin good when he went over three beers and had eight." I avoided this reporting and he then said I was going to be disappointed because he had failed the test. I related to his depression upon failing the test; also his wish to know his wife's reaction and that he could discuss this with her; she was sympathetic and concerned. He then described how everything had been going so well between him and her that he began to feel it was so good, that drinking one more would be okay and that ended up to eight. He takes full responsibility; he had nothing to complain about to account for his test failure; he can discuss his feeling of depression about this failure; but also he feels the test helped him see things clearer about his drinking and also about how things really are for real; everything is clearer even if it isn't all good.

Reprinted with permission of Family Service of the Cincinnati Area.

VIGNETTE #3

The denial system is frequently reactivated during treatment because the alcoholic almost instinctively turns to alcohol during times of stress until sobriety has become a firmly established way of life. He protects this system with all sorts of rationalization which means that confrontation is repeatedly necessary.

Mr. F. was an investment broker whose ability was above average but earnings were far below his potential because of his drinking. When his job was threatened and his wife threatened to return to live with her parents 500 miles away and take the children with her he finally decided he would have to get help if he wanted to keep his job and re-unite his family. His wife had told him that she would not return until he had six months of sobriety, and despite dozens of long distance calls from a pleading husband, she held to that decision.

As an aid to sobriety, Mr. F. was taking Antabuse, which would make him severly ill if he took a single drink and, as with many alcoholics, served as a deterrant.

During the interviews he had told the worker that his only recreation, apart from an occasional movie, was to spend weekends with a friend who had a hunting lodge in a neighboring state. The outdoor activity was invigorating, and the sport was an effective antidote to his tension, and the companionship relieved his loneliness.

The worker usually asked if Mr. F. was continuing to take Antabuse and for many weeks the answer was "Yes." One morning, however, it changed to "No." Mr. F. explained that he had not had any sexual relationships with other girls since his wife left and the need had become almost intolerable. There was, he said, an after hours bar near the hunting lodge and one of the more attractive waitresses had been suggested as a possible solution to his problem.

Mr. F. hesitated but then went on to say that he couldn't very well go to the bar and establish the necessary relationship unless he had a few drinks, so he had stopped taking the medication to make this possible.

The story was possible and yet absurd and the worker bluntly told him so. While it was true that Mr. F. did not live and work in one of the swingingest cities in the country, it was equally true that girls were available to him without too much trouble and certainly a man did not have to go to an after-hours bar in another state to find a sex partner.

Mr. F., the worker pointed out, had fabricated this elaborate tale to justify his taking a drink. When thus confronted, the client agreed and added the girl was working that night which was a matter of indifference since he was more interested in alcohol than sex. He had said before that "not drinking" was a continuing problem and he decided to see if he could get away with it.

He added that he was glad his bluff had been called and while he did not promise he would never try again, he seemed relieved to know that the worker would continue to help him but would not permit deceptions to go unchallenged.

VIGNETTE #4

FAMILY THERAPY SESSIONS

Note: These sessions are culled from an ongoing record and do not show the beginning or end. (They include the alcoholic, his wife, and teen-age daughter.)

1. Therapist noted that daughter sat in chair near his. When her mother moved to sit in therapist's chair, daughter motioned for her to sit next to the

father. The session went rather well and wife gave patient permission to buy a new car which she had refused for a long time. It was obvious that this gesture enhanced his self-esteem and when prompted by the therapist, he said it showed his wife had respect for his judgment. He added she has recently been more cordial and this has reduced his desire to drink. Wife replied that it was not lack of respect that caused her to nag but concern for her husband's well-being. This message seemed to get across to the husband but it was certainly more difficult to make her realize that her "bitching and sniffing his breath" each night might well send him out to the nearest bar.

2. Family came despite bad weather. The car was purchased but has not been used because of the road condition. Mrs. Q. wants to wait until summer. Anyway, she noted, Mr. Q. had not been able to get his license back and she was openly pleased. She said he has to learn the facts of life and he deserved his punishment for Driving While Intoxicated. That started an argument because the patient resented the word "punished." She said she didn't mean it. The daughter reported a practical joke played by patient who returned from bowling and tried to make them think he was drunk. His wife failed to see the humor. Daughter is generally on side of patient.

Wife dominated much of the session. She said she knows her husband very well and when he drinks he "gets nutty." She knew when she married him that he drank heavily but she thought love for her would make him stop. They didn't have a child for the first five years because of financial difficulties. Patient interrupted testily to say that when daughter was born, his wife gave total attention to child. Worker asked if they ever discussed the problem. They said yes, but it seemed doubtful if the discussion had much meaning. Drinking of patient increased and as time went by, wife became mother to both child and husband. He resented this but did nothing to discourage it.

3. Started again with reminiscences about patient's drinking years and the discussion became heated with all three sometimes talking at once. Therapist suggested exploring ways in which members of family could express their anger constructively. Wife said she was afraid to show anger because she might "get killed" or have her "head punched through the wall." Daughter heatedly challenged this. There was no resolution.

4. Wife upset because her husband goes to the bar although he doesn't drink. Worker asked him why and he said he was lonely. Daughter said her mother should not try to control the patient. Most of the session devoted to discussing ways Mrs. Q. might alter her patterns of behavior. She said she knows she will have to change but they will have to give her time. Both husband and daughter attacked and told her how "wrong" it was to try to control.

5. Session filled with recriminations. Much of it centered on disagreement over daughter's independence, her efforts to look older with a new wig in upswept hair style. Wife thinks present controls are necessary for daughter's own protection. Patient scoffed.

6. Session was a reciprocal name-calling contest. Worker pointed out how they made life miserable for each other and if this continued the future was not promising. Mrs. Q. cried and showed her dependence on patient and he

seemed to understand that their inability to separate was related to mutual dependency although he appeared to grasp, intellectually at least, that the somewhat unhealthy mutual dependency needs made it impossible to give the kind of affection and concern to each other that a successful marriage requires. Throughout the daughter sat with a supercilious look on her face and occasionally made smart alecky comments that irritated everyone.

Reprinted with permission of Washingtonian Hospital, Boston, Massachusetts.

VIGNETTE #5

When Mr. and Mrs. M. came to the clinic they presented the classic picture of the domineering wife and the harassed husband. She was a large woman with a rasping insistent voice and he was slightly less than average size for a man. In the first interview, Mrs. M. tried to answer all questions whether or not they were directed to her.

"Why did you first start drinking excessively?" the interviewer asked Mr. M.

Mrs. M. replied instantly. "Oh, he'll tell you it is only about two years but it's really seven or eight."

The interviewer tried again. "How much do you drink during the day?"

"At least a fifth," replied Mrs. M.

Mr. M. shrugged his shoulders helplessly.

This went on despite the interviewer's best efforts, which included telling Mrs. M. what she was doing. Indeed, it continued for many interviews and, on one occasion, the worker casually commented to Mr. M. that it was a nice day. "Yes, it is," replied Mrs. M.

The worker constantly pointed out what was happening and asked whether it was the same at home. Of course it was.

It became apparent that Mr. M.'s drinking had severely disrupted the family. He had been a most inadequate father and an irresponsible husband although he had a fairly good job, but he had not had many promotions and his wife constantly reminded him that he lacked ambition and if he cared about his family he would have tried to get ahead.

Mrs. M. had retaliated to her husband's behavior by lavishing all her affection and attention on her son. They did things together, leaving Mr. M. on his own. This might not have been so bad but they could not function independently —they were always derogatory about Mr. M., blamed him for all that had gone wrong, ridiculed his failures. It is sometimes healthy for non-alcoholic members of the family to act independently in the face of the alcoholic's refusal to seek help, but is not healthy to add disparagement and attack to that independence.

There were two areas of concentration in trying to help this family. One was to persuade Mrs. M. to cease and desist and give her husband a *chance* to help himself. He needed at least the opportunity to function, and he enlisted her trust by taking Antabuse, a medication which would make him violently ill if he drank. This effort was not a stunning success.

A concurrent effort was made to convince Mr. M. that he could only function with some self-esteem and confidence if he gave up drinking. His drinking was his wife's most potent weapon as well as an agent of self-destruction for him. This was more successful.

The M's were asked to participate in group therapy. The group approached them pretty much as the therapist had in individual and joint interviews. Mrs. M. left the group after six sessions because she could not tolerate "being blamed for everything and being looked upon as on ogre." Mr. M. continued in the group and in sobriety developed the ability to meet his wife on almost equal terms. When this happened, she returned to the group. After eighteen months, the marriage was functioning and acceptable. Mr. M. was sober. Mrs. M. almost permitted him to be a man and she learned that she had to release her son, then nineteen, to grow up, and that she could not use him as a substitute husband without disastrous results.

VIGNETTE #6

Mrs. T. has been depressed all month. She finally told me that in many ways she was happier when Mr. T. drank. With encouragement she confessed that he seems indifferent sexually. When he was drinking he demanded lovemaking frequently — sometimes as often as once a day, although aspirations sometimes exceeded ability to perform. Now he is indifferent and frequency of intercourse is down to once a week or even two weeks. It was explained that there is usually a change in a couple's sexual interaction with sobriety and Mrs. T. was encouraged to ask her husband if anything was wrong, instead of brooding in silence. She did, and he laughed. He explained it isn't that he cares for her less, "but I don't have to prove I'm a man now." With this reassurance she was able to accept the quality of sexual relations as being at least as important as quantity.

VIGNETTE #7

Couple X were college-educated, middle-class, economically stable people in their early forties. They had been married for 17 years and had two children, a girl nine years old and a pre-teen boy. Mr. X has been a heavy drinker since entering the army during World War II. He was not ready to refer to himself as an alcoholic, but would admit a drinking problem, having had to be hospitalized for it two years previously. He had had occasional periods of sobriety, the longest one being six months. Although he was a successful man in business, it was understood with his employer that drinking would mean the end of his job, with the result that Mr. X did his drinking largely at home. Mr. X had great personal charm and a usually comfortable sense of humor which could become biting and sarcastic when he wished. His charm and ready wit provided a defense that proved difficult to penetrate. In physical appearance he was large and generally attractive. Superfically he gave the impression of warmth, competence, and geniality. In the group, probably only the counselors were initially aware of his tremendous underlying anxiety, hostility, and dependency.

Mrs. X was an attractive small woman, overtly exhibiting relatively few of the controlling rigid traits we are beginning to associate with the wives of alcoholics we have counseled and studied. She had some insight into her role in their problems and gave the impression of genuinely wanting to gain more. In the beginning both the X's seemed to be quite well motivated. This was a self-referral; Mr. X came in "from the street" and demanded an immediate interview. None of the previous help his wife had suggested for him, including psychiatry, had been satisfactory. His wife had already been to see a lawyer and planned to leave him at a specific date in the near future. At first he said he didn't care, and he was going to make it the "dirtiest divorce action" on record. Finally he decided he didn't want to go through with it, and at the last minute came to marriage council.

One of the most verbally active members of the group, Mr. X interacted with all other members. Unlike his behavior in individual counseling he rarely directly expressed any hostility. This came out in veiled humor. In many instances he adopted the counseling role of recognition of feeling and of giving verbal support. From the beginning the X's made what seemed to be steady gradual progress in the relationship to each other. Soon after the group started they began having sex relations for the first time in a year.

At about the sixteenth session the counselors became aware of subtle changes in Mr. X's behavior. He was less verbal. His comments began to reflect bitterness rather than humor and there were times when he seemed moody and remote from the group. Our observations were augmented by an individual interview requested by Mrs. X. She was quite apprehensive about her husband's behavior. He was drinking heavily, had had episodes of violence, verbalized being fed up with his job, and was exhibiting a generalized sort of restlessness which was familiar to her from the past. Her worry included his sexual advances to their nine-year-old daughter. This had happened before, but as far as Mrs. X knew, there had been no episodes of it since they had come to marriage council. Superficially Mr. X. remained about the same. His behavior had not penetrated enough into the group sessions for his interaction with group members to be changed. Right through the twentieth session he was still comparatively active in the group, seemed interested in the others and interacted frequently with his wife. This, surprisingly, was the X's last session.

Before the next session met he left home following a drinking episode and had himself committed to a state hospital. Mrs. X attempted to cooperate with him around his voluntary hospitalization, but by now his hostility was out in the open. He left the hospital and his refusal to avail himself further of any psychiatric or counseling help was the determining factor in her decision to get a divorce.

Mrs. X. was previously described as having fewer of the characteristic neurotic traits we often see in these wives. Had her own neurotic needs been greater she might not have been able to initiate a move out of the marriage. At our last contact with her the divorce was final, her husband had gone to the West Coast and she was making an apparently satisfactory adjustment in her life with the children. Although one might have hoped for a different conclusion the results in this case were not without merit. The degree of psychopathology in Mr. X. precluded a satisfactory marital relationship and at that time, he was determined not to have further assistance. We felt that the group had helped him to look at himself, and conceivably in the future his group experience may provide the foundation on which he can develop further ability to function more adequately with intensive therapy. Mrs. X. used the group constructively in determining what she wanted from her life, in recognizing the limitations her marriage imposed, and in changing the situation.

Reprinted from Genevieve Burton, "Group Counseling with Alcoholic Husbands and Their Nonalcoholic Wives," *Journal of Marriage and the Family*, Vol. 24, No. 1 (February, 1962), pp. 56-61. Reprinted with permission.

Community Resources for Alcoholics

CHAPTER VIII

THIS BOOK HAS emphasized the social agency as a major community resource for the treatment of alcoholics and their families. The myth that alcoholism is or should be the exclusive franchise of specialized agencies must be buried with the disease concept. All competent professional caretakers, including or perhaps especially social workers, are qualified to help alcoholics. The cooperation of other disciplines such as medicine can be enlisted when necessary but that does not mean primary responsibility should be shifted.

Every alcoholic should be helped as completely as possible when he asks for help. There is no reason why an alcoholic should be shunted from agency to clinic to agency, but it happens all the time. A man who asks for help in a social agency is likely to be told that alcoholism is primarily a medical problem so he should see a doctor. The physician who either does not want to be bothered or has read much and understood little in psychoanalytic literature tells the alcoholic that alcoholism is a symptom of unresolved conflicts submerged deep in the psyche so "get thee to a psychiatrist." Whether or not the patient follows that suggestion may depend on the amount of his bank balance and his attitude toward psychiatrists.

The game has many variations but if played too long the alcoholic is discouraged and heads for the nearest bar, where he tries to forget that no one seems to want to help him. Yet any of these or other professionals could provide something that might start him on the road to sobriety and a useful life. (J.V., in Vignette #1, is an example of an alcoholic shunted from place to place.)

When all this is said, however, the fact remains that some agencies are not equipped to work with all alcoholics who knock at the door, that some alcoholics cannot constructively use the services of a particular agency, and that others may need more than one kind of help. A knowledge of community resources available to alcoholics and their families is, therefore, indispensible to social workers.

ALCOHOLICS ANONYMOUS, AL-ANON, AND ALATEEN

Almost since its beginning in 1935 when two alcoholics—Dr. Robert Smith of Akron, Ohio, and Bill Wilson, a Wall Street broker—found hope in mutual support after all else had failed, Alcoholics Anonymous has been regarded as the greatest single therapeutic tool in the treatment of alcoholism. Many professionals as well as those who had recovered under its auspices saw it as the *only* successful program for alcoholics.

That judgment still has strong advocates. It remains part of the fundamental faith of many early members of AA and their disciples. There are professionals who feel that once an adequate diagnosis has been made and medical care rendered if necessary, a referral to AA fulfills the therapists's responsibility and if a client fails to follow through he apparently doesn't want help.

It isn't that simple and the attitude is no longer as prevalent as in former years. The effectiveness of other kinds of help was recognized in the book *Alcoholics Anonymous Comes of Age,* published by AA. Also, co-founder Bill Wilson was one of the first to challenge his fellow members to take their heads out of the sand. He wrote a now-classic article, "Let's Be Friendly to Our Friends," in which he stressed the need for other services.

Perhaps the time will come when it will be possible to suggest, without risking a charge of sacrilege, that the number of professionals working with alcoholics may be doing so just as effectively as AA. It is just that they are reaching different populations, with some healthy overlapping.

Unfortunately, there is still considerable conflict between Alcoholics Anonymous and the professionals; the responsibility, which must be shared by both, arises largely from misunderstanding. Milton Maxwell, who made the best study of this conflict, found no unified view of AA on the part of professionals. The attitudes ranged from abyssmal ignorance and sometimes contempt to understanding and appreciation. The attitude of AA members toward professionals likewise ranged from hostility and ignorance to appreciation and understanding.

He found that most professionals, including social workers, were willing to make referrals to Alcoholics Anonymous but that willingness was frequently little more than a function of their own inability and/or unwillingness to help alcoholics themselves. Consequently, the referrals were ineffective.

Professionals have complained that AA has consistently wanted everybody to know about AA and to refer to it but refused to reciprocate by telling prospects about other treatment resources and recommending them. They have also been offended by the stubborn views of many AA members that (1) only an alcoholic can help another alcoholic, thus ruling out professional competence, and (2) the AA program is complete in itself.

The members of AA have complained, with justification, of condescension on the part of some professionals. They are also critical of the rigidity of clinic and agency schedules, the need for appointments, and the use of fact sheets and other "irrelevant" paper work. They feel that professionals do not understand the urgency of the alcoholic's condition and do not go all out as AA people do.[1]

Open communication is essential because Alcoholics Anonymous is a major resource in most communities. It has advantages that are difficult to surpass and groups are available almost everywhere. Even isolated individuals can be members through correspondence with the central office.

The only requirement for membership in AA is a desire to stop drinking and anyone who says he is a member is. Membership is free and there are no dues, although voluntary contributions are collected to defray expenses. This openness and the absence of formal requirements have therapeutic significance for victims of a disorder long stigmatized by our society. The foundation blocks of the program are the Twelve Steps and Twelve Traditions listed at the end of this chapter.

Alcoholics Anonymous gives the alcoholic, a generally alienated person, a sense of belonging. As John Park Lee has said: "No one asks

[1] Milton Maxwell, "An Exploratory Study: Alcoholics Anonymous and Professional Relations," Selected Papers, 15th Annual Meeting, North American Association of Alcoholism Programs, 1964. (Washington, D.C.: NAAAP, 1964), pp. 115-130.

him where he has been; no one asks if he is sorry; no one suggests that he ought to be ashamed of himself; nobody points a finger of scorn." [2] The new member of AA has a lot to get off his chest and a lot to learn and the fact that an AA group can be permissive, tolerant, and accepting is, in the words of Maxwell, "part of its genius."

If the crucial ingredient of recovery from alcoholism is to enable the alcoholic to find satisfactions in sobriety superior to those found in drinking or to learn a way of life that does not depend on alcohol, Alcoholics Anonymous may offer the most complete answer *for those who can use its approach.* It can be an encompassing experience that provides an emotionally satisfying alternative to chronic drinking. It has been described by Maxwell as follows:

> First, the A.A. subculture provides the member with much more objective knowledge about alcohol and particularly about alcoholism. This includes a redefinition of alcoholism as an illness rather than as moral degeneracy.
>
> Second, the A.A. subculture requires and facilitates an honest facing of the connection between drinking and stressful situations; the alcoholic begins to define his disorder as involving an obsession of the mind. The impotency of will power to handle the obsession and the necessity of other help are emphasized. Myths and rationalizations concerning drinking are debunked. The "screwy alcoholic thinking" is dissected and exposed, frequently in a humorous fashion.
>
> Anxieties against drinking are buttressed. Alcohol is associated with all the harm it has done to the alcoholic and with the tragic increase rather than the solution of problems. The member is given perspective on the first drink–that he will always be just one drink from a drunk, and that he can never again drink socially. He is taught that he can "arrest" his problem but that he will always remain an alcoholic. This fact is reinforced each time he presides and introduces himself with "I'm Joe Doakes and I'm an alcoholic." Then, to handle the anxiety aroused by the dread of a lifetime without alcohol, he is provided with the "24-hour plan"–sobriety just one day at a time. Because of his association and identification with sobriety models, the A.A. system is made easier to accept and learn. Then when he steps out to help a new prospect (Twelfth-Step calls), he furthers his learning by becoming a teacher and a representative of the A.A. way of thinking and acting. Thus,

[2] John Park Lee, "Alcoholic Anonymous as a Community Resource," *Social Work,* Vol. 5, No. 4 (October, 1960), p. 22.

the A.A. ideology not only attacks vigorously the use of alcohol for the relief of stress, it provides alternative methods of tension relief.[3]

The focal point of AA activity is the group meeting and members are exhorted to attend regularly. What he gets at these meetings has been well described by John Park Lee.[4]

1. He gets hope—hope that he can recover. "As he looks at the AA group, he consciously or subconsciously says to himself, "If they can do it, I can."
2. He is received back as a member of the human race. This is of incalculable importance to a person who suffers from rejection and a "loneliness so intense that few non-alcoholics with the greatest power of empathy can appreciate it."
3. He is compelled to face the fact of his alcoholism. His trumped-up explanations for drinking are brushed aside and he is told that he is drinking because he is an alcoholic and cannot help himself. He is further told that unless he accepts the fact that he is powerless over alcohol and that his life has become unmanageable, he will be unable to recover.
4. The alcoholic learns to accept himself as a human being free of unattainable concepts of perfection. This means that everyone has strengths and weaknesses, virtues and flaws, and that in every day there is likely to be some success and some failure. He may, through the group, learn to accept himself, live with himself, and, in so doing, learn how to live with other human beings.
5. The alcoholic in AA is introduced to what many feel is its basic source of strength; the relationship with God as the members understand Him. This, says Lee, "is not a creed to which the members are asked to adhere; there is no theological description of the Deity. Rather there is the admonition to the new member that if he would remain sober, he must develop some concept of God which will be good enough for him to rely on to enable him to break the grip of the alcoholic obsession that is destroying his life."

Perhaps, as many have said, no one can really understand the AA program by merely reading about it. The interested social worker should attend meetings and talk to members.

The completeness of the program led some to the conclusion that a dependency theory of alcoholism could offer some explanation for the

[3] Milton A. Maxwell, "Alcoholic Anonymous: An Interpretation," included in *Society, Culture and Drinking Patterns,* David J. Pittman and Charles R. Snyder, eds. (New York: John Wiley and Sons, Inc., 1962), p. 583.
[4] Lee, *op. cit.,* pp. 21-22.

success of Alcoholics Anonymous. Nevertheless, it is true that the indulgence of dependency needs in adulthood is correlated with a low frequency of drunkenness. The program of Alcoholics Anonymous can encourage dependence, but, as in all therapeutic processes, the goal is to help the alcoholic to grow away from this dependence to reach a healthy level of independence. He is then encouraged to help others achieve the same growth.

As the result of an intensive study of the life history of a successful AA member, Hanfmann hypothesized that the alcoholics for whom that fellowship is the answer may be "those in whose life for one reason or another, belongingness with a group of peers has been, from childhood on, a significant or even the most significant relationship."[5] (See Vignette #2)

Whatever the reason for joining or for success, it must be remembered that people use AA in different ways. According to Maxwell, ". . . Some seem to float upon group support with little change in attitude or behavior other than the maintenance of sobriety. For some AA becomes a rather exclusive social home or a kind of sect. For others it is a social home, but less exclusive, and a place where good AA therapy goes on. For still others, there is real personality change and continued growth in maturity. Furthermore, the functions may change for a given member over the years. We also note that some stay close to AA for the rest of their lives (not all for the same reason) and that others spread out in their friendships and activities and that some of these move through AA rather quickly and on out into the larger society."[6]

With all its merits, Alcoholics Anonymous is not a universal panacea for alcoholics and in some ways it has suffered from excessive adulation. The fact that it cannot and does not help all alcoholics bears repetition and referrals should be made carefully and with understanding of its limitations. There should also be an awareness that what attracts some repels others.

Alcoholics Anonymous is a highly *social* fellowship and is most effective with those who can readily interact with others even if that interaction is superficial at the outset. Trice reported that those who successfully affiliated were persons who could easily share basic emotional reactions with others and who easily adapted themselves to the casual give and take that develops before and after meetings.

An essential element of most AA meetings, for example, is the coffee hour, where conviviality is at a peak. This is fine for Mr. and Mrs.

[5] "A.A. Joiners and Nonjoiners," *Connecticut Review on Alcoholism*, Vol. 2, No. 4 (December, 1959), p. 2 (quoted).
[6] Milton Maxwell, "An Exploratory Study: Alcoholics Anonymous and Professional Relations," in Pittman and Snyder, *op. cit.*

Gregarious but many withdrawn persons are intimidated. True, older members will, with the best of motives, reach out and try to involve the loner but may only cause further withdrawal. Such a person may be far more accessible to the one-to-one contact in a clinic or agency, although he may one day reach a point where he can comfortably affiliate with AA.

There is also a need—at least some neophytes feel there is a need—to stand up and be counted. Claire, an alcoholic character in Edward Albee's play, *A Delicate Balance,* rather mockingly recounts her experience when she stood up and said, " 'My name is Claire and I am an . . . alcoholic.' Now, I was supposed to go on, *you* know, say how bad I was, and didn't want to be, and How It Happened, and What I Wanted to Happen, and Would They Help Me Help Myself . . . but I just stood there for a . . . ten seconds maybe, and then I curtsied; I made my little girl curtsy, and on my little girl feet I padded back to my chair."

Most AA meetings feature a lead speaker who tells of his experience with and recovery from alcoholism. (Vignette #3) Not all are as balanced as the vignette. Some speakers emphasize their wild adventures and newcomers cannot identify with them. Their reaction may be: "If that's what you have to be to qualify as an alcoholic, then I'm not one." The wife of a prosperous merchant drank a fifth a night but always at home. She had visited bars perhaps only a dozen times in her life. The gaudy autobiographies of the first two AA speakers she heard quickly turned her off. She could not identify and did not return, although she later realized these were the exception.

AA is a *spiritual* fellowship which, beyond cavil, is one of its greatest strengths but it is not for everybody. Staunch members say it should be but that doesn't make it so. Again, Claire, in Albee's drama, when asked if they laughed at her, replied: "Well, an agnostic in the holy of holies doesn't get much camaraderie, a little patronizing, maybe. Oh, they were taken by the *vaudeville,* don't misunderstand me. But the one lady was nice. She came up to me later and said, 'You've taken the first step, dear.' " That is more cynical than most reactions but it does happen.

AA emphatically rejects any description of itself as a *religious* group and the welcome mat is out for all, including atheists and agnostics. But even the word spiritual has doctrinal implications and many persons balk at turning their lives over to a "power greater than ourselves" and to "God, as we understand Him." To say that the "greater power" can be anything, including the group itself, and that "God, as we understand Him" permits the widest latitude, may not persuade the client who is so hostile to organized religion that he will not swallow any of that

"God stuff" no matter how attractively it is packaged.

Inadequate motivation can be a deterrant to AA affiliation. In general, AA does not help the alcoholic who lacks strong motivation within himself because it does not reach out. The alcoholic must admit his own illness, and, while practice varies from one community to another, he must usually make the initial call for help himself. A call from a spouse, relative, physician, or social worker is interpreted as casting doubt on the quality of his motivation and will not be answered.

Insistence on total and life-long abstinence is a barrier for some but is an institutionalized policy of AA. It may be a desirable goal for most alcoholics but the credo that this is necessary for all has been challenged.

According to AA, lifetime abstinence can only be achieved by resolving to remain sober 24 hours at time. A popular slogan is: "Easy does it–one day at a time." The thinking is that it is the longest period most alcoholics can foresee without becoming fearful. If he renews the pledge every 24 hours, he has it made. Again, it works for some and not for others.

The totality of involvement overwhelms some people. New members may be told they can take from the program what they can use, but it doesn't always work that way. In many groups there are pressures and a person comes to identify himself solely as an alcoholic rather than as a human being who has a problem with drinking. He perceives himself and other alcoholics as being unique and a few are convinced they wear halos because they have recovered from alcoholism. AA is most beneficial to those who can gradually decrease their dependency and enter into other personal relationships and activities.

One barrier to affiliation that is frequently overlooked is *social class*. Alcoholics Anonymous is, as Bailey and Leach have convincingly documented, a middle- to upper-class movement. Like most other helping resources, it reflects the standards of society and has failed to reach the lower socio-economic groups.[7]

The social worker who is thinking of Alcoholics Anonymous for a client has to consider the various factors in relation to that individual. Which AA group is best? How does the client see AA and what misconceptions does he have? As with any skillful referral, the particular advantages of a resource must be matched to the particular and present needs of the client. Professional referral to AA frequently leaves something to be desired; far too many professionals confuse recommendation with referral. Also, it should be emphasized that there are times that

---

[7] Margaret B. Bailey and Barry Leach, *Alcoholics Anonymous Pathway to Recovery* (New York: The National Council on Alcoholism, Inc., 1965), p. 11.

a professional can help a person to return to Alcoholics Anonymous. (Vignette #4)

Al-Anon, a counterpart of Alcoholics Anonymous organized to help relatives and friends of alcoholics, is similar in structure and philosophy. Most members are wives of alcoholics although some groups include a few men married to alcoholic women. There is also a scattering of parents and other relatives. The Al-Anon statement of purpose says the members "are banded together to solve their common problems of fear, insecurity, lack of understanding of the alcoholic, and other warped family relationships associated with alcoholism."[8] It is necessary for the alcoholic spouse or relative to be a member of AA; Al-Anon is open to all who have friends or relatives or spouses with drinking problems.

A woman who can use Al-Anon learns from contacts with others in a similar situation that her husband is a sick person (there is considerable emphasis on the disease concept), that he is the one who must decide to stop drinking although she might be able to help, but not through nagging, cajoling, or pleading. She learns that while some acts on her part may trigger drinking episodes, she does not have to bear the burden of guilt for making him an alcoholic. She also learns that it is possible for her to change and create a better life for herself and her children, even if her husband continues to drink.

In principle, Al-Anon does not "give specific advice to members on family finances, separation, divorce, sex, legal matters, medical, psychiatric, or clerical aid. Instead, its members *suggest* only what has been helpful in their own situation, and *refer* the relatives of the alcoholic to professional sources for help. . . ."[9] Anyone who attends Al-Anon meetings discovers how uncertain the distinction is between suggestion and advice.

Al-Anon also declares its belief that affiliation with AA is not the *only* way to sobriety for the alcoholic but most Al-Anon members and groups believe it is the *best* way. It has been the experience of this writer that Al-Anon groups have been increasingly cordial to professional visitors and discussions following presentations are invariably spirited.

Flawed communication has not been the exclusive responsibility of either group. Margaret Bailey has pointed out that in the past many social workers have been unfamiliar with Al-Anon as a resource for wives of alcoholics and others "have expressed doubts about the wisdom of referring clients to a completely non-professional self-help group." She adds: "Professional help and Al-Anon affiliation need not be mutually

[8] *Living With an Alcoholic* (New York: Al-Anon Family Group Headquarters, 1960).
[9] M. Trudy, "Al-Anon As a Family Treatment Tool In Alcoholism," North American Association of Alcoholism, Programs Report #14.

exclusive or rivalrous, since the two methods contributed in different, but complimentary ways to a common goal–recovery of the family from the destructive effects of alcoholism."[10]

In a study done for the National Council on Alcoholism, Dr. Bailey reported that when husbands were members of AA, their sobriety was strongly related to their membership "but the likelihood of sobriety was increased when the wives participated in Al-Anon."

As with Alcoholics Anonymous, Al-Anon is not for everyone and referrals have to be made carefully, in accordance with the needs of the individual. Al-Anon, too, is a highly social fellowship; it is spiritual, and it can become a way of life to the exclusion of other contacts. Its twelve steps are the same as those of Alcoholics Anonymous although the application has to be tailored to the non-alcoholic. In the first step, the Al-Anon member admits that she is powerless over alcohol, meaning that she is powerless over its use by and the effect on the alcoholic. Employed constructively, the steps are highly effective but misinterpretation or misuse has dangers. The fourth step, for example, demands a searching self-inventory and some women carry this to such masochistic extremes that they become powerless over everything. They seem to enjoy believing they are the sicker ones in the marriages. As Al-Anon has matured, this kind of misuse has been discouraged but not eliminated.

The second fellowship derivative from Alcoholics Anonymous is Alateen which, as the name implies, has a membership of the teenage children of alcoholics. The basic idea is expressed in the credo: "If my mother or father never stops drinking I still must be the one to decide what to do about myself. If not, then I am using the crutch of alcohol as an excuse to live badly and cheat myself of all the good things that could be in my life. I will no longer apologize, hide, and make excuses for myself. I love my parent, and do understand he or she is sick and needs help. I will try to understand and help where it is the right kind of help. I will learn to accept that I cannot change another, only myself."[11]

Alateen has not enjoyed the popularity of the parent groups and even in large cities there are few groups. Nevertheless, some teenagers can use it and the availability of groups is obtainable from local AA or Al-Anon offices or their central offices as listed in the appendix.

HOSPITALS

As indicated in Chapter One, general hospitals have been notoriously reluctant to admit alcoholics. The pleas of those concerned with alco-

[10] Margaret B. Bailey, "Al-Anon Family Groups As an Aid to Wives of Alcoholics," *Social Work*, Vol. 10, No. 1 (January, 1965).

[11] Bettye Marsh, "Problem Drinkers," *Focus on Alcoholism*, Newsletter published by Washington State Department of Health, Olympia, Washington, Vol. 10, No. 3 (May-June, 1969), p. 5.

holism were supported in 1956 by the American Hospital Association and the American Medical Association House of Delegates with an additional statement by the American Psychiatric Association in 1965, but intake policies and attitudes have been slow to change.

Hospital personnel, too, often regard alcoholics as nuisances at best and thoroughly obnoxious and disruptive at worst. As most alcoholics who are admitted for their alcoholism come through the emergency service, they tend to be dirty, disheveled, loud, and demanding, and professionals react with hostility. Nobody wants them. Social workers denounce medical personnel for their indifference to alcoholics who obviously need medical attention, while the medical personnel complain that the so-called experts in social rehabilitation seem unable to do whatever is necessary to prevent alcoholics from reappearing in the emergency room time and again.

It is important for the social worker to recognize which alcoholics need hospitalization. There are some, for example, who do not seem to be able to stop drinking unless they are removed, at least temporarily, from their social environment. Unfortunately, if this is the only reason for referral, it may require divine intervention to get the client admitted and that is seldom available.

Alcoholics with severe medical complications resulting from prolonged and intensive drinking need hospitalization. Some of these may be emergencies involving coma, head injury, malnutrition, pneumonia, or delirium tremens. The latter, one of the most dramatic consequences of alcoholism, is an extreme state of agitation which may include hallucinations, convulsions, and general disorientation. Delirium tremens is regarded by many as a condition that can be fatal. It is the one thing that opens the doors of most hospitals to alcoholics.

Even when alcoholics are admitted to hospitals, the results are discouraging. Competent medical care is provided but the patient is discharged without follow-up or referral to an appropriate community agency. This means that the alcoholic has been sobered up and physically repaired, but without help in learning how to live without alcohol, he is almost certain to return to drinking and the hospital. Except for the fact that it offers more comfortable surroundings and more medical care, the hospital can be just as much a part of the revolving-door process as the courts.

There have been a few innovative programs to demonstrate what can be done. One such evolved over a period of years at Mendocino State Hospital in California. It was discovered that alcoholics will search out and become meaningfully involved in their own treatment if the program is designed to meet their specialized needs. The multiple symptoms of alcoholism argue strongly for a multi-dimensional approach employing a variety of therapeutic techniques. The Mendocino program has encouraged many treatment modalities; however, basic to the total program has been the involvement of the recipient, the alcoholic himself, in choosing the type of services he receives. This should appeal to those who advocate the health and welfare principle of mobilizing the strengths of the individual to help himself.

> Many alcoholics, because of the nature of some of the emotional problems accompanying or underlying their illness, or because of their stressful environmental situation, need more than just the hour or two of individual or group therapy per week usually available to them on an outpatient basis. At the same time, it is important because they are still reasonably well integrated–both in terms of their personalities and in terms of family and community–that they do not undergo a period of prolonged hospitalization away from family and community. There is every reason to believe–although it yet remains to be widely demonstrated–that a day hospital type of facility would meet the needs of this group admirably. It would provide them with the wide variety of therapeutic modalities available in specialized hospitals–pharmacotherapy, individual and group therapy, occupational therapy–and yet permit continued intimate relationships with family and community. Providing a hospital setting for several hours a day, that is so often badly needed to interrupt the "snowballing" process so many alcoholics follow–(stress causing drinking–causing more severe reaction from family–more stress–more drinking–more reaction). At the same time the patient remains involved enough with his problems of adjustment in his environment that he is constantly motivated to seek help during his hospital hours to find ways of coping, other than by drinking. Many times patients undergoing prolonged periods of hospitalization do very well, only to fail miserably on their return to a stressful situation with which they are ill-prepared to cope and for which they receive no help when they are most in need.
>
> One group is that which, because of their alcoholism, has shown a rather marked deterioration of their personal and social lives, to say nothing of their physical deterioration. This group needs a period of several weeks of hospitalization for the purpose, pure and simple, of being restored to a fairly de-

cent physical condition. Many are malnourished, dehydrated, confused, and often suffering from transient or permanent brain damage precluding their ability to cooperate in any prolonged treatment program in the community; to say nothing of being totally lacking in the type of emotional support from families or others necessary to carry out such a program. In addition to time needed for physical restoration, time is also needed for a rehabilitation program designed to restore previous work habits, social and recreational habits, and healthier patterns of living in general—with a return to some element of self-respect and hope.[12]

A few hospitals, usually under pressure from Alcoholics Anonymous, have established special wards for alcoholics. Segregation is a dubious and unnecessary practice in most cases and the participation of Alcoholics Anonymous too frequently means domination. AA sponsorship is required for admission and hospitalization is limited to one visit. This restriction is supposed to test the patient's sincerity and willingness to seek permanent sobriety.

A spiritual atmosphere frequently permeates these premises and the soul may receive more attention than the body. A writer describes a place called Good Shepherd Hall as "a haven of serenity for the tortured mind and body of the often panic-stricken alcoholic on the verge of the dreaded delirium tremens. There is a large lounge with comfortable chairs, pictures of The Last Supper and a tranquil country scene. Perhaps, for the first time in years, the alcoholic is allowed to relax long enough to ease his anxiety and to contemplate the future."[13]

The potential for social workers in hospitals in working with alcoholics is almost limitless, especially in follow-up care, but it remains largely potential. First, the emphasis is to get rid of the alcoholic as soon as possible so the social worker never sees him. Second, there is a strong feeling among medical personnel that the treatment of alcoholism is not within social work competence. This was expressed by the writer who assigned to social workers the role of easing the alcoholic through his hangover and preparing him for psychiatric referral.

General hospitals fall far short of meeting their responsibilities to alcoholics but the need should be kept in perspective. There is a widespread impression that hospitalization should be available to all or at least the majority of alcoholics. That is not true. The complaint is not,

[12] Joseph Adelstein, M.D., *A Conference Report—Planning for Coordinated Alcoholism Services on a State and Local Level,* United States Public Health Service, NIMH, Washington, D.C., 1963, pp. 31-32.

[13] Theodore Van Dorn, *Drunk's Diary* (New York: Philosophical Library, Inc., 1966), p. 47.

or should not be, that hospitals refuse to take all alcoholics, but that they does require their services.

Alcoholism is an out-patient problem for the majority of clients. This is confirmed by many authorities, including physicians. Dr. Fred E. do not even accept the small percentage of the alcoholic population that Lawrence wrote: "In the last analysis the alcoholic must be able to function as a member of organized society and to remain abstinent from alcohol within the environment of that society if his alcoholism is to be arrested. The decision to hospitalize the alcoholic patient should not be made without carefully considering his social, economic and psychiatric needs as well as the medical symptoms. Frequently the alcoholic patient is maintaining a very tenuous adjustment that may be broken by a relatively brief period of hospitalization and be extremely difficult to restore. . . . "[14] There are unquestionably some patients who use a hospital as a further retreat from reality—a cushion between themselves and reality rather than a bridge to help them reach a more normal life.

The de-emphasis on hospitalization may continue as alcoholism is increasingly seen as a behavioral disorder rather than a physical disease. Dr. Griffith Edwards has said that treatment in the future may "develop on the basis of very much more close and adequate analysis of the patient's lack of social skills, and will treat him in the setting of these difficulties rather than conceiving of alcoholism too much in terms of the medical model of an 'illness' which can be treated in a hospital."[15]

DETOXIFICATION CENTERS

In recent years, there has been rising interest in the establishment of special detoxification centers. They have usually been thought of in relation to the public intoxication offender as an alternative to jail.

When the District of Columbia planned a detoxification center, it was decided that it "should deal with simple intoxication only. Seriously ill patients, even though intoxicated, should be treated in a fully equipped hospital or other appropriate medical or psychiatric facility." The center "should function as an improvement over the police drunk tank for simple intoxication cases but not as a hospital substitute for inebriates who are seriously ill."[16]

The planners also recognized that any detoxification center had to be an integrated component of a comprehensive alcoholism treatment sys-

[14] Fred E. Lawrence, M.D., "The Out-Patient Management of the Alcoholic," *Quarterly Journal on the Study of Alcohol* Supplement No. 1 (November, 1961), p. 120.
[15] Griffith Edwards, M.D., "The Role of Therapy," Proceedings of the 28th International Congress on Alcohol and Alcoholism (Highland Park, New Jersey: Hillhouse Press), p. 221.
[16] Richard J. Tatham, "Detoxification Center: A Public Health Alternative for the 'Drunk Tank,' " *Federal Probation,* Vol. 33, No. 4 (December, 1969), p. 47.

tem rather than an isolated facility. This was in line with the recognition by the President's Task Force on Drunkenness that the chronic offender is not likely to change a life pattern of drinking after a few days of sobriety in a detoxification center. After-care is urgently needed and might as well begin with mobilization of existing community resources, including Alcoholics Anonymous, hospitals, clinics, social agencies, vocational rehabilitation, and many others.[17]

There is little opposition to the idea that some alcoholics, typified by the chronic drunkenness offenders, need detoxification before they can be reached for additional help. The construction of new buildings at enormous cost, however, is questioned by some planners. After all, the hospitals are already here. A study prepared by the Philadelphia Diagnostic and Relocation Service Corporation emphasized that very point and argued that the responsibility for a detoxification program should be shared by the hospitals of the city. Some hospitals are not operating at or near capacity and "it is important that the total medical community share the responsibility of the alcoholism program and not allow a 'dumping ground' to be created."[18]

JAILS

The crusade on behalf of the establishment of detoxification centers was organized partly because most people recognized the futility of incarceration in jails as they now exist. The fact remains that a few detoxification centers will not make jails obsolete because the former can care for only a small number of alcoholics. Despite a dozen or a hundred court decisions, there will be thousands of alcoholics in jails and workhouses for years to come.

It is far from an ideal situation but as it will be changed slowly, it may be necessary for community planners to give some consideration to constructive programs in this existing facility. The difficulties cannot be overstated but a few programs have indicated that some steps in this direction are not impossible.

Parenthetically, it is interesting to note some research that indicates that jails are not necessarily medieval torture chambers for all alcoholic inmates. Rubington, quoting a study by Samuel Sidlofsky in Toronto wrote:

> Firstly, jail is not quite as punitive as it was intended. In addition, it neither deters nor resocializes. Secondly, most of its

[17] Task Force Report, *Drunkenness, The President's Commission on Law Enforcement and Administration of Justice* (Washington, D.C.: U.S. Government Printing Office, 1967).

[18] Irving Shandler, *et al.*, *Alternatives to Arrest* (Philadelphia: Philadelphia Diagnostic and Relocation Service Corporation, 1967), p. 47.

> harshest aspects are mitigated, at least for the men Sidlofsky studied. Loss of freedom was only minimal, physical hardships were rare (some men actually gained weight), little sex deprivation was felt by a group of relatively inactive men sexually, and given their meager effective relationships "on the outside," there was little here for the jail to disrupt.
>
> Conversely, the jail offered these three sets of rewards: a stable environment, a substitute social system, and a quasi-familial setting. On the street men had to make decisions about uncertain moments, not to say about their future. On the street, their positions with regards to others was amorphous if not highly disesteemed. On the street, there were few who would care or show an interest in them. All this, the jail reverses.[19]

A major problem is to determine which alcoholics can be helped in jails and training personnel to do the work.

HALFWAY HOUSES

The American Association of Halfway Houses has described the halfway house as a transitional facility in a community providing group residency for alcoholics. It provides guidance, supervision, and personal services in those areas of adjustment that will enable the alcoholic to move into independent living in normal surroundings.[20]

Thomas Richards, director of one of the most successful halfway houses in the country, says "The halfway house must succeed in providing a warm and satisfying group experience, and, at the same time, include an element of challenge. The alcoholic must be exposed to this challenge, not protected from it. He may turn from it, run out and get drunk, because he does not fit or is unwilling to try, but he must be exposed to it. Sooner or later, there will be a knock-down, drag-out fight between what he is and what he'd like to be. This may never be faced in the service center, in the protection of the larger, self-contained institution, but it should be faced in the halfway house."[21]

In the same paper he points out that "The halfway house is an experience in group living and an exposure to group therapy. The members of the group will be influenced by each other as well as by the therapist. Since it is a small group, however, it can more readily be directed or manipulated by one person; therefore the therapist should avoid extremes

[19] Earl Rubington, "The Alcoholic and the Jail," *Federal Probation,* Vol. 29, No. 2 (June, 1965), p. 31.
[20] Personal communication from Leonard Bochee, President of the American Association of Halfway Houses, 1971.
[21] Thomas Richards, "The AA Halfway House and Service Center," a paper included in *Alcoholism: The Total Treatment Approach,* Ronald J. Catanzarro, M.D., ed. (Springfield, Illinois: Charles C. Thomas, 1968).

in overdirection or permissiveness. Out of this group experience can come solid, enduring friendships—the building of relationships which will strengthen the individual's will to live. It is most important that this develop between the men themselves, rather than contribute toward a dependent relationship between therapist and client. Continual reiteration of former drinking escapades soon palls. The counselor can make his greatest contribution by raising the level of discussion to include all those things that one can do and be, once freed from the tyranny of the bottle."

According to Cahn, there are about 120 halfway houses in the country, not counting various kinds of shelters indigenous to Skid Row.[22] Those for men outnumber those for women three to one, and in bed count seven to one.

In terms of purpose, Rubington has observed that the names of many houses "signify a state of mind that may be obtained through membership, e.g., Sobriety House, Serenity House, Hope House. Others symbolize that residents are in transit somewhere and that membership may ease the transition, e.g., Compass Club, Beacon House, Harbor Light Center. Still others take the name of religious figures who befriended the sick and the needy or who gave special help to alcoholics; St. Jude's House is an example of the first, Matt Talbot Inn is an example of the second. Others are named for state alcoholism programs; still others have names which conceal more than they reveal, as Studio Club. Some just call themselves Halfway House."[23]

Whatever they call themselves, most halfway houses rely on the therapeutic methods described by Cahn:

1. The therapeutic milieu—a strong anti-drinking culture—is maintained by the expulsion of those who break the abstinence principle and is reinforced by the manager's process, primary group peer relationships, status distributed in terms of ability to abstain, and the acceptance of all residents as first-class citizens who have an opportunity to recapture lost self-esteem and personal dignity. The halfway house is socially well structured and has well-defined lines of authority and unequivocally stated rules so that all may understand what is expected of them and how they are supposed to behave. Those who cannot fit in leave quickly.
2. The intensive use of Alcoholics Anonymous. Residents are

[22] Sidney Cahn, "Alcoholism Halfway Houses: Relationship to Other Programs and Facilities," *Social Work,* Vol. 4, No. 2 (April, 1969).
[23] Earl Rubington, "The Future of the Halfway House," *Quarterly Journal on Studies of Alcohol,* Vol. 31, No. 1 (March, 1970), p. 170.

expected to attend anywhere from one to five AA meetings a week, and it is usual for at least one AA meeting to be held on the premises. All the other facilities for the care of problem drinkers, such as specialized wards, outpatient clinics, and other psychiatric facilities, also utilize AA but not to the same extent.

3. The residents compare notes and discuss their problems with one another. These discussions provide important opportunities for them to express their feelings. Yet this type of verbalization, while therapeutic in some cases, should not be considered a cure-all and, in a few cases, might be contraindicated.[24]

Social workers employed in jails, hospitals, clinics, and similar facilities might well see the halfway house as having considerable potential for some clients. There is little doubt that it does offer a valuable link in the rehabilitation chain. Again, a skillful referral matches the needs of the client with the services of the facility.

BOARDING HOMES

The range of services required for alcoholics in various stages has not been established. All that is certain is that more is needed than exists. For example, halfway houses have traditionally been associated with homeless or Skid Row alcoholics, and, to the extent that staffing and financing was adequate, they have served their purpose. But they do not provide enough for all Skid Row alcoholics. What is needed for some, wrote Shandler, is special boarding homes which provide a quasi-family situation. These men, long rejected by their families, need to be with someone who cares about them and to have the luxury of caring about other human beings. They are not halfway houses but "all the way" homes for men who do not need institutionalization but cannot make it on their own.

OTHER RESOURCES

The all-pervasive character of alcoholism makes almost every helping facility in the community a potential resource. Those who regard alcoholism as partly a spiritual illness, for example, would enlist the church as an essential ally. Bill Wilson once said: "Before AA we were trying to find God in a bottle." Clinebell sees abundant evidence that "there is a search for a spiritual experience involved in what the alcoholic is looking for in alcohol. For him, it is a kind of chemical religion." He

[24] Cahn, *op. cit.*

adds: "Full recovery from alcoholism involves the recovery or discovery of a religious view of life—of a conviction that life has meaning and value. This life of faith, of trust, growth and meaning, can be achieved in various ways, but certainly organized religion has a major concern for helping alcoholics to find it."[25]

Many, including large numbers of alcoholics, might question the need of spiritual help for all. Nevertheless, some do need it and few social workers can provide that kind of counseling.

Other resources include vocational rehabilitation agencies, courts, and legal aid groups. They do not require extended discussion. It is important to re-emphasize a recurrent theme in this section—the need for coordination and the working together of helping facilities as required. This is extremely rare in the field of alcoholism and offers a challenge and opportunity to those in community organization.

THE TWELVE STEPS

1. "We admitted we were powerless over alcohol—that our lives had become unmanageable."
2. "Came to believe that a Power greater than ourselves could restore us to sanity."
3. "Made a decision to turn our will and our lives over to the care of God as we understood Him."
4. "Made a searching and fearless moral inventory of ourselves."
5. "Admitted to God, to ourselves, and to another human being, the exact nature of our wrongs."
6. "Were entirely ready to have God remove all these defects of character."
7. "Humbly asked Him to remove our shortcomings."
8. "Made a list of all persons we had harmed, and became willing to make amends to them all."
9. "Made direct amends to such people whenever possible, except when to do so would injure them or others."
10. "Continued to take personal inventory and when we were wrong promptly admitted it."
11. "Sought through prayer and meditation to improve our conscious contact with God as we understood Him, praying only for knowledge of His will for us and the power to carry that out."
12. "Having had a spiritual awakening as the result of these steps, we tried to carry this message to alcoholics, and to practice these principles in all our affairs."

THE TWELVE TRADITIONS

1. "Our common welfare should come first; personal recovery depends upon A.A. unity."

[25] Howard J. Clinebell, "Philosophical-Religious Factors in the Etiology and Treatment of Alcoholism," *Quarterly Journal of Studies on Alcohol,* Vol. 24, No. 3 (September, 1963), p. 476.

2. "For our group purpose there is but one ultimate authority—a loving God as He may express Himself in our group conscience. Our leaders are but trusted servants; they do not govern."
3. "The only requirement for A.A. membership is a desire to stop drinking."
4. "Each group should be autonomous except in matters affecting other groups or A.A. as a whole."
5. "Each group has but one primary purpose—to carry its message to the alcoholic who still suffers."
6. "An A.A. group ought never endorse, finance, or lend the A.A. name to any related facility or outside enterprise, lest problems of money, property and prestige divert us from our primary purpose."
7. "Every A.A. group ought to be fully self-supporting, declining outside contributions."
8. "Alcoholics Anonymous should remain forever non-professional, but our service centers may employ special workers."
9. "A.A., as such, ought never be organized; but we may create service boards or committees directly responsible to those they serve."
10. "Alcoholics Anonymous has no opinion on outside issues; hence the A.A. name ought never be drawn into public controversy."
11. "Our public relations policy is based on attraction rather than promotion; we need always maintain personal anonymity at the level of press, radio, and films."
12. "Anonymity is the spiritual foundation of our traditions, ever reminding us to place principles before personalities."

VIGNETTE #1

J. V., a woman in her fifties, was a welfare client who had been referred to the Welfare Department by the Municipal Court where she had been arraigned several times on drunk and disorderly charges over a span of two years. At the time of referral she had been evicted from her flea bag hotel room for nonpayment of rent and she urgently needed housing and financial assistance.

The Welfare Department heard nothing from her for a month after the initial contact but they later discovered she had gone to a hospital and pleaded for admission because she was sick and had no food or lodging. The hospital referred her to the jail as a "temporary lodger." Later she went to another hospital for sore feet. The doctors found liver cirrhosis and a cardiac condition. They just found them; they didn't do anything about them. So after a binge she returned to the Welfare Department.

J. V. was raised in luxury. Her father became wealthy in the construction business although he lost heavily in the Depression. He died when she was 13 and she never knew him well. She rather liked her mother who was a "real snob" and associated only with the "best people." As a child J.V. was pampered by her mother and a maternal aunt, and she could get anything she wanted from them. She was an only child but grew up with a male cousin who became a prominent industrialist. He used his inheritance as a springboard to riches; she dissipated hers. After she became an alcoholic her cousin wrote occasional checks for ten or twenty dollars but later abandoned her completely. She told a therapist she always thought she was far brighter than her cousin, and, when she was a relief client, commented: "Just think what a combination it would be with Allen's money and my brains."

J. V. attended an exclusive school for girls and had two years of college before she left to marry a business man with whom she lived only intermittently for three years before divorcing him. Her second marriage was to an actor who never achieved stardom, but he was highly regarded and his name was well known to theatregoers of the 1930's and 1940's. This also ended in divorce. A few years prior to going on welfare, J. V. lived with a man, but as her drinking increased, he deserted.

J. V. had been a writer most of her working life, first a newspaper reporter, then a script writer for radio, and later she and her husband went to Hollywood where he acted in movies and they collaborated on scripts.

J. V. had her first drink at 26 and for several years drank moderately, but after the death of her mother began to drink excessively. The increased drinking made it difficult to keep jobs or find new ones and her marital problems became severe. Her last employment in writing was ten years prior to this referral when she wrote a women's column for a newspaper. She returned to Cleveland and took a job at a nursing home for alcoholics. The drinking continued and there were personality clashes between J. V. and the employer's wife. She was dismissed and the downward spiral continued.

J. V. was unemployed for seven years and got some help from her family but they finally rejected her and she ended on welfare. She was assigned to a retraining program and employed as a typist at the county workhouse part-time. At first, she seemed to find satisfaction in knowing that her work was good, but she always felt it was beneath her. Writing was her profession and being a clerical worker corroded her pride.

She drank heavily, appeared at work with hangovers, and made it clear that she regarded her co-workers as hopeless dolts. At one point a supervisor suggested that J. V. take a Civil Service examination so she could be considered for full-time employment. She agreed but failed to follow through. A woman of less intelligence and ability did take the exam and got the job. J. V. was furious. She blamed her supervisor, was hostile to all employees, and would not accept the fact that the other person had earned the job in competitive examination. The other woman was "a stupid idiot and had no right to get the job above me."

She drank more and went on more frequent binges. She was arrested and it was uncertain in any month whether she would be a civilian worker or an inmate. Inevitably, she was fired.

Sporadically, J. V. attended AA meetings and had many sponsors, all of whom she viewed as "dimwitted." She said she had "more sponsors than Jack Benny."

Finally, she was referred to the Center on Alcoholism. She was gross, obese, and, when intoxicated, almost grotesque. Nevertheless, it was possible to imagine that in her youth she had been as attractive as she said she was, and she had a picture in her wallet to prove it. But now she was slovenly and unwashed. In every hospital nurses had to forcibly put her in a tub or under a shower.

The welfare worker brought her to the first three sessions in a taxi. She was depressed and saw no point in trying. The therapist suggested to a dubious welfare lady that J. V. should be trusted to keep future appointments alone. It was tried and it did work for a while. She continued to drink, often heavily, and one Monday morning a cleaning lady found 30 empty wine bottles in J.V.'s room at the Y.W.C.A. Delicate negotiations were required to prevent her eviction.

As the interviews continued, J. V. bitterly complained that she had been unjustly maligned, and, like Lear, she was more sinned against than sinner. She found out that the therapist was moonlighting with some success as a freelance writer and immediately knew he would understand her. She brought in faded samples of her own work, all done long ago and some of it faraway. Also, there were letters from familiar names in literature and the theatre. She lived in the past. She seemed to be one of those persons, described by Herman Hesse in *Demian,* "surrounded by the loneliness and mortal cold of the universe. Very many are caught forever in this impasse and for the rest of their lives cling painfully to an irrevocable past, the dream of the lost paradise–which is the worst and most ruthless of dreams."

The focus of therapy was on bringing her to an awareness and an ability to cope with present reality. This unsettled the welfare worker who thought the therapist should be exploring the murky terrain of J. V.'s psyche for infantile clues to a "character disorder."

J. V. tried to manipulate the therapist when she didn't get what she wanted on demand. She had achieved this with others, including the welfare worker, when she did nothing but sit and wait. Now she wanted to write again and it was suggested that only she could do it. Interviews were arranged with the editor of a trade paper and the editor of a newspaper in a nearby city. She did not keep either appointment. She avoided both by getting drunk.

The next visit with the therapist was a stormy one. J. V. denounced everyone, including the therapist, for her failure. He replied he was "goddamned sick and tired of watching her waste away by drinking and listening to her whining excuses." She had promised many times to produce some writing, no matter how elementary, as a start. She refused to discuss it; "she would talk only of the past or how badly she is now treated." Besides, how can anyone work in an environment devoid of intellectual stimulation?

A few weeks later she threatened suicide. A psychiatrist saw this as part of her insatiable desire for attention and recognition which no person or group could possibly satisfy. "She is certainly capable of suicide at any time," he noted, "but uses this as a threat to get action from those who are interested."

In one interview it was pointed out that she had to project her feeling of unworthiness on those around and that she used this projection as a defense against depression. She agreed but left the office, got drunk, and was arrested.

Finally, it seemed best to hospitalize her again. After that she was lost. At best she was on the community carousel of hospitals, courts, and jails. It was an old story that ended with her battered and beaten body found in a sleazy hotel room.

VIGNETTE #2

Sam had successfully affiliated with AA at the age of 44 after years of excessive drinking. He was a success from his very first contact with the group and had only one "slip" in three years, an event that in no way endangered his sobriety or general pattern of abstinence.

Sam's membership in a group of boys of his own age started when he was five or six. This alliance with neighborhood friends became for him the most important source of security and of satisfaction of his emotional needs. He began in childhood to handle his problems "by the device of extensive affiliation with companions" and continued to do so through adolescence and in maturity. Sam's drinking was never solitary, even in the worst phases of his alcoholism. Typically, he drank with friends in bars and taverns. If he had liquor in the house, he did not touch it without company. Even on the mornings when he had the "shakes" he went to a bar for that first drink for a "cure." When Sam, feeling his health threatened after several hospitalizations, finally decided to seek help for his alcoholism, this was no more a solitary act than his other pursuits had been. He and a friend together went to AA and together stopped drinking at once.

Sam immediately found AA congenial, accepted its program, enjoyed its casual social contacts, and gave it an important place in his life activities. His previous experience of the give-and-take of group life and the central position that affiliation with equals held in his personality organization "fitted him perfectly for participation now insured for him the continued rewards of pleasant personal interaction and of group support." For people such as Sam, Hanfmann suggested, "the transfer of allegiance to the group is an easy and natural process and the therapeutic results of this transference may be immediate."

Reprinted from "A.A. Joiners and Nonjoiners," *Connecticut Review on Alcoholism,* Vol. 2, No. 4 (December, 1959).

VIGNETTE #3

MY NAME IS EMMA

All my life I have wanted someone to lean on. When I got married, I stopped depending on my mother and father and started depending on my husband. I did not want responsibility of any kind. I was willing to do anything as long as someone else was responsible.

My husband died suddenly of a heart attack. I took my little eight-year-old girl and went back to my mother. My husband was gone, but I still had mother. I stayed with mother and daddy for three months, then I wanted to go back to my own home, but I wanted mother to stay with me. She did part of the time, and when she wasn't at my house, I was at hers with her.

One day I got a phone call at work that my mother had been badly burned. I had to go home first and get someone to drive my car to the hospital. I thought mother had just burned her hand real bad. But when we got to the hospital mother was in the emergency room. I went up and down the hall looking for my sister. I saw a man lying down on a bed with both hands in bandages to his elbows. I never thought about daddy being burned, too.

I saw my sister. I asked her about mother. She said they still had her in the emergency room. She said daddy was right down the hall. He had third degree burns on his hands. He had tried to put the flames out that were covering my mother. The only part of her that was not burned was her feet. She lived two days.

I was completely lost.

Daddy was good to me, but he, too, wanted someone to lean on. I tried to go on and did all right for a while. Then in December, just before Christmas, I was baking a cake one night when the phone rang and it was some friends who asked me to come over and play cards with them. At first I told them I couldn't come. They said if I didn't come they would come after me. So I went.

When I got there they had another couple there and a bottle of whiskey and a bottle of gin. At first I did not drink with them. I was surprised to see the girls drinking, but I thought so much of this friend, I thought if she did it then it couldn't be too wrong, so I started drinking too. I didn't get drunk but I felt crazy.

I got home all right but the next morning I was so sick I thought I'll never do that again, but I did, again and again, until I didn't want to go on without it.

One day after about three days and nights of drinking, my family found me in bad shape. I didn't know any of them. I was swelled up so much my little girl said I looked like a monster. They took me to the doctor and I got over that one, but it didn't stop me. I would go for two or three days not eating and didn't go to work. Then I went into a coma or whatever you call it, only this time when my family came to see me, they had to call the doctor. He told them to tell me to come in and talk to him when I got over being sick.

I went to see him and he suggested AA, but I told him I was not an alcoholic. He just shook his head.

I kept right on staying away from work without calling until someone told me to call in and tell them I was sick. So I started doing that. I really was sick, but I caused myself to be sick. I didn't know what day of the week it was, or what month. When I would close my eyes, I could see things which weren't there. I was put on "leave of absence" from work to get straightened out.

Then I started coming to AA. I am ready and willing to do anything so I'll never get that awful feeling again, and I believe with the help of God and a group of people that understand me here in AA, I am on the way to recovery.

Reprinted with permission from *The AA Grapevine,* August, 1967.

VIGNETTE #4

Mr. D. walked into the office of the Cleveland Center on Alcoholism on a sultry June afternoon. Despite the oppressive temperature, he wore a frayed, dirty, sweat-soaked woolen shirt. Trickles of perspiration moistened the stubble that covered his beet-red face. His breath was fetid with the smell of cheap wine that was a staple of his daily diet. It would have been difficult to guess that he had, for many years, been a successful certified public accountant.

The man told his story in painful, halting phrases. Sometimes his weary voice was barely audible. He had lived with loneliness and despair for so long that he seemed to forget or not to care that someone was listening to him. .

He spoke of the past as if searching for clues to the present. He wanted answers to tormenting questions. Why had his wife divorced him and taken their child? Why, after eighteen years, had he lost his job as chief accountant for a large corporation? Why, after that, had he lost three more jobs in quick succession? Why was a man with his abilities living in a shabby rooming house with its suffocating atmosphere of defeat? Why were his only companions misery and sickness?

Vaguely, he conceded that the answers were related to fifteen years of excessive drinking. People had tried to help although their help was often misguided. His wife had threatened and cajoled. On Friday night she might threaten to leave him unless he stopped drinking but when that didn't work she bought liquor on Saturday and drank with him in the hope that he could practice moderation if he drank at home with her. When this also failed she was infuriated and frustrated. Then she nagged and he retaliated by drinking more. It made no sense but there seemed to be no stopping.

Mr. D. was a good accountant–the best in the office–so his employer was patient. He accepted excuses for reports that were inexcusably late. He covered for Mr. D.'s costly, embarrassing blunders even while he threatened dismissal. But the unexecuted threats accomplished nothing. Mr. D. drank more, was absent more frequently, and made bigger and costlier mistakes. The company could no longer afford to carry him.

Family, friends, colleagues all tried to tell Mr. D. what was happening, but, like most alcoholics, he accused them of meddling. Drinking, he insisted, was his own business and others should understand that he needed a few harmless shots now and then to keep him going. He was always ready with quotes from authorities who advocated a drink before dinner to stimulate a jaded appetite or one to induce sleep by providing relaxation after a tense day.

The only mistake was excess and he didn't see how anyone could accuse him of that. There was nothing wrong with having a few drinks with clients for business reasons. Besides, some of the clients drank more than he did. When he worked, he worked hard and a little liquid recreation was good for any man.

Mr. D. could not or would not understand that a few drinks might be fine for 14 out of 15 of those who consumed alcohol because they could control their drinking. Drinking did not destroy their family relationships, their work, or their health. They might even get drunk occasionally without any lasting effects other than a hangover. But he was the fifteenth man. Drinking did impair his functioning on a continuous basis and he had lost the ability to choose when and where he would drink or get drunk.

Crisis followed crisis. Mr. D. lost his job, his family, and his self-respect. He half-heartedly tried to get help from a variety of sources but nothing worked. He finally came to the Center because he had heard about it from a friend. After all, he "couldn't lose anything by stopping in" and he "didn't have anything else to do anyway!" The Center might help, he said, although his skepticism was obvious.

Three years before we saw him, Mr. D. had attended some meetings of Alcoholics Anonymous with a friend. Unfortunately, he devoted most of his time to finding flaws rather than to understanding and working with the program. He contemptuously divided the members into two categories–hypocrites and revivalists. The incessant chatter of the social hour at the end of the meeting made him uncomfortable. Besides, the chairs were hard. Neverthless, Mr. D. did stay sober for three months. Then he went on a real wing ding because he was "fed up."

Even during the course of the first interview at the Center, Mr. D. seemed to relax a little. His hostility softened slightly and an occasional note of hope punctuated his threnody of self-pity. He agreed to a second visit although his attitude was that of trying anything, no matter how ridiculous.

Mr. D. did not keep his next appointment. Almost three months passed before we saw him again. Then he was desperate. While drunk he had wrecked his car and he was fined heavily and sentenced to 60 days in jail.

During the next few weeks he was seen by several members of the Center staff. An internist arranged for minor but essential medical care. Psychiatric evaluation and psychological tests clarified some problems. Emotional recovery accompanied a renewed sense of physical well-being.

The caseworker saw him every week. She helped him to recognize the futility of looking back in anger and of drinking to destruction in an effort to erase the memory of a tortured childhood or a turbulent marriage. The past could not be changed by alcohol but a productive future depended on sobriety.

She compelled him to face reality. Those who had tried in the past had not been responsible for his failure. He had failed because of his refusal to invest enough of himself in getting well. The absurdity of his indictment of Alcoholics Anonymous was one illustration. Just because he would not use the program at that time he was envious of those who did. Just because he was afraid he couldn't make the grade, he pretended scorn for those who could and used this counterfeit scorn as an excuse to get out and return to drinking. Moreover, it was probably his own severely damaged self-image that prevented him from *letting* the group accept him.

The discussion of his former relationship with Alcoholics Anonymous was well-timed. Despite a new awareness of and interest in the potential rewards of life, and despite a newly acquired job and occasional social activities, Mr. D. was still lonely and lost. The walls of his solitary room sometimes threatened to close in and crush him.

The caseworker emphasized the need for fellowship. Now that he thought better of himself, he no longer had to fear what others might think. He was ready to accept and be accepted. Why not try Alcoholics Anonymous again but really try it this time? He needed to find all possible satisfactions to replace drinking. He needed a new way of life.

Mr. D. was dubious but he was persuaded to call the central office of Alcoholics Anonymous. No miracle followed. He was still shy and awkward, and, at first, he thought everyone was looking at him. This time, however, he recognized his discomfort for what it was. He worked at the program and did find a new way of life. He also discovered, as have all successful members, that the fellowship does not hamper individuality and that each person can work his own program within the goals of A.A.

He learned that one can sometimes rely on others for help but that he must rely primarily on himself. In Alcoholics Anonymous he found a new set of values and a new direction in life. He learned that sobriety does not solve problems but it permits one to work effectively at their solution. Above all, he learned that he was not alone and had the feeling of having joined the human race again.

Mr. D. has been sober for three years. He is impressed with this long period of sobriety but he is not complacent. He goes on from one day to another. He does not compare himself with others who may not have been as successful. He is helped to maintain his own sobriety through helping others to achieve their sobriety.

The history of Mr. D. emphasizes the need for many community resources to work together to help alcoholics. There is no single answer to their illness. For some individuals counseling is enough. For others, the fellowship of Alcoholics Anonymous is enough. Many need both. Mr. D. might not have returned to Alcoholics Anonymous without clinical aid, but he might not have maintained sobriety unless he had returned to A.A. because he needed the way of life he found with them.

There are many alcoholics like Mr. D. The community will receive high returns on its investment if it provides those resources that are needed and the climate in which alcoholics can use them without fear of stigma.

Reprinted from Herman Krimmel and Helen R. Spears, "Profiles in Progress, The Open Door at the Cleveland Center on Alcoholism," Cleveland Center on Alcoholism, 1965.

CHAPTER IX

Notes on Prevention

EVERYONE IS FOR the prevention of alcoholism just as they are for the prevention of drug addiction, delinquency, venereal disease, and scores of other ills that blight our society. Professionals are for it but seem almost powerless to do much about it. The power structure represented on agency boards of trustees, frequently more enamoured of lofty words than of social action, find few words loftier than "prevention." It is one of the most used or misused words in their lexicon.

Prevention is, as Dr. Wittman has said, a seductive word. "It creates in the mind of the professional person an ideal of some unknown but effective resource or method which, if properly identified and used, will dissolve existing social dysfunction into tangible social usefulness." [1] In the field of alcoholism, as in many others, those resources and methods have defied identification or, if they have been identified, they have not

[1] Milton Wittman, "Preventive Social Work: A Goal for Practice and Education," *Social Work* (January, 1961).

been used. The only measure of primary prevention is a significant decrease in the incidence of alcoholism and that apparently has not happened.

There are many who see primary prevention, creating conditions that will eliminate the source of the illness or behavior disorder, as being accomplished through education. Educating who, for what purpose, and how? Frequently, the words *education* and *prevention* are used almost synonymously with the implication that if we educate children properly about drinking, they will not become alcoholics. There is no evidence to justify that conclusion. Alcohol education has an important place in a drinking society but to suggest that it will prevent alcoholism is egregious nonsense.

That is not a popular position because alcohol education has been widely sold by its medicine men who are quick to suggest that skeptics should be cast into outer darkness where their voices will not corrupt the faithful. The fact remains that alcoholics do not drink excessively because they are ignorant of the effects of alcohol. On the contrary, they drink because they know very well what alcohol will do for them. It will provide dreams of glory, escape from the actualities of existence, and serve as a temporary anodyne to the pain of living. Alcoholics did not become what they are because of lack of knowledge. Most have read the books, seen the films, heard the lectures, and they know more about the effects of alcohol than many non-alcoholics. They became alcoholics because their ability to cope was flawed and they needed an easy way out. The prevention of alcoholism is not accomplished by teaching facts about the effect on the brain of a certain number of drinks in a certain number of hours. It may be accomplished by emphasis on the normal healthy growth of a child because a mature, balanced, integrated person is unlikely to become an alcoholic.

The gimmicks suggested by otherwise rational people have mild entertainment value but they are not likely to make the grade as preventive measures. Children, it is said, should be taught *how* to drink. They should learn to sip alcoholic beverages with their meals so drinking in itself is not emphasized. The Italians were standard models for the virtues of this approach, but in recent years increasing numbers of Italians have disappointed their fans by turning to alcoholism.

A few authorities, better trained in the principles of publicity than those of education, have attracted brief notoriety by proposing that children should be taught *how* to drink while in school— beginning, perhaps, in the fifth grade with a practice course in the proper and moderate use of wine. It is doubtful that this would prevent alcoholism, but it would make a lot of fifth-graders happy.

The fallacy in the theory of prevention by education, especially with the emphasis on how to drink moderately and sensibly, is that most alcoholics did that successfully during many years of social drinking. There is no evidence that alcohol was more important to them in that period than it was to their friends. It became more important when the condition of their lives became unendurable and they lacked healthy coping resources.

CHANGING ATTITUDES

There is increasing acceptance of the idea that much alcoholism will be prevented if the attitudes of society toward drinking are changed. One writer noted that "many students of alcoholism and alcohol problems are agreed that if we are ever to do anything in prevention we must begin with the American drinking practices and attitudes."[2]

Dr. Marvin Block has said that two of the major causes of alcoholism are toleration of drunken behavior and social pressures to drink. "The public attitude toward drinking must be changed to an extent that at no time will any individual drink excessively."[3] If Dr. Block sees that as an attainable goal, he must be a man of unbounded optimism.

Plaut is one of those who is enthusiastic about a change in attitudes as an effective preventive measure. He wants people to obtain perspective on their own drinking behavior through "a detached and objective examination of current practices and beliefs relating to alcohol." He thinks the social pressure to drink should be reduced, with a responsibility for the host to serve non-alcoholic as well as alcoholic beverages and he calls on advertisers to help party-givers to feel comfortable in doing this. He would like to clarify and emphasize the distinctions between acceptable and unacceptable drinking. He would also discourage drinking for its own sake and encourage the integration of drinking with other activities. He thinks less potent spirits would help and would give a tax incentive to manufacturers of lower alcoholic content. But alcoholics have to get drunk so they would just drink more. He is cautious in his endorsement of alcohol education as a means to these ends because he feels that what goes under the name of education to prevent alcoholism is actually education about alcoholism.[4]

As indicated in Chapter Three, *Theories of Causation of Alcoholism,* the attitudes of society do influence the incidence of alcoholism. Orthodox Jews are not likely to become alcoholics because of the powerful

[2] David Hancock, "We Can Reduce and Prevent Alcohol Problems by Changing Drinking Attitudes and Practices," Selected Papers, 21st Annual Meeting NAAAP, Washington, D.C., pp. 23-26.
[3] Marvin A. Block, M.D., "Preventive Treatment of Alcoholism," *Modern Treatment,* Vol. 3, No. 3 (May, 1966), p. 451.
[4] Thomas F. A. Plaut, *Alcohol Problems, A Report to the Nation by the Cooperative Commission on the Study of Alcoholism,* (New York: Oxford University Press, 1967), p. 122.

cultural sanctions against drunkenness. Where these sanctions do not exist, the risk of alcoholism increases. The inevitable question is whether the prevention of alcoholism is worthwhile unless the alternatives are better. The prevention of alcoholism is a pyrrhic victory if those who might have become alcoholics turn to narcotics, compulsive gambling, or schizophrenia. Chafetz, linking attitudes to education, said: "If we are ever going to prevent alcoholism as an emotional illness we need to develop healthy attitudes in people, starting when they are young. This means teaching them about alcohol – about its proper use and their social responsibilities toward it. Alcoholics are troubled people who have turned to alcohol to solve emotional and social problems. If we instill the proper attitudes toward alcohol, troubled people will select safer ways to feed their neuroses."[5]

Perhaps, but if Dr. Chafetz and Dr. Block are typical, the medical profession has a buoyant faith that is not easily shared by others. Troubled people, conditioned against the excessive use of alcohol, are likely to select other ways of coping with their problems but it seems naive to assume they will necessarily select "safer" ways.

PREVENTION BY CONTROL

The effort to control excessive drinking by law goes back to the Code of Hammurabi in 2250 B.C. Under this law priestesses were forbidden to engage in the business of selling liquor or to enter a tavern for the purpose of drinking. The penalty for the latter was burning at the stake.

Most societies have attempted to curb drinking by decree but without much success. In ancient China, the Duke of Chou limited the use of alcoholic beverages to religious feasts only to discover that *all* feasts had become ceremonies of devotion. The Hindus, in the late Vidic period, made the manufacture, giving, sale, acceptance, or use of any alcoholic beverage punishable by death. Under the laws of Maru, any Brahman imbibing liquor was supposed to commit suicide, but, as with many commandments in later epochs, this was honored more in the breach than the observance. The use of breath purifiers to avoid detection, incidentally, is an old Brahman custom. Also members of Hindu cults who wanted to drink openly merely recited a holy incantation over the liquor and thus obtained absolution in advance for sinning.

One of the most comprehensive efforts to eliminate the "evil" consequences of drink was our own eighteenth amendment to the Constitution which was the culmination of a century of dedicated crusading by temperance groups. It, too, failed. By over-shooting the mark, total prohibi-

[5] "Should Children Be Taught to Drink," a panel discussion with Theodore Berland, *Today's Health,* Vol. 47, No. 2 (February, 1969), p. 47.

tion encourages the behavior it is designed to prevent. During prohibition, breaking the law became the most popular way to voice dissent. Thousands of upright citizens who never dreamed of violating other laws puffed with pride as they boasted of smuggling liquor through customs or manufacturing their own. "The ingenuity of convivial man," noted one writer, "is usually more than equal to the restraints imposed upon him."

Total prohibition finds justification in the extreme premise that, as Bacon has said, "all use of alcohol is one and the same thing and, naturally, all users of alcohol form a single type of person. One word for the action – *Drink*. One word for the category of people – *Drinker*."[6] Nevertheless, in talking about prevention, prohibition has an indisputable, albeit simple-minded, logic. If all alcohol were banned from society there would be no alcoholism, just as if the driving of automobiles was outlawed, there would be no more traffic fatalities. But cars will be manufactured and driven and fruits will ferment. Distillers and winemakers will continue to make available the liquids that flow in the wassail bowls.

Despite the tireless efforts to impose prohibition, most men have known that it isn't practical. St. John Chrysostom, a fourth-century priest in the Greek Orthodox Church observed in Homilies: "I hear many cry, 'Were there no wine! O folly! O madness!' Is it wine that causes the abuse? No. [For] if you say 'Would there no wine!' because of drunkards, then you must say, going on by degrees, 'Would there were no night!' because of the thieves. 'Would there were no light!' because of the informers, and 'Would there were no women!' because of adultery."

Despite its apparent failure, the eighteenth amendment did have an impact. Even as it was repealed, as Bacon points out, "the legislatures still accepted the basic tenets of the Classic Movement philosophy (even though they attacked and disclaimed Prohibition). All the States adopted the position that alcohol was potentially a specific, unique and massive evil and that the realization of the evils depended upon availability; therefore, they planned to control the evils by one and only one method – controlling availability; the only difference in their position was this – the final or absolute and total control of availability, namely Prohibition, was in itself bad. Otherwise one can see little difference."[7]

It is interesting to note that social workers first became active in the field of alcoholism by aligning themselves with the prohibition movement. Their concern was with exploited laborers and the wives of children who were the victims when husbands and fathers squandered the contents of their pay envelopes behind the swinging doors of saloons.

[6] Selden D. Bacon, "The Classic Temperence Movement of the U.S.A.: Impact Today on Attitudes, Action and Research," *British Journal of Addictions*, Vol. 62 (1967), p. 9.
[7] *Ibid.*, pp. 10-11.

Social workers of that day may have been on the wrong side of the liquor debate but at least they did sincerely want to improve the condition of man and, among the helping professionals, were almost alone in their dedication to social action.

PUBLIC HEALTH APPROACH

There are many who recognize the futility of legal sanctions in the prevention of alcoholism, are skeptical of the effect of alcohol education, and doubt that miracles will come from changing attitudes about drinking. Some of these suggest that only a public health approach can be effective. This means the problem is studied and measures for control are developed while, at the same time, there is a coordinated effort to apply preventive techniques that will eliminate the problem as a factor in human life. This may challenge those in community organization, but one public health official has warned of the necessity for looking at certain principles in public health concerning preventive techniques and relating them to alcoholism. Dr. John R. Philip, one-time Chief of California's Division of Alcoholic Rehabilitation, noted the lack of similarity between alcoholism and other problems more susceptible to the public health approach. He outlined the principles as follows:

1. *Can we measure the problem?* In most illnesses or diseases there are methods or techniques for actual measurement of the problem to determine precise incidence and prevalence figures. At the present time we are largely lacking adequate methods of measuring the problem of alcoholism. We have ways of estimating the size of the problem, but we do not have techniques and tools for simple, precise counts and measurements.
2. *Do we have a preventive technique which will prevent the illness or the disease when it is applied on an individual basis?* Such preventive techniques are well known with other health problems, as for example the use of cowpox vaccine to inoculate against smallpox, the use of polio vaccine to immunize against the paralytic effects of polio, the boiling of water to prevent enteric disease, and so on. These are merely illustrations of a preventive technique which, when applied to an individual, will prevent the occurrence of illness or disease in that individual. Looking at alcoholism, we realize again that we lack precise techniques or methods of preventing the occurrence of alcoholism in any given individual. Good progress is being made in methods of detecting and uncovering the early alcoholic, but we do not have a

preventive technique at the present time with which we can actually prevent the occurrence of alcoholism in any given individual.

3. *If we have a preventive technique, is it susceptible to or adaptable to mass application?* Illustrating again the use of cowpox vaccine, polio vaccine, and other preventive techniques successfully applied in the individual, these techniques are adaptable for mass application. Purification of public water supplies prevents water-born diseases in the community.
4. *Is the mass application of these preventive techniques economically feasible?*
5. *Can we evaluate our results, after we have applied our preventive techniques on a mass basis?*

Actually, since the answer to question number two for alcoholism has been "No," it follows that the answer to the rest of these three questions is also "No." Well—where does this leave us? I have just enunciated five principles in public health, five criteria to determine the preventability of a problem, the answer to all of which needs to be "Yes" before one can expect to initiate an effective public health program to reduce or eliminate the illness in question. Where does this leave us in the field of alcoholism? At this moment, we are apparently forced to admit that we are without the scientific knowledge and without the proven tools and techniques to eliminate or even to reduce the problem of alcoholism.[8]

Dr. Philip wrote that paper a decade ago and things haven't changed much. Does this mean primary prevention is impossible? Realistically, it seems to have about the same possibilities as it has in other areas of social pathology. Those in the field frequently talk as if alcoholism can be prevented as an isolated illness, but, as with other social problems, primary prevention depends on creating a better and more humane society which gives more people healthy alternatives to destructive defenses. It means, in a word, massive social action.

SECONDARY PREVENTION

What most of us mean when we talk about prevention in alcoholism is secondary prevention, which means early identification and, if possible, prompt intervention. If successful, this strategy can prevent years of agony for the alcoholic and his family.

Unfortunately, it doesn't work in many cases. The helping person may

[8] John R. Philip, "Alcoholism Is a Public Health Problem," paper presented at 11th Annual Meeting of the North American Association of Alcoholism Programs, 1960 (mimeo).

be the relationship between the drinking behavior of the alcoholic and the problems associated with it. The alcoholic, as we have said previously, may not see or he may choose to ignore this relationship. Many alcoholics say they regret they were ignored so long but admit they would have been unapproachable in the early stages. "I needed all the props knocked out from under me," a recovered alcoholic told a symposium at the University of Oregon Medical School. Said another: "It had to hit me pretty hard before I would give in."[9] These comments may provide a clue as to why it is difficult to reach young alcoholics. They are having a ball and there will be plenty of time to "settle down."

Despite these reservations there is ample reason for attempted intervention in the early stages. Some discouragement can be avoided if we bear in mind that alcoholics, like other people, have different needs and different responses at different times. With many, repeated efforts are necessary.

Tertiary Prevention

There is a tendency to scoff at treatment as a preventive measure, but it may be the most important of all. Some authorities have declared that the public health point of view might justify a comparative disregard for the current alcoholic population so that efforts could be concentrated on prevention of future alcoholism. Contemporary alcoholics, according to this reasoning, will eventually disappear with or without treatment.

This is a restricted view of treatment because alcoholics affect so many around them. We have seen what can be done to children, for example, and it can easily be argued that a treated alcoholic father or mother is likely to provide a more stable home which can prevent future problems. This is not to lose sight of the real enemy which is, as Perlman has pointed out, "the social conditions that pollute social living, not only among the poor – although there the social smog thickens – but across total communities."[10]

What, then, are the immediate and possibly attainable goals. We turn again to Dr. Philip, who seemed to be so pessimistic about the public health approach. He suggested the following:

1. Citizens who recognize that there are some people who cannot drink in moderation and that these people should not be blamed for the condition that made them alcoholics.
2. Police officers who have some knowledge of alcoholism, and who, in addition to this, consider helping alcoholics as well as protecting the rights of others as part of their job.

[9] *The Oregonian,* Portland, Oregon, September 28, 1964, p. 14.
[10] Helen Harris Perlman, "Casework and 'the Diminished Man,'" *Social Casework,* Vol. 51, No. 4 (April, 1970), pp. 216-224.

3. Courts and laws which recognize that help for the alcoholic is far more effective than punishment.
4. Physicians who are willing and are competent to treat alcoholics and who will use their skills to join with others in the community to offer help for the alcoholic.
5. General hospitals whose beds are as available to acutely intoxicated alcoholics as they are to people with other acute medical problems, and nursing staffs who recognize that there is more to alcoholism than intoxication.
6. Clergymen who are aware of the spiritual problems faced by alcoholics and their families and who are prepared to use their counselling skills to help rather than to condemn.
7. Social agencies which offer help to families where alcoholism has intensified or created social problems and use their skills also to help the individual alcoholic.
8. Local health departments that feel as much responsibility towards alcoholism as they do toward any other public health problem.
9. Employers who recognize the early symptoms of alcoholism in employees and who protect the investment they may have in these people by getting help for them before their jobs are jeopardized.
10. Schools that teach objectively.
11. Medical and mental health clinics with the desire and skill to provide treatment services for alcoholics.
12. An informed and organized community.

How do we go about accomplishing these rather immediate goals which visualize an informed and organized citizenry and the incorporation of the appropriate understanding and skills in the armamentarium of a variety of professional people to assist in the treatment and rehabilitation of the alcoholic? I would like to come back to two words I emphasized earlier – we do this through organized community effort. This means involving as many people as possible . . .[11]

Although Dr. Philip doesn't say so specifically, that is part of the role and skill of the social worker. While we are working toward the realization of a Brave New World, his outlined steps could provide a fair start.

[11] Philip, *op. cit.*

Bibliography

Note: This bibliography does not purport to be complete in any respect. At best, it is an introduction to the literature and there has been an effort to include publications that will be useful to faculty and students in schools of social work.

The amount of written material on alcohol and alcoholism is incredibly voluminous. Perhaps the most complete bibliography available is the International Bibliography of Studies on Alcohol edited by Mark Keller and published in two volumes by the Rutgers Center of Alcohol Studies, 1966. A card index system that records almost everything published in the field and is continually updated is the Classified Abstract Archive of the Alcoholic Literature. This is available in some medical libraries, Divisions of Alcoholism in State Health Departments and, occasionally, at the offices of local Councils on Alcoholism.

BOOKS

Alcoholics Anonymous. New York: Alcoholics Anonymous Publishing Company, revised edition, 1955. This is known among AA members as the "Big Book." It was written from the early experiences and is a "must" for anyone who wants to understand the origins of the fellowship.

Alcoholics Anonymous Comes of Age. New York: Alcoholics Anonymous Publishing Company, 1960. Shows an interesting development and broadening of AA thinking after the fellowship had gained the security to recognize the contributions of resources other than AA in the rehabilitation of alcoholics.

Al-Anon Faces Alcoholism. New York: Al-Anon Family Group Headquarters, 1965.

Anonymous. *The Drinking Game and How to Beat It.* New York: Simon and Schuster, 1968. One of the more palatable accounts by an alcoholic of the trials and tribulations of recovery.

Bacon, Margaret and Mary Brush Jones. *Teen-Age Drinking.* New York: Thomas Y. Crowell, 1968. One of the best discussions of an aspect of the alcohol problem not covered in the foregoing text. Also includes general material about drinking and alcoholism.

Bailey, Margaret. *Alcoholism and Family Casework.* New York: Community Council of Greater New York, 1968. One of the best publications in the field written by a social worker. Come to think of it, one of the best written by anyone.

Bell, R. Gordon, M.D. *Escape from Addiction.* New York: McGraw Hill Book Company, 1970.

Blane, Howard T. *The Personality of the Alcoholic.* New York: Harper & Row, 1968.

Blum, Eva Marie and Richard H. *Alcoholism; Modern Psychological Approaches to Treatment.* San Francisco: Jossey-Bass, Inc., 1967.

Cahn, Sidney. *The Treatment of Alcoholics.* New York: Oxford University Press, 1970. Contains an excellent discussion of community resources.

Calahan, Don. *Problem Drinker.* San Francisco: Jossey-Bass, Inc., 1970.

Catanzarro, Ronald, M.D. (ed.). *Alcoholism; The Total Treatment Approach.* Springfield, Illinois: Charles C. Thomas, 1968. Giant size, but inept in the selection of papers, especially those in social work. Includes a few that are excellent, however, such as the one of "Drinking in the Bahamas" and another on halfway houses by Tom Richards.

Chafetz, Morris E., M.D. *et al. Frontiers of Alcoholism.* New York: Science House, 1970.

Clinebell, Howard J., Jr. *Understanding and Counselling the Alcoholic.* Nashville, Tennessee: Abingdon Press, 1968. One does not have to agree with the author on all points but this is one of the *best* general works in the field. Clinebell is a clergyman and his orientation is evident but not obtrusive.

Cohen, Pauline C. and Merton S. Krause. *Casework with the Wives of Alcoholics.* New York: Family Service Association of America, 1971.

Cross, Jay N. *Guide to the Community Control of Alcoholism.* New York: Public Health Association, 1968.

Demone, Harold W. Jr. and Morris E. Chafetz, M.D. *Alcoholism and Society.* New York: Oxford University Press, 1962.

Fox, Ruth, M.D. (ed.). *Alcoholism; Behavioral Research, Therapeutic Approaches.* New York: Springer Publishing Company, 1967.

Hoff, Ebbe C., M.D. and Ruth Fox, M.D. *Aspects of Alcoholism.* Philadelphia: J. B. Lippincott Company, 1963. Two small hardback volumes developed by Roche Laboratories to summarize the various aspects of alcoholism for physicians.

Jellenik, E. M. *The Disease Concept of Alcoholism.* New Haven, Connecticut: Hillhouse Press, 1960. The towering classic in the field of alcoholism. The prose is turgid and difficult but the concepts have had a profound effect.

Keller, John E. *Ministering to Alcoholics.* Minneapolis: Augsburg Publishing House, 1966.

Maddox, George L. (ed.). *The Domesticated Drug.* New Haven, Connecticut: College and University Press Services, Inc., 1970.

Mann, Marty. *New Primer on Alcoholism.* New York: Holt, Rinehart and Winston, revised edition, 1958.

McAndrew, Craig. *Drunken Comportment.* Chicago: Aldine Publishing Company, 1969.

McCarthy, Raymond (ed.). *Drinking and Intoxication.* New Haven: College and University Press, 1959.

McCord, William and Joan McCord. *Origins of Alcoholism.* Berkeley, California: Stanford University, 1960.

Pittman, David J. and C. Wayne Gordon. *The Revolving Door.* Glencoe, Illinois: The Free Press, 1958. Probably the best study of the chronic court offender.

Pittman, David J. and Charles R. Snyder. *Society, Culture and Drinking Patterns.* New York: John Wiley and Sons, 1962. One of the most comprehensive anthologies in the field.

Plaut, Thomas F. A. *Alcohol Problems: A Report to the Nation by the Cooperative Commission on the Study of Alcoholism.* New York: Oxford University Press, 1967. If this does not quite live up to the expectations of those who looked for apocalyptic revelations from the five years labor of the commission, it is still one of the best overall discussions of the problem.

Trice, Harrison M. *Alcoholism in America.* New York: McGraw Hill Book Company, 1966.

"Understanding Alcohlism." *The Annals of the American Academy of Political and Social Science.* January, 1958. After more than a decade this remains one of the best collections of papers in the field.

Whitney, Elizabeth D. (ed.). *World Dialogue on Alcohol and Drug Dependence.* Boston: Beacon Press, 1970.

Wilkinson, Rupert. *The Prevention of Drinking Problems; Alcohol Control and Cultural Influences.* New York: Oxford University Press, 1970.

PAMPHLETS

"Alcohol and Alcoholism." Public Health Service Publication No. 1640. Department of Health Education and Welfare, Washington, D.C., 1967.

Cohen, Pauline. "How to Help the Alcoholic." Public Affairs Pamphlet No. 452. New York, 1970.

Kellermann, Joseph L. "A Merry-Go-Round Named Denial." Charlotte, North Carolina, Council on Alcoholism. This is a MUST. An extremely skillful presentation of the systems that operate with a family.

Kellermann, Joseph L. "Guide for the Family of an Alcoholic." Available from Kemper Insurance Company, Chicago, Illinois.

Pittman, David J. and Sterne, Muriel W. "Alcoholism, Community Agency Attitudes and Their Impact on Treatment Services." U. S. Department of Health Education and Welfare, Public Health Service Publication No. 1273. Washington, D.C., 1963.

The President's Commission on Law Enforcement and Administration of Justice. "Task Force Report: Drunkenness." U. S. Government Printing Office, Washington, D.C., 1967.

PERIODICALS

Quarterly Journal of Studies on Alcohol. Publications Division, Rutgers Center of Alcohol Studies, New Brunswick, New Jersey. This is the leading journal in the field and is indispensible for anyone engaged in research or those who want to keep informed of current thinking.

Addictions. A small quarterly published by the Alcoholism Research Foundation of Ontario, 33 Russell Street, Toronto, 4, Ontario. They do not send this publication to non-professionals outside Ontario so requests for subscriptions must indicate professional interest.

The British Journal of Addiction. Headington Hall, Oxford, England. Distributed in U. S. through Pergamon Press, New York.

SELECTED PAPERS

Bacon, Selden D. "The Classic Temperance Movement of the U.S.A.: Impact Today on Attitudes, Action and Research." *British Journal of Addiction.* Vol. 62, (1967), pp. 5-18. This is the best brief account of attempts to control drinking behavior through temperance.

Bailey, Margaret B. "The Family Agency's Role in Treating the Wife of an Alcoholic." *Social Casework.* (May, 1963). pp. 273-279.

Bailey, Margaret B., P. Haberman, and H. Alksne. "Outcome of Marriages: Endurance, Termination and Recovery." *Quarterly Journal of Studies on Alcohol.* Vol. 23, No. 4 (December, 1962), pp. 610-623.

Blumberg, Leonard, *et al.* "The Development, Major Goals and Strategies of a Skid Row Program: Philadelphia." *Quarterly Journal of Studies on Alcohol.* Vol. 27, No. 2 (June, 1966), pp. 242-258.

Burnett, William H. "The Court's Challenge." Report #44, North American Association of Alcoholism Programs.

Burton, Genevieve. "The Alcoholic and His Community Search for Help." *American Journal of Public Health.*" Vol. 50, No. 7 (July, 1960), pp. 980-988.

Burton, Genevieve and Howard M. Kaplan. "Sexual Behavior and Adjustment of Married Alcoholics." *Quarterly Journal of Studies on Alcohol.* Vol. 29, No. 3 (September, 1968), pp. 603-609.

Carstairs, G. M. "Daru and Bhang." *Quarterly Journal of Studies on Alcohol.* Vol. 15 (June, 1954), pp. 220-237. One of the classic studies of cultural influences on drinking.

Fox, Ruth. "A Multidisciplinary Approach to the Treatment of Alcoholism." *The American Journal of Psychiatry.* Vol. 123, No. 7 (January, 1967), pp. 769-778.

Fox, Ruth. "The Alcoholic Spouse." Reprinted by the National Council on Alcoholism, Inc., from Neurotic Interaction in Marriage. V. W. Eisenstein (ed.). New York: Basic Books, 1956.

Jackson, J. K. "The Adjustment of the Family to the Crisis of Alcoholism." Reprint from: *Quarterly Journal of Studies on Alcohol,* Vol. 15, No. 4 (December, 1954), pp. 562-568.

Kepner, Elaine. "Application of Learning Theory to the Etiology and Treatment of Alcoholism." Reprint from *Quarterly Journal of Studies on Alcohol.* Vol. 25, No. 2 (June, 1964).

Kogan, Kate L. and Joan K. Jackson. "Stress, Personality and Emotional Disturbance in Wives of Alcoholics." *Quarterly Journal of Alcohol Studies.* Vol. 26, No. 3 (September, 1965), pp. 486-495.

Kogan, Kate L. and Joan K. Jackson. "Role Perceptions in Wives of Alcoholics and Non-Alcoholics." *Quarterly Journal of Studies on Alcohol.* Vol. 24, No. 4 (December, 1963), pp. 627-639.

Krimmel, Herman E. and D. Bruce Falkey. "Short-Term Treatment of Alcoholics." *Social Work.* Vol. 7, No. 3 (July, 1962), pp. 102-107.

Krimmel, Herman E. "Alcoholism — A Social Problem for Social Workers." Paper presented at National Conference on Social Welfare, Dallas, Texas, May, 1967. Mimeo. Available from Cleveland Center on Alcoholism and Drug Abuse.

Krimmel, Herman E. "Reaching the Unreached Alcoholic." Presented at National Conference on Social Welfare, San Francisco, 1968. Mimeo. Available from Cleveland Center on Alcoholism and Drug Abuse.

Peltenberg, Catherine. "Casework with the Alcoholic Patient." *Social Casework*. Vol. 38, No. 2 (February, 1956), pp. 81-85.

Plaut, Thomas F. A. "Alcoholism and Community Caretakers; Programs and Policies." *Social Work*. Vol. 12, No. 3 (July, 1967).

Rubington, Earl. "The Future of the Halfway House." *Quarterly Journal of Studies on Alcohol*. Vol. 31, No. 1 (March, 1970), pp. 167-174. (Reprints available)

Tiebout, Harry M., M.D. "Alcoholics Anonymous — An Experiment of Nature." *Quarterly Journal of Alcohol Studies*. Vol. 22, No. 1 (March, 1961), pp. 52-68. (Reprinted by National Council on Alcoholism)

Tiebout, Harry M., M.D. "Crisis and Surrender in Treating Alcoholism." *Quarterly Journal of Studies on Alcohol*. Vol. 26, No. 3 (September, 1965), pp. 496-497.

RESOURCES FOR INFORMATION AND PUBLICATIONS

National Center for Prevention and Control of Alcoholism
National Institute of Mental Health
5454 Wisconsin Avenue
Chevy Chase, Maryland 20015

North American Association of Alcohol Programs
1130 — 17th Street, N. W.
Washington, D. C. 20036

National Council on Alcoholism
2 Park Avenue
New York, New York 10016

Alcoholics Anonymous
General Office
305 East 45th Street
New York, New York 10017

Rutgers Center for Alcohol Studies
Rutgers University
New Brunswick, New Jersey 08903

Association of Halfway House Alcoholism
Programs of North America, Inc.
334 Mounds Boulevard
St. Paul, Minnesota 55106